GEOGARDENING

By

C. M. GOETHE

● Author of Sierran Cabin From Skyscraper; War Profits and Better Babies; Pomegranate Blossom; Where Queen and Pope Failed; New Wine from Old Bottles; Luther Wong, Coolie; Gambling for Dulces; A Playground Hard by a Temple of Hate; Children of Loneliness; Immigration into New France; Peons Need Not Apply; Filipino Immigration Viewed as a Peril; Russia's Future and Ours; Guano; Extinction of the Inca Highcastes; Eugenics in Postage Stamps; Sunworshipping Conservation; Gretchen of Hildesheim, (a story of the *Klenigartenvertrieb*) ; Bird Music for the Blind; Czechoslovakia Caught in a Nutcracker; Overpopulation in Java; Dr. Jan Mjoen's Windern Laboratorium; Eugenic Aspects of Famine in Hindustan; France's Code de La Famille; Eugenist at Cromagnon; Eugenic Aspects of Life in the Sahara; Albuquerque—And After; 45% College Women Do Not Marry; Is Population Pessimism Justified?; Eugenical Studies in Korea; Eugenical Aspects of Iceland's Conquest of Illiteracy; Europe's Mistress System; Finland's Heterogeneity.

PRINTED IN THE UNITED STATES OF AMERICA
BY
THE KEYSTONE PRESS
SACRAMENTO, CALIFORNIA.

DEDICATION

TO THE MEMORY OF MY WIFE,
GEOGARDENING PAL,

and to

the thousands of her fellow-members of the Garden Clubs of America, who always have "mothered" seedlings as devotedly as they do the wee bairns . . . They thus have helped keep alive, nationwide, (and despite constantly-increasing urban congestion) interest in Gardening, and, incidentally, in The Soil, that source of all Food essential to the Renewal-of-Life. They thus have helped perpetuate our Republic.

"The most splendidly poetic building in the world . . . modelled and painted more frequently than any other building in the world. . . Word pictures of it are numberless. . . It can only be described as a dream in marble."

(The Encyclopedia Brittanica)

THE TAJ MAHAL (POIGNANT LOVE-POEM IN MARBLE) AND ITS GARDEN

Taj Mahal was built by the sorrowing Grand Mogul, Shah Jahan, for his queen, Mahal. She died, (1629), at the birth of their 8th child. One account says the Shah spent on her tomb 31,748,026 rupees (and this at slave-labor costs!) . . . Pundits in Hindustan grudgingly concede Shah Jahan sent to France for its master architect, Austin of Bordeaux. The inlays of precious stones, as well as the formal gardening, suggest Italian influence. Some critics, however, say "Persian" . . The interior of the Taj is ornamented with flowers and fruits. The inlays of diamonds, rubies, emeralds, sapphires, have been pried out by looting soldiers. The remaining agates, jaspers, even lapis lazuli, give a glimpse of its original beauty. The silver doors, too, are gone. They were melted as loot. Even a British viceroy once suggested dismantling the Taj, that its marbles might be sold.

"The builders of the Taj planned like Titans, finished like jewelers."

"GEOGARDENING: THE CULTIVATION, FOR FLOW-
ERS OR FOOD, OF GARDEN PLANTS . . . . . THE
TRACKING OF THE SAME TO THEIR WILD BEGIN-
NINGS . . . THE STUDY THEREOF IN THEIR NA-
TIVE HAUNTS TO BETTER UNDERSTAND THEIR
ORIGINS, THEIR FAMILY TIES, THEIR 'SAUVAGE'
ENVIRONMENTS, THEIR HISTORY OF NATURAL,
THEN OF ARTIFICIAL SELECTION, THE POSSIBIL-
ITIES OF INCREASED IMPROVEMENT THROUGH
SUCH ARTIFICIAL SELECTIONS . . . THE ENJOY-
MENT OF MEMORIES OF SUCH WANDERLUSTING."

● This is a tale of a Gardenlover. He found in his garden's annuals and perennials, its shrubs and trees, constant
stimuli to steal away a-wanderlusting. This, that he might
know more about whence came his posies, . . . that his
love for them might intelligently deepen—that his hours
in that Garden (his escape from Life's insistent calls to
Duty) might have telescoped into them: Appreciation and
Knowledge and Historical Memories. These, he was certain would enrich, at an ever-accelerated rate, his enjoyment of that Garden.

COTTAGE NEAR SHAKESPEARE'S STRATFORD ON AVON

In rural England, even the humblest thatched-roof cottage has its bit of blossoming.

"God gave us memory
That we might have
Roses in December."

(Photograph, copyrighted by C. M. Goethe from "War Profits . . . And Better Babies.")

GARDEN OF PREMIER CLEMENCEAU, BRITTANY

The garden of the "Tiger of France" War-Premier Clemenceau at his country home in Brittany. It was at this, his Garden-refuge, that a neighbor sneered: "You are too old for that job." He replied, "Nevertheless I am an octogenarian who plants trees!"

"THE PLEASURE OF ANY TRAVEL SHOULD BE THREE-FOLD: (1) THE ANTICIPATION THEREOF. (2) THE ACTUAL JOURNEY ITSELF. (3) THE READING AFTER THE RETURN, AND REFLECTION THREON."

"The biologist-president, Thomas Jefferson, 'Long Tom' as the people affectionately called him, was a fellow livable and lovable. He reverenced women, adored children, DELIGHTED IN FLOWERS."

Donald Peattie, Reader's Digest, 4/43.

XOCHIMILCO'S COLORFUL "FLOATING" GARDENS

Xochimilco's name roots in the Aztec *xochitl*, or flower. Apparently some warlike tribe, whose ancestors may have crossed the Bering Sea on the ice, cut their bloody way down to this land of delights. There they built an Amerind Venice. Their *chinampas* or Floating Gardens at that time actually floated. They were made by weaving sticks into a raft. (The peons to this day still weave a *petate*, or mat, of rushes which, stretched on an earth floor, form their only bed). Upon these wood-woven rafts was piled the rich lake-muck. Such soil, with abundant moisture plus a tropical sun, meant floral wealth. These garden-rafts could support human habitations. In fact, one senses the redskins' protective strategy paralleled that of the prehistoric Swiss lake-dwellers . . .

Gradually bird-dispersed, water-borne, also wind-carried tree seeds sprouted on the *chinampas*. These, more and more, became anchored as roots penetrated the lake bottom. . . To have known xochimilco's floating gardens in the opening decade of our century was to have enjoyed one of the world's greatest geo-gardening thrills. Today they are tourist-spoiled. There one once met smiling Carmens, each coiffure brightened with a red poppy. In place of these flower girls, now are whining beggars. These cry: *"Diez centavos, senor, y vaya Usted con Dios!"*

FOREWORD

"After all, the dominant stimulus is color." Thus spoke, aboard a tiny trading ship off the Somaliland coast, the veteran head of the Botany Department of a European university. "Look at these Somali dandies. Their kinky hair is dyed red as a rose, one is yellow as a sunflower. That skinny Negro, has, within the year, made the pilgrimage to Mecca. His hair has the hue of a new-clipped lawn. Green, the color of plants, still stirs profoundly the soul of the desert-dwelling Mohammedan."

The Professor was, to steal a metaphor from Freemasonary, a Thirtythird-degree Geogardener. From his own little, but world-famed, botanical garden, he had gone a-wanderlusting across Siberia. There he had reveled in days of journeying thru orange-red Oriental poppies. He had threaded narrow, snow-choked Hima-layan passes, to descend into Tibetan meadows carpeted with blue poppies. These, he declared, seemed, at a distance, to be mountain lakes reflecting the blue of Heaven. He had botanized in the purple lantana tangles of Java. He had penetrated deep into the rain forests of Ecuador. Therein he had studied the color attraction that blossoms held for hummingbirds. He was positive that color dominated, not only primitive man, but lower vertebrates, even insects . . .

Thus he spake, standing at the vessel's rail, and watching the varicolored-coiffured Negroes loading the captain's purchases of palm nuts. He philosophized: "The reason there is a steady stream of palm-nut baskets coming over the vessel's side is, that our shrewd skipper had stocked his trading vessel with colorful junk dear to the savage negro heart." There were, it is true, barrels of black high silk hats. These had been gathered from secondhand clothing stores of London, of Paris. But there were, also strings of brightcolored beads. What seemed, however, to attract most attention were bales of flimsy near-silk neckerchiefs. Some flashed brilliant hues, bright purples, striking yellows, flaming reds. A few had that color dearest to Islamic souls, the sacred green of Mohammed. From the boastful darky, just back from wondrous Mecca, these extracted triple tales of his palm nuts.

The freighter had run in as close as possible inshore. Out had come a few native *dhows*. The fuzzy-haired negroes had clambered upon the freighter's side. Soon it was evident there was good trading ashore. The freighter's long boat, the first mate in charge, then had been lowered. The male citizens of Somaliland soon had put their respective harems at work. These women had gathered ivory-palm nuts, that later would be converted into coat buttons for European men. Meantime the lazy menfolk were leaning against palmtree trunks, directing the work. By midday, these ebony Apollos were strutting around in high silk hats. A half-dozen kerchiefs were around one buck's neck—and little else of clothing, save a G-string. It was noticeable that what was left over, in beads and kerchiefs, had gone, rather unequitably, to his youngest wife. This happened, too, despite the elder ones having worked far more efficiently!

The whole day had been like what, some years later, could be described as the unfolding of a motion picture. The dominant note, to our Geogardener, seemed to be savage love of color. Opportunities today, to thus observe such primitive origins of human behavior, are disappearing as rapidly as the melting of a Spitzenbergen glacier's nose under the 24-hours-per day sunlight of the Midnight Sun. Perhaps, therefore, this Somaliland incident may help answer this question:-

Why does one garden? Ask one's best friend, one's neighbor, a dozen, a score of folks from various walks of life. . . As to VEGETABLE gardens, the answer revolves around: "Food." With our Victory Gardens, many said "Helping Win the War" . . . Additional comments are: "It's lots of fun". . . "Everybody's doing it" . . . "Relief to work with one's hands" . . . "Back-to-the-soil" . . . "Thrilling to watch something grow". . . If, "Why a FLOWER garden?" the response may be "Always did like wildflowers". Further questioning elicits: "Their color attracted". . .

The joy of color IS all embracing. It is deeply primeval. . . Note a savage's pleasure in beads of jade, of gold, of even brightly-colored glass. Observe the frankly uncontrolled urge in certain races, as the Burmese, to dress in bright colors.

Study the highly refined balancing of color values in women's gowns, millinery. This reached new heights in Paris before World War I. Fascinating it was there to see world-famous designers' efforts in attiring:- (1) The tall, blue-eyed, golden-haired daughter of an English Earl, (2) A velvet-eyed, jet-haired odalesque from old Constantinople, (3) The spoilt, already obese, young wife of a Colombian emerald-king. She was dubbed *"mestizo"*, and probably only 1/16 Castilian, with 1/16 negroid, 7/8 Amerind.

Color has appeal, indeed, both to the savage and to the sophisticated. It is no accident that one of the best French cook books of the Chateau Age opens with: "The first essential of a successful chef is an imagination sufficiently vivid that he can sense the color values of the food he prepares when it reaches the master's table."

C. M. G.

"LIQUIDATED" DR. VAVILOV

The day the final proofs of this book are returned to the printer, there arrives Mr. Dobzhansky's "Homage to Nikolai Ivanovitch Vavilov, martyr of Genetics".* Dr. Vavilov's American friends long had worried about what was happening behind the Soviet's Iron Curtain. After V-E Day, some disquieting rumors about "liquidation" filtered thru. This year all hope has melted.

What may interest the reader is author Dobzhansky's comment about this hero's geogardening: "Vavilov journeyed and collected in 60 countries." . . . He further mentions Dr. Vavilov's "monumental study," also his most important research contribution: "THE CENTERS OF ORIGIN OF CULTIVATED PLANTS." The undersigned never before had heard of same. He grasps, however, the unlimited possibilities of systematic search for "valuable genes in existing varieties, thoroughbred AS WELL AS PRIMITIVE . . . AT CENTERS OF ORIGIN."

DR. VAVILOV, THEN, WAS A KING OF GEOGARDENERS. His martyrdom came on a charge of "DISSIPATING HIS EFFORTS BY SENDING EXPEDITIONS TO MANY FOREIGN LANDS, INSTEAD OF CONFINING HIMSELF TO STUDIES ON LOCAL VARIETIES IN THE U.S.S.R.

This modest book was written with the hope that it might increase gardening pleasure, might help reduce biological illiteracy, might stimulate interest in genetics and eugenics. Here is a salute to the memory of the Great Master, Vavilov, who died because of his devotion to "the Mendelian-Morganian heresy."

(*Journal of Heredity 8-'47)

———————

"When 19,000,000 Victory gardens were wanted, advertising threw in all the skill of its copywriters; everyone from Henry Aldrich to Elsie, the Cow, had a garden. 20,000,000 gardens according to the Department of Agriculture, produced 8,000,000 tons of food."

Don Wharton, Reader's Digest, 744, page 104.

TABLE OF CONTENTS

TABLE OF CONTENTS

LIST OF ILLUSTRATIONS

LIST OF ILLUSTRATIONS

LIST OF ILLUSTRATIONS

LIST OF ILLUSTRATIONS

WALLABY, LURED BY MANDARIN PEEL, POSES ON AN OUTCROP
in an Arid-Australia Acacia Forest

Here the author also found his first platypus. The acacia forest that ringed said rockridge sheltered thousands of scarlet parrots. These flashed like blazing meteors against the massed golden acacia bloom background.

Australia's flora has enriched U. S. A. gardens. Acacias, beefwoods, (also called "she-oaks"), eucalypts, of some 15 or more grevilleas, also those typical "Down-under" flowers which the kiddies call "bottlebrushes"—All these are "Aussie" gifts to us.

The culture of Britain's Dominions, particularly of Australia, of New Zealand, and of Canada has in each instance an origin common also to U. S. A. If garden acacias awaken thoughts of our allies from the Land of the Platypus, the Emu, the Cockatoo, the Teddy-bear, the Kangaroo, if seeing their fuzzy yellow bloom helps strengthen the ties that already bind our English-speaking groups—then geogardening has "done its bit."

CHAPTER 1

ACACIA

Give us the WATTLE'S gold
And the dew-laden air,
And the loveliness bold
Loneliest landscapes wear.

(James Lister Cuthbertson.)

IT WAS in the acacia-dotted African "bush" that our Geogardener saw the height of male independence. He had come thither in the Hamburg trading-tramp, mentioned in the Foreword.

To know, however, the acacia in all its glory, one must go a-wanderlusting to Australia. There the name of "Wattle" is given to one species of acacia, same has a shiny brown foot-long seed. It is much like its cousin, the "women's-tongues" tree of Barbadoes. The name "Wattle" may be a throw-back, perhaps, to when our savage Anglo-Saxon ancestors lived in their first habitations, huts of "wattle-and-daub." "Down-Under," you may enjoy one of the rarest treats of the Nature-lover*: An Acacia forest in its Antipodes' spring's full bloom. October brings parrots flashing red against its yellow flowers. Mother *wallabies* hop under the feathery, yellow-starred branches. Their young blink at you from the kangaroo-like pouch. You may even find, as did our Geogardener, the uncouth duckbill or platypus. Lyrebirds here are love-dancing under the tree ferns. In the rain pattering on the acacia, the cucaburra's demoniacal laughter will make you grasp why the settlers dubbed Aussie's kingfisher: "Laughing Jackass."

"Gold of the tangled wilderness of wattle,
Break in the lone green hollows of the hills,
Come with thy saffron diadem, and scatter
Odour of Araby that haunts the air;
Queen of the woodland, rival of the roses,
Spring in the yellow trees of thy hair."

(James Lister Cuthbertson.)

Australia's really lush acacias are found on the fairly-well-watered Eastern coastal-plain. In South New South Wales, also in Victoria, they are interspersed,—along with millions of graceful

---

* An at-home reminder of an Australian color-feast is the landing of a flock of bluebirds in an acacia in bloom.

tree ferns—under the tall eucalyptus. In places this growth almost partakes of a rain-forest type. As one advances westward and inland toward the Never-Never desert, the acacias become more stunted. It is out there that, in World War II, so many city-raised American G. I.'s have been lonesome. Thus arose the oft-repeated soldier yarn: "After the first week you talk to yourself. The next week you talk to the lizards. The third week, you just let the lizards talk to you."

The acacia is as well adjusted to aridity-plus-high-temperature as the cactus in Arizona, or the cactus-like euphorbias in the African desert. The thorny acacias indeed are, in certain African deserts, as characteristic as the leafless euphorbias. . .

The acacia blooms abundantly in late winter along the French Riviera, when the Nice stock are at their height of pink and purples, heightened by whites. The acacia then adds its share by massing its yellow blooms against vistas of that bluest of seas, that which warrants the French calling that littoral the "Cote Azure".

The French, always quick to utilize color values, make sweets of yellow acacia blooms much as they do of purple violets. Both will come to you atop French pastries. A single bloom thriftily will crown one pastry with the same Scotch-like caution that a Schwartzwald housewife will similarly use a preserved blueberry. At Frejus, our Geogardener was reading Julius Ceasar in the *Forum Julii*. This was at what was once a seaport. It is now several miles inland. There the Conqueror of Gaul, jealous of unfriendly Marseilles, tried to establish a rival port. At this study of Roman history, our Geogardener found his landlady had included in his lunch acacia-bloom pastries . . .

Eastern friends are to be your dinner guests on New Year's Day in California. After breakfast, you check over your garden for indoor decorations. Your favorite acacia carefully had been placed, a decade ago, in a sunny, wind-sheltered spot. It rewards you, on this January 1st, with a half-dozen branch-tips in bloom. You therefore decorate your table with its fuzzy, yellow blossoms. Australians reproduce, on Christmas-gift calendars, these acacia flowers. They then are transformed into baby faces with eyes, nose, rosebud mouth.

Your pleased guests compare your native Golden State with blizzard-news from back home. One starts a discussion of the flora of acacia's homeland:—The Australian "Down-Under." You add to your New Year's resolution another—to track the acacia to its native haunt. Your GEOGARDENING has commenced!

The "acacia" concept, to a few, may stimulate memories of the deserts of East Africa, or, across the Red Sea, of Arabia. When an acacia there is wounded, the sap that flows is not pitch, as in a pine, but a clear mucilaginous gum that forms in beads. It is the "gum Arabic" of commerce. This is the basis of good mucilage.

The acacia is an example of the various devices of seed distribution. Those who can read a trailside as a book find everywhere evidence of the care Mother Nature takes to insure THAT REPRODUCTION SHALL BE ADEQUATE. Our Geogardener found one species of acacia (1) whose seedpod is light as paper. Each pod had 5 to 9 almost weightless seeds. (2) Each pod was TWISTED. Here was a mechanism as efficient to catch wind as a windmill. It is fascinating to watch the action of these seeds in a gale. They travel long distances as they spin over a hard surface. They are really as marvelous in this as are the seeds of the Linden. Nearby is another species of acacia with a *straight* pod having also the weight of a lead pencil. The twisted pods spread over a wide triangle in this one gale, (the mother tree is apex) . . . The heavy-podded species remained close to the parent tree.

Yes, acacia bloom in garden clump, or street-side forestry stimulated Geogardener's memories of where acacia grows wild in Africa, in Arabia, in Australia.

"*I'm sick of fog and yellow gloom,*
    Of faces strange, and alien eyes,
Your London is a vault, a tomb,
    To those born 'neath Australian skies.
O land of gold and burning blue,
    I'm crying like a child for you!"

Dorothy Frances McCrae

STONE SEATS, BACCHUS THEATRE
Acanthus Land is the Land of the Greeks.

Above photograph shows stone seats in the ancient Theatre of Bacchus below Anthens' Acropolis. Here, in Pericles' lifetime, were played the never-to-be-forgotten tragedies.

An example of the brainpower of ancient Greeks is brilliant Erathosthenes. He was employed at Alexandria by the King to educate the Crown Prince . . . Throughout Egypt were certain milestone poles. Erathosthenes once made a trip, past these, up-Nile to Syene. This city was built at the equator's crossing of the Nile. This Greek intellectual noticed the milestone pole there, at the summer solstice, cast no noonday shadow. There was, however, a shadow at Alexandria. He knew the number of paces' or human steps, between Alexandria and Syene. He measured that day's shadow at Alexandria. So penetrating was his mathematical mind, he was able from that date to compute, with startling accuracy, the size of the earth, of the sun, and of the moon. From such facts, he was able to make a forecast of an eclipse . . . Greece lost forever her research strains through cross-breeding with overseas' low-powers . . . U. S. A.'s research men also are a great asset. We need them to lift us out of biological illiteracy. We will locate more of them when more children have "home museums" of botanical, zoological, geological finds. Children enjoy collecting "specimens" on weekends and vacations. Gardens, too, contain a wealth of material. Kiddies thus acquire a knowledge of Nature's laws as a sponge absorbs water. Wise librarians will suggest data about butterfly nets, cigar-box insect collections, home aquariums, (fresh water or seaside), science reading . . . Our photo on page 7 is another view where the black and white Acanthus grows wild, to-wit, at Athens. When your Acanthus blooms remember Greece is Acanthus Land.

CHAPTER 2

ACANTHUS

THE MYSTERIOUS "Man-with-the-Iron-Mask" was imprisoned on Sainte Honorat Island. It lies off France's Juan-les-Pins. The tiny islet is rich in history. Here the Saracens,—(who, at nearby Arles, built their watchtowers on Roman-amphitheater-walls as a foundation)—raided again and again. Charles V held Francis I prisoner there. Its vicinity is linked, too, with Napoleonic legend.

Our Geogardener crossed in a small rowboat from Juan-les-Pins to Sainte Honorat. He landed on a beach KNOTTED WITH ACANTHUS. This had advanced, almost mangrove-like, to the swish of high tide. There he first saw, growing wild, the many-lobed leaf. This the nature-loving Greeks, in the days of Aristophanes, Demosthenes, Pericles, wove into their architectural motifs.

Behind this beach, in whose sand acanthus grows thus luxuriously, is an ancient monastery. It had a reputation for its very excellent wine. For centuries, its vineyards had been cultivated with the heavy square-hoe. This was hardly lighter in weight than the Neolithic stone hoe of 3,000 years earlier. With these, mankind's first gardens had been cultivated. Such gardening is back-breaking work. The "Man-With-The-Hoe" is, indeed, symbolic of that "hard labor" that once terrified the culprit when the sentencing judge said sternly: "Ten years at HARD LABOR". . .

In Sainte Honorat's monastery garden, our Geogardener witnessed an amusing example of the power of organized public opinion. The younger monks had overcome the opposition of their Superior as to hoe-work. . . A tiny tractor had been unloaded. It had been moved up the beach, where, like sand-verbenas in California, the acanthus had bound the drifting sands. The young monks, sandaled, and in their long robes, were trying to navigate the tiny tractor between rows of vines. From the manner in which priestly togas tangled in the tractor, one grasped why war-plant women had taken to slacks. . .

Compare acanthus' flowers with regular corollas—such as poppies, buttercups, wild roses. The former's bloom seems, as to symmetry of petals, like Shakespeare's King Richard III: "Scarce half made up." Perhaps a better simile would be to describe it as a reversed Andy Gump. Instead of being chin-less, however, it is *all* chin and no upper face. The tall stalks are, however, as many-flowered as delphinium or hollyhock. The bizarre bloom sports a purplish-green umbrella above. This is a convenient landing-place for visiting insects. . .

Cailfornia deserts have a relative of the acanthus family, (the Acanthaceae). It is the chuperosa, (*Beloperone Californica*) . . . "Daddee, gimme nickel to buy candy!" . . . This, before the whites came, was not heard from desert papooses. They had their "candy," nevertheless. For sweets they ate the coral-red, trumpet-shaped blooms of the chuperosa. This plant is the one American member of the acanthus family. It is found in the Lower-Lower Sonoran Zone in our Mexican-Border states. It is like the buckeye of the Upper-Lower Sonoran in Caledonian thrift. Both are so canny as to moisture-thrift, they shed their leaves when hot weather comes.

Spencer, in "Faerie Queen", compared the life of our garden flowers with the brief span of human life. "Man is like that flower, so fresh at morn, yet which fades at evening late." In an age intensely more practical than Spencer's, man draws another lesson from gardening. He observes the eugenic possibilities of improvement of strains by aiding Natural Selection with Artificial Selection. . . He sees the value of co-operation, in the continued expansion of the Sunflower Family* . . . He discovers therefrom also the consequent possibility of the reduction of war to a minimum thru such cooperation. . . He watches the working of the Differential Birth Rates Law, as seen by the garden displacement of, for example, a less desirable variety of gladiolus† by a better one. . . He notices, out of his gardening, the constant struggle, by weeding, to reduce competition working against flowers. This is, of course, a garden parallel of Galton's Eugenics.

---

* See Frontpiece Sierran Cabin . . . From Skyscraper.
† See Gladiolus Chapter herein.

CARYATIDES, THE ACROPOLIS, ATHENS

The architecture of Ancient Greece remains after 2 milleniums, the world's classic model. These brainy men fathomed the mystery of evolution in the Before-Christ era. Their research was forgotten until Darwin. The intervening Dark Ages came partly because the Greek intellectuals ended immigration control. Then commenced inter-marriage based on money—not intellect. Photo above is from the Land where grow wild Acanthus. Statice, Calendula and Camomile, also the Almond and the Olive.

ATHEN'S PARTHENON. UPHILL FROM SOCRATES' TOMB
(Acanthus Land)

Socrates, condemned to drink the hemlock because he dared express his thoughts, personifies those who still struggle for Free Speech. That the Atlantic Charter found it necessary to emphasize the Free-Speech right proves above . . . Socrates was one of those powerful intellects that, in his time, gave Athens "The Golden Age." . . . Sir Francis Galton, founder of Eugenics, declared even the brilliant Victorian Age of Britain was as far below Athens' Golden Age as it was above the culture of African primitives . . . Athens' success, unconsciously, was due to eugenical family life. Marriage was limited to mates of the highest physical and mental inheritance. Read about "Kiths" in Dr. Elsworth Huntington's "Mainsprings of Civilization."

PEON EXTRACTING PULQUE

The agave's use is an example of native resourcefulness. From it the Aztecs made a molasses-like sugar, resembling that of the maple. The agave is the plant from which pulque is made. (See "My Duenna's pink-hued Pulque" herein). Maguey sugar is fermented much as that of the toddy palm in Hindustan. Back in Toltec days the fibre formed the basis of paper. Like the yucca's, it made excellent binding twine. It thus became the chief basis of Mexican-Amerind textiles. One sometimes sees the thick curved leaves used as a combined tile and thatch for the crude huts. In some the beds are mats on the bare ground. Agave's thorns were used as needles as far back as when our savage ancestors made them of bone.

CHAPTER 3

AGAVE

"Cuando tineo dinero
Se llamaban 'DON TOMAS.'
Pero cuando no tengo dinero
Se llamaban 'TOMAS'—no mas"

(When I have pocketsful of money.
They flatteringly call me 'MY LORD THOMAS.'
But when I have no money,
They bluntly dub me merely 'TOMMY.')

(Folk-song from Agave Land)

WHERE yesteryear, courtship was by "playing bear" thru barred window, one of our Georgardener's family was stricken with a Mexican fever. Removed to a hospital, she was, ten days later, convalescing. The head nurse asked "Why worry? Your patient is improving." Our Geogardener answered "That I know. I now am disturbed about no replies to my mail to my office." "What stamps do you use?" "Why, of course, the common adhesives." "That is the reason for non-reply. Jose, our mailcarrier, soaks off the 5¢-value foreign-mail stamps. Each buys a drink of pulque at the corner *pulqueria.* Go to General Post Office. Buy envelopes with *embossed* stamps." Our Geogardener did. Soon the mail flowed as of old . . .

The pulque traffic in this century's first decade was very heavy. Whole trains thereof sped daily from the agave, or *maguey,* plantations into Mexico City. Even residence sections were dotted with *pulquerias,* resembling in number the American saloons of that day.

When one sees a "century plant" in a New England garden, one may travel in his imagination, geogardener-style, to Aztec Land. Down there, the agave's bloom-stalk is cut down. Its base then is basined into a bucket-sized cup. Its life-blood, the sap, accumulates therein. This becomes the favorite Mexican intoxicant—*"pulque."*

The agave, or maguey, is a gangster-type of plant. An amarylid, it has grown to be as tough as a Sicilian Black-hand. It has had centuries of fierce struggle. It has withstood blistering heat, rainless months that sometimes lengthened into years, and, most terrifying of all, desiccating winds that brought disheartening sandstorms. Its giant leaves thus have come to have a leathery overcoating. Such leaves are efficient reservoirs of precious moisture. They also constitute a defense system against Sol's javelins. This is so

YUCCA

While geogardening in blistered
Agave-land, one gained memories of
venison-jerky, mulliganed over the only
possible fuel—Yucca stalks. A cold tortilla, smeared with what Pepita declared
was yucca-blossom honey, completed
the repast.

effective that it would make a Prussian General Staff turn pea-
green, and apple-green, and nile-green, and bottle-green, and jade,
and emerald with verdant envy. Since it thus can stand almost
any type of unjust gardening treatment, it succeeded in persisting
when New England Clipper captains brought it from Vera
Cruz to Nantucket and to Salem. As to frequency of bloom in the
North, agave is as tardy as war-time mail to Honolulu. The week
after Pearl Harbor, a Honolulu man insists he wrote Philadelphia
for war-garden seeds. Months afterward they arrived. He opened
his package. It contained 6 full grown carrots, 2 heads lettuce. The
agave was similarly reluctant in flowering regularly in Massachusetts. Its striking, but years-apart blossoms earned it the sobriquet
of "Century Plant."

* For a tale of the Amerinds of Agave Land, see the author's "Manuelito of the Red Serape."

V.

Then comes temp-ta-tion
To mix his po-tion
IN MY DU-EN-NA'S
PINK-HUED PUL-QUE.
And now she's snooz-ing.
And now she's snor-ing
And now it's ea-sy
To steal her key.

VI.

Across the pa-tio,
In feet red-stock-ing'd,
I steal quite mouse-like
To steel-grilled gate.
There's Juan Bau-tis-ta
With his fleet mus-tang
Duen-na's scream-ing . . .
But she's too late.

VII.

In red se-ra-pe
High peak'd som-bre-ro
MY Juan Bau-tis-ta
He flees with me.
Across the des-ert,
In the pale moon-light,
Thru cac-tus ghost-like
He flees with me.

A few codices were sent by the Conquistadores to Europe. Their value was not appreciated at first, however. Prescott tells of some of these. The Mendoza Codex was lost for more than a century. It finally reappeared in Oxford's Bodleian library. . . . The brilliantly colored one of Rome's Borgian collection became a plaything of servant's children. Humboldt tells us of its being painted on deerskin. This saved it from these youngsters' sundry attempts to burn the priceless treasure. . . *The painting of the Dresden Codex is on agave.*

SENESCENT IN AGERATUM LAND

Ageratum is more imperialistic than Agave. Its domain extends from Aztec Land thru to Inca Land and indeed with an Eastern arm into Venezuela. There one species is shrubby. Our Geogardener found it forming chaparral on a precipitous, arid hillside. 2,000 feet below, and across the barranca, crept around the trail's hair pins a snake-like line of a pack train of burros. Field-glasses showed their loads were coffee bags. We turned back to study bush ageratum. The flowers were mostly light blue. A few were white. They were almost identical twins in resemblance to the charming ageratum of our home garden borders.

Far down South America's West Coast were other species. Our Geogardener collected ageratum, also calceolaria in flowers growing in interstices of paving stones of the old Inca Fortress of Sacsahuaman above Cuzeo. This was near where above picture was taken in the land where the breakfast cereal is chunyo of frozen potato flakes.

CHAPTER 4

AGERATUM

MacGregor yarned about an Aberdeen baker and his customer's dog. Each morning the dog appeared at the baker-shop, basket-handle in mouth. The basket contained three pennies, wrapped in newspaper. The dog returned daily with 3 oatcakes. One day the baker remarked "Sandy, 'tis good ye have an honest baker. . . I could easily cheat the dog." . . . "I'll wager a guinea ye could not!" . . . Soon 2 guinea-pieces were in the stakeholder's hands . . . Next morning the baker placed only 2 oatcakes in the basket. The dog trotted homeward. The baker telephoned "Sandy, the guineas be mine". He turned, because the dog was back—barking loudly, and, with him, was a policeman!

MacGregor continued: "We Scots can afford to tell jokes about ourselves, for we have the proud consciousness that our careful thrift has a high survival value. Without it, we never could have had our high birthrate!" . . . Among garden flowers, one of the highest birthrates is ageratum's. Careful as are the Scots of all resources tending to maintain life, ageratum is fully as efficient as is any Scot in maintaining continuance-of-life. Look, either beneath the wild ageratum plants anywhere from Mexico to Peru or Venezuela, or beneath your garden ageratum in late fall or early spring. You will be amazed at the number of seedlings.

Ageratum's soft blues are most pleasing as contrasts in color-schemes of either pink or yellow. It was one of the first cultivated flowers our Geogardener succeeded in tracing to its native haunts. He found it wild first in Mexico, then in Guatemala, Venezuela, later in the Peruvian highlands.

Ageratum, therefore, from its bonnie, blue-blossomed border whispers about towering Mexican volcanoes: Orizaba, Iztaccihuatl*, Popocatapet-atl.

Ageratum stimulates memories of olive-seed carvers at Mazatlan, cutting these pits into fascinating monkeys. Its blue blossoms, gathered even in December in sheltered nooks in Sacramento, talk of Juan Panduro, modelling humans from clay at Guadalajara, of

* This Aztec suffix: "atl" recalls, too, another Geogardening adventure tracing chocolate to its origin. "Chocol-atl" was the name of the favorite Aztec drink. The proud feather-robed Montezuma offered chocol-atl to the steel-clad Cortes. It reminds us of Aztec "Coyo-atl." This was the all-wise, wild-wolf, or coyote that, out of his wisdom, guided the redskin thru life's crises. It stimulates memories of "avoc-atl," or "alligator pear." This, an exotic luxury of yesteryear's men's clubs, became the basis of the great California avocado industry of today.

drawnwork-vendors at Aguacalientes. A flattering "Señora" glides into "Señorita" when this wrinkled squaw grasps she has not awakened an urge to buy. Ageratum awakens memories, too, of the obsidian quarries at West Coast Itzlan. From those came the volcanic glass for the knives that slashed out the palpitating heart of the war-sacrificial victim atop Anahuac's *teocalli*. Ageratum will tell you, too, of the hot winds among the banana foliage at Tapachula, 'way down on the Guatemala border. . .

Ageratum will stimulate recollections of wild ageratum blooming above a beach where started a ride across that frontier in a dugout canoe. It was made of an avocado trunk. Down in that land, the liberty-loving *quetzal* is enshrined in the name of the Guatemalan dollar. It will not let you forget when the Indio caught an iguana. You feasted on its chicken-like meat, decorated with the yolk-rich eggs of this noiseless lizard. The stew was flavored with rare herbs, according to a technique handed down from the days of the temple-building Mayas.

Ageratum also revives memories of still farther south—in the semi-deserts of Salvador—with giant blue, also red, green-and-yellow macaws—of parrots a-nesting in banks of volcanic pumice, like bank swallows up north—of those feathered garbage-gatherers, the funereal *zapilotes*—of a score of fly-catchers, vermillions, also scissor-tails, on an airplant-weighted telegraph wire across the road from the *fonda,* while you breakfasted on sustaining *tortillas.*

Ageratum tells you of the day you gathered it growing among the stones of the Fortress of Sacsahuaman which once looked down upon the goldtiled Sungod temples of holy Cuzco below.

COLONNADE OF THE TEMPLE OF THE SUN, BAALBEK

Wild-Almond Land also is Fattail-Sheep Land. It commences with the coast of ancient Sidon and Tyre. It runs thru Baalbek of the mightiest stones of all architecture. Here, if you are polite, you gulp down that most greasy of dishes, fattail sheep. Your host is honoring you, as we of U. S. A. would with a turkey dinner. Wild-Almond Land (or Fattail-Sheep Land, if you prefer) runs across Arabistan, Iraquistan, Iranistan, Afghanistan to the Hindustan of which is written:

"A FATTAILED SHEEP, who did not want to die, bleated lamentably at my tent-door. He was scuffling with the Prime Minister, and the Director General of Public Education, and he was a royal gift to me . . . The Prime Minister adjusted his turban. It had fallen off in the struggle . . . I dispatched 2 bottles as a foretaste and . . . the sheep entered into another incarnation."

(Kipling: Namgay Doola)

CHAPTER 5

ALMOND

OUR GEOGARDENER had been a California almond-grower over several decades. He knew, from experience, the ups-and-downs of the almond business. He grasped that the almond, like its Anatolian neighbor, the apricot, was most exacting about geography. Happening to be in Egypt one winter, he decided to visit Transjordania and the Grand Leban, to try to find wild-almond nuts.

He was successful. Incidentally, however, found himself caught in the Druse Rebellion. The young Druse who assisted in locating the wild almonds was the son of a rebel chieftain. This son and his sister had been educated in U.S.A. The girl told of her first day in an American women's college classroom. She spoke little English. Her classmates, the night before, taught her the alleged ritual for "first-day-at-school". The professor happened to be a handsome bachelor of about 35. When he entered, she rose from the front-row seat where the conspirators had planted her, dropped on one knee, placed her left hand over her heart, rolled her eyes heavenward and repeated, as instructed, the magic formula: "I love you, gol'darn you."

Her brother was blue-eyed, flaxen-haired. One wondered, in this area of brunettes, whether he might not have been a "throwback" to Roman days. This seemed possible because, in the corner of the stone wall outside their dwelling, (where the crowded camels took shelter during the sandstorm), there was, upside-down, a stone with a Roman inscription. It evidently had been taken from an old Roman bridge. One could make out enuf lettering that the "XV Legion from Gaul" had been constructing here "roads and bridges". This now was French-mandated territory. Had perhaps, golden-haired, Gallic soldiers once planted the Roman Eagles there? . . .

The wild-almond "trees" were scrubby, almost bushlike. This Druse had a few wild nuts. They were very much smaller than even our Texas Prolific, which runs more to frost-hardiness than to size like the IXL. One was reminded of the stories of out China-way how peach strains had been built up, thru many centuries, by observant and highly intelligent Buddhist priests, eager that THEIR monastery's fruit should be a little larger, a little better flavored than the common run in the neighborhood.

This blond young Druse told of their grievances against their French masters. His tribe had held their land since time immemorial. They objected to forcibly receiving immigrants. The French, under "divide-and-rule" strategy had planted, under the guise of "accepting unfortunate refugees," those Armenians who were being forced out of Turkey under the Young Turks' "Turkey-for-the-Turks" slogan. Our Druse complained his folk, docile agriculturists, were no match, commercially, against the over-shrewd, ruthless Armenians. To make matters worse, now had come the almond-eyed Tonquinese. A few were soldiers. Most of them, however, were Oriental coolies. He mathematically contrasted the Druse living standard with U.S.A.'s, with Indo-China's. He declared it was this: U.S.A.'s $4 per day of 8 hours. Druse's 40c per day of 10 hours. Indo-China's 4c per day of 12-14 hours. . .

Many of California's most productive almond orchards are on hill-lands once considered worthless except for sheep-range. They ranked with Ozark hill-billy lands: "Where you get that calf?" "Traded my farm for it." "Farm? Whole farm for a calf?" "Yes, man came along . . . Wanted to trade calf for 1 acre. . . . When I found he couldn't read or write, I slipped the whole 160 acres into the deed."

One's liking of almonds may be horticultural or gustatorial. One may enjoy, in March, a flowering twig of almond blossoms from his California orchard, or perhaps a double-pink, grown for flower effect alone. Tourists go to Sicily to view its almond orchards in blossom-time. Most folk find pleasure in munching a few salted almonds. . . One may taste, with gusto, a green-almond soup at a Spanish restaurant. One may have canned green-almonds in a compote as an unexpected treat at a hotel-de luxe in the Dolomites. In the Schartzwald, sliced almonds came on a *"toertchen."* Highly-colored almond-paste, as *marzipan*, may be one's dessert in Luebeck. Almonds appear as *"mandel"* in a dish of cottage cheese in a Falzerego Pass inn's renowned dessert.

If, however, one wants the electric thrill of finding the "sauvage" almond so as to contemplate the eugenistic building-up, from the wild one, then he must go a-wanderlusting to the Levant of the Crusaders. There, in the land of the Druses, certain Oriental rug dyes are dissolved in camel's milk. . . There sabot-makers work cottonwood blocks into cheap footgear. . . There fat-tail sheep, bleating piteously are led to the slaughter toward a greasy *pilau* . . . There hoary cedars of Lebanon whisper of the building of the Temple of Solomon the Wise, and of the coming of the Queen of Sheba.

This is Wild Almond Land. There is no better example of the gains of Artificial Selection than the finding there of hard-shelled fingernail-sized wild almonds, then comparing them with the giant papershells of our best orchards.

The almond is also used medicinally by Old-wives* in the Near East. At least they consider "Bitter Almond" valuable in the fevers only too common there. "Milk-of-Almond" also "Sweet Almond" are not entirely unknown in certain pharmacies. An array of "herbs" and similar "vegetable" curatives forms the display of many an "herb doctor" in our cities.

---

* "One of the most important aspects of primitive medicine is the pharmacopoeia of most primitive tribes. Except for a very few regions, like the Arctic and Melanasia, where drug lore has been developed only slightly, an amazing percentage of the herbs, barks and roots used by the natives—a percentage which is far above the mathematical probability of random sampling—is of objective medicinal value." Dr. E. H. Ackerknecht, Transactions, Section of Anthropology, N. Y. Academy of Sciences, 1145, page 26.

CARAVANASARY, WILD-ALMOND LAND

Wild-Almond Land is almost identical with Camel-land. Camel colts always fascinate kiddies. A Geogardener well may analyze his urge to go a-wanderlusting—may ask, himself how much thereof had beginnings in the circus' "lions, an' tigers, an' camels, an' ele'funts."

All thru the wild-almond range are caravan-serai's, or inns. These cater to camel drivers. Among their freight are goatskins of dates or dried apricots. They also transport other goodies such as almonds. Geogardening in these lands is for sauvage artichoke, narcissus, ranunculus, anemone and an occasional gladiolus. Such wanderlusting brings by-products. Not the least of these is patriotism. One comes to have a deep appreciation of American business morals. Compare date-market haggling for a half hour with one-price "5 & 10" buying.

Is not American living standard worth eugenic conservation?

(B) BULBOUS SPECIES
"The clustering anemones
Their pretty secrets tell."

(Hafiz.)

PRIEST WITH ANCIENT CODEX

The Holy Land also might be called Anemone Land, Cyclamen Land, Ranunculus Land. Much of this area is semi-arid . . . Hence one finds here, as in California's Central Valley, also in Corsica, in Provance's limestone deserts, in the rock-deserts of Algeria, an abundance of bulbous plants. The bulb is one of Nature's devices for persistence through continued weeks of burning heat and aridity. Then the plant that already has flowered shrivels to the ground-line. Beneath, there is warehoused, in that bulb, all that is needed for next year's blooms.

CHAPTER 6

ANEMONE

Ah, ah, Cytherea! Adonis is dead.
She wept tear after tear, with the blood which was shed;
And both turned into flowers for the earth's garden close;
Her tears, to the WIND-FLOWER,—his blood to the ROSE.
                (E. B. Browning—A Lament for Adonis. St. 6.)

"Within the woods,
Whose young and half-transparent leaves
Scarce cast a shade,
Gay circles of ANEMONES
Danced on their stalks."
                        Bryant—The Old Man's Counsel.

"The ANEMONE in snowy hood."
                (Mary Clemmer's "Good-Bye, Sweetheart!")

"WIND-SHAKEN FLOWER" is the meaning of the Latin whence arose "anemone". Anemones have no petals. Their sepals however make them attractive. We have several charming species native to U.S.A. These include Arizona's "Canyon anemone". California's redwood belt has the dainty wood-anemone (A. queriquefolia). This is also found in the southern Appalachians. Other Alleghany species are: A. trifolia and A. virginiaca. A. parviflora is Asiatic, and is as well a native of our mountains. When, however, our Geogardener started tracking our garden species back to their native haunts, his trail led (a) transPacific, to Japan, (b) transAtlantic, to the Anatolian-Persian area.

In October, Cailfornia gardens display massed color in white-, in magenta-, and in pink-Japanese anemones. Do not look for these in the gardens of Nippon along side their chrysanthemums, the dwarf-pines, the stone lanterns. To have the geogardening thrill, go back into the Hinterland. Go a-wanderlusting far behind over-commercialized Yokohama, over-industrialized Osaka. Journey to where bits of old Japan persist. Travel to where wrinkled peasants' heads are bound in blue-and-white sweat-towels. There the *kago* may still be hired. A half-dozen runtish coolies will shoulder you along the narrow bamboo-lined trails. There even a foreigner is still greeted with the courtesy persisting from *samuri* days. There one may find the untouched, primitive flora of Japan. There one will find in spring wild hydrangeas, in autumn wild anemones.

A fine territory for such adventures is in the Back-of-Beyond behind Nikko, up Chuzenji way. There one's English friend, long resident in Japan may recount Japanese yarns. These show the little brown men have their jokes about their thrifty as do we. We are inclined to locate ours, geographically, in Caledonia. The Scots themselves restrict them to Aberdeen. A wanderer among the Nipponese misses said geography, can, however, smile at the joke. Here is one: Two samuri discussed spending. Tokagawa remarked: "My fan lasts me for years. When fanning, I open but one segment at a time." "I must criticize you for being a reckless spendthrift. I hold my fan open also at only one segment. You, however, wear yours out fanning! I hold mine stationary and wave my head!"

Geogardening in this anemone country meant, before World War I, primitive travelling. The typical Japanese inn contained never a table, never a chair. One slept on pads laid on the floor-matting. One's bedroom, however, had rare charm because of flower-arrangement. Opposite the unrolled *kakemona* on the right there would be, on the left, a vase of cloisonne. This usually contained but a single flower, sometimes just one anemone.

Our January-blooming species are native to Anatolia and to Persia. Each depends upon a kind of bulb for reproduction.

Gardening falls far short of geogardening. The latter expands mere gardening into vistas of intellectual enjoyment. These are far greater in extent than one may at first dream. Gardening may include merely jotting down, on a printed form, quantity, catalogue number, and price, then enclosing a check. Geogardening includes adventures as fascinating as any of Conan Doyle's Sherlock Holmes, or one in an Austin Freeman novel. One is not content with penciling in: 12 #4,627 (which means "anemone")—$1.20. One wants to know about origins. Where does anemone, fuchsia, paeony grow wild or *"sauvage."* Such curiosity may take one to Holland's kaleidoscopic bulb-polders with their ribbons of red and pinks and whites and purples. From thence one trail winds, in the case of anemone, to the Holy Land, to the Grand Leban, to Damascus, to Bagdad, and, yesteryear, along camel trails to them, yet unheralded Teheran.

> *"The fairy-corm'd, flesh-hued ANEMONE,*
> *With its fair sisters, called by country people*
> *'Fair maids o' the spring.'"*
>
>   (James N. Barker.)

En route Jerusalem, (above), to the Sea of Galilee, (below), our Geogardener halted to study wild anemone, cyclamen, ranunculus in dust-soil in lava cracks . . . His chauffeur had been instructed, by the Biblical pundits, to go to the point nearest to where Christ preached The Sermon on the Mount . . . Its lava outcrop was surrounded by thorn bushes, source of the "Crown-of-Thorns." There one reread the undying Sermon. Came a new glimpse: Much of 20th Century eugenics was therein. "Which of you, by taking thought, can add one cubit to his stature?" . . . The need of nature study had new force in "Behold the fowls of the air" and "consider the lilies." . . . "Cast not your pearls before swine" awakened memories of Greeks, of Horace . . . "Wide is the gate and broad is the way that leadeth to destruction" seemed to give new ideas as to EXCESSIVE birth control of our Talented leading to eventual extinction.* Negative Eugenics was anticipated by "Every tree that bringeth not forth good fruit is hewn down and cast into the fire" . . . Crowning all was the folly of expecting "grapes from thorns, figs from thistles." "The Highpowered" in contrast with morons: "Ye are the salt of the earth," also "Ye are the light of the world." What greater stimulus to eugenic planning could one find than building the house on a rock, contrasted with choosing the sands.

---

* See study of Extinction-trend of the Samaritans, (Eugenics Pamphlet No. 47).

CHAPTER 7

APRICOT

The specific name of Apricot, Prunus armenica, locates its Asian oasis' beginnings. When you eat fresh apricots, canned apricots, glacé apricots, why not give your imagination full play? Dream of diamond-brilliant desert stars looking down on Oriental intrigue, of burnoosed sheiks on prancing Arabians, of caravans of swaying camels, their sheepskins bursting with sun-dried apricots, of black-eyed girls peeping at you from latticed windows, of fierce eunuchs guarding harem doorways.

The apricot indeed has entree to the most exclusive harems. It there ranks with ruddy pomegrantes and with the prized golden-brown *deglet noors*. Not that our Geogardener ever dared attempt passing those sacred portals. However, coax a tired eunuch coming off duty, to accept an extra cup or two of thick black, Turkish coffee—(you know the kind: wherein a spoon sticks upright in the ropy syrup-like concoction)—and soon you'd be a-hearing grateful gossip. Yes, the damsels of the harem esteem the apricot—fresh or candied—as of the upper-level aristocracy. The men folks are not far behind. If you have cameled the trail of the Damascus Hinterland for days—even when geogardening—and the sandstorms have filled eyes and ears, nostrils, mouth and lungs with razor-sharp sand

MOSQUE OF SULIMAN THE MAGNIFICENT IN APRICOT-SHADED DAMASCUS

—if you would give your left hand for a bath—when your disagreeable *oont, oont, oont,* has tried persistently to nibble your
ear or your elbow with that cavernous, dribbling mouth at the end
of his hairy slide-trombone neck—when your eyes are weary of the
desert glare—and your hipbones are ready to come through your
saddle-skin—when—all of a sudden—you come to The Rim, and,
beyond and below, you see the full-leaved oasis of apricot trees that
is Damascus—Well! you then, and only then, come to know why
green is sacred to Allah!

Geogardening peach or apricot toward *sauvage* beginning calls
for more than Sherlock Holmes' skill. You may find almond cousins
that seem primitive. Our Geogardener, however, never found the
wild apricot. Peaches, well, sometimes. A saffron-robed Buddhist
priest, much farther East, finally may have judged you to be what
the South American calls *"simpatico."* He then will unbosom. If
you praise his tiny but toothsome peaches, he may tell you of tradi-
tions of centuries of competition between monastery gardens in improving that gift of Heaven—the peach. He will describe a persistent selection over centuries. This must have improved the almost
bitter wild peaches. He will tell you imaginative legends about the
peach-blossomed gardens of the Land of the Immortals. Like the
search for those fruit-yielding Rosales, the sauvage apricot—your

Trays of Dried Fruit in Apricot   In Apricot Land
Land Market   French Engineers have installed
                         faucets in lieu of wells.

Geogardening for the wild peach will probably yield you no more than—(but they are worth the whole cost)—glimpses of Different Lives!

Of course, "they" are all roses, too. But "they" have learned, thru long experience, that the kitchen's a safer door to security than that of a "beauty shoppe." So we find them around bandanaed Dinah, with her fruit-canning, her jelly-making, her jams— yes, and even her shortcakes. "They" are the perhaps less ornamental, but highly useful—the gastronomical Rosaceae. They're not versed in hairdo's or powdered noses, or highly-colored finger nails, like the Eclipses, the Hoovers, the MacArthurs, or their somewhat elder sister roses, the LaMarques, the Marshal Niels, not to mention The Madam Testouts—if you are thinking of the French branch of the family—the Karl Drutschkes if you lean toward the

At the crook of this street in Scutari, under the shadow of the minaret, while the muezzin was calling the Faithful to prayer, there passed a dozen camels. Each had "saddle bags" of sheepskin. Following them to the caravanserai enclosed, their unloading was followed by bargaining for the inevitable dried apricots.

The bred-in-the-narrow regard of the Mohammedan for green as the sacred color sometimes results in startling effects. The green turban (evidence of having made the Mecca pilgrimage within the year) usually is pleasing. One is startled, however, at seeing a Pathan coming thru the Khyber pass with a beard stained—not red or yellow—but green. And, in Africa, where the under-sized Somali negroes dye their kinky hair orange or henna our geogardener saw one, with hair colored green. Again, 'twas evidence of the Mecca trek.

Nazis—or the American Beauties—if you be Yank or Reb . . .

The utilitarian "theys" include the apples, the pears, the peaches, the plums, the prunes, yes—and the strawberries, the blackberries, the raspberries, the salmonberries, the Loganberries, the Youngberries, the phenomenalberries. (Hope we've not overlooked any "among those present").

The clan of the "theys" is far flung. Their nectarines are also called "Australian peaches." The pears rub elbow with what remained of France's aristocracy after 1790—and our apricot moves in the best society, under the Star-and-Crescent, whether Turkey-red or Morocco-green.

DESERT SCENE IN APRICOT LAND

While geogardening to discover wild artichokes, a Californian learns that the adobe bricks of his Golden State's missions are of a culture that filtered to Mexican-California through Spain from Africa-of-the-Moors. (See 'dobe wall in above photograph. Note, too, the peasant hoeing). American-pioneer stock's inventive genius substituted tractor-drawn plows for such back-breaking hoe-work. This same ability to invent gave U. S. A. the punch-card system that was one of the indispensable factors in our World War II victory. Is such an asset not worth eugenic conservation?

CHAPTER 8

ARTICHOKE

R UTS WORN by Roman chariot-wheels into street-paving stones are still visible at Timgad. It was a desert outpost of the Roman Empire. It was near here our Geogardener found his first wild artichokes. Their large, purple-blue, thistle-like blooms grow as wildflowers in French Africa.* They were growing along a fissure in the rock below a Bedouin camp. Our Geogardener had to fight for his first one. The wild artichokes grew unpleasantly close to the Bedouin's camel's-hair tents. The snarling dogs of none-too-friendly Bedouins disputed our Geogardener's right to collect specimens. The desert-dwellers made, at first, no effort to call off their ferocious herd-dogs. However, the flash of a bright-yellow, near-silk neckerchief opened negotiations. Soon it became possible not only to gather the desired botanical specimens, but to photograph their camp. The headman, who spoke a little French, later wanted to sell a strip of the cloth of their tents. He asserted it was *"veritable"* camel's hair. . . .

The artichoke, one historian asserts, most appropriately could be the coat-of-arms of the House of Savoy. That dynasty managed to persist from the Middle Age days of its first little barony. This was in what is now France's *Department de Haut-Savoie*. Since then it had continued until the years of boastful Il Duce Mussolini. Said historian asserts: "Italy was like an artichoke, for Savoy to consume, leaf by leaf". Truly, from its first hill-fortress in the Savoyard highlands, the White-Cross-on-the-Field-of-Red saw annexed, toward southern horizons, castle after castle. Lands were added from Piedmont to Rome, then to Naples of the Two Sicilies. Absorbed, too, was Sardinia. Thence leaping to Africa, Tripolitania, Cyrenaica, Libya were absorbed.

There is a French school of medicine that values highly an extract of artichoke. The pith-helmeted Britisher, back from Hindustan, growls at his "liver". For this complaint, these Gallic doctors assert, artichoke extract is as valuable a corrective as are the famed waters of Vichy.

The artichoke, thru centuries of desert environment, has evolved an effective weapon. It is one that is most valuable in a

---

* See the author's "Immigration into New France." This tale of French Africa describes the forces at work in the North African population-mass.

sparse-vegetation environment, like its North Africa rock-desert. That weapon is the thorn. It tends to prevent foraging by mammals. The thorn is common to desert plants of various orders. These range from the catclaw of the pea family to the cacti—which sprang from the pre-Rosales. . .

The artichoke also illustrates how desert plants tend to become moisture-conservors. This giant thistle must survive the dryness of summer-shade temperatures up to 130°. Each plant, therefore, builds up a perfect "thatch" of accumulated dead leaves. These, radiating from the stem in every direction, accumulate year after year. One artichoke has thus a circle thereof with, say, a 20-inch diameter. The soil, under this thatch, remains as moist as tho it had showered within the hour. The terrain beyond its parasoled circumference may have been sun-parched for months. Herein one sees another of the thousands of examples of efficiency in Mother Nature's evolution upward. 'Tis only Man, endowed with reason, who reverses this process.

Some hold our first garden cultivation of wild plants was in desert oases. He who goes a-geogardening (whether to Persia whose ancient rugs may have supported the first table bouquets or to the Western Sahara) is always fascinated by irrigation—even if the blossom depended on a turbaned burnoosed A r a b with his water route a distended pigskin.

Desert pigskin water supply. Compare YOUR merely turning a faucet. How about U. S. A. living standard?

The artichoke is a member of the Thistle Tribe of the Compositae.* The artichoke's cousin, the Caledonian thistle, is the bonnet-piece of several Scottish clans. Among these are the Royal Stewarts, with their blue-plus-green-on-red plaid. Their clan, based on Brittany, became the royal stewards of King Henry I. Other thistle-badge clans are the Stewarts of Appin, a Highland clan, and the Stewarts of Athole, rare fighting men. At Culloden, these

* See "Sierran Cabin from Skyscraper" for an account of the successful evolution of the Compositae. It is a tale of cooperation. A parallel in International Relations therein is drawn.

Athole Stewarts, along with the Camerons, formed the right wing, which completely routed the opposing Hanoverians. . .

Natural Selection has tended to elevate the thistles and other composits to top-place among all plants. . . The same Darwinian Natural Selection has worked for centuries among humans as persistently as it does among wild elephants, tigers, coyotes, rabbits pinetrees, buttercups, lilies, roses, campanulas, snapdragons, sunflowers. It has lifted man from the stooping, bent-kneed Neanderthalers to the Aristotles, the Shakespeares, the Pasteurs, the Edisons . . . It has remained for the Talented of the last few decades to reverse Natural Selection by EXCESSIVE birth control . . .

The artichoke's clansfolk, the thistles, always are worth study. One day our Geogardener found, beside an El Dorado National Forest trail, Sierran thistles flaunting their red-purple banners. One attracted a Calliope hummingbird. A few moments later, a zebra-swallowtail fed thereon. It systematically circled around the brilliantly-colored flowerhead. Bird- also insect-aviator landed easily. Let, however, a deer attempt feeding thereon. Then lips and tongue swiftly telegraph the deer brain the message: "Too thorny". This Sierran thistle's flowerhead had 67 sepal-like bracts. Each of these had one terminal barb, several lateral ones. These spines also are as effective as barbwire in stimulating rabbit feeding elsewhere. . . Thus is fortified the magenta-tipped flower which tops the seed with the silky wings, folk-named "thistle-down." . .

The days of miracles are not over. There is one floral miracle in every thistle bloom, artichoke or Sierran. These miracles include the publicity-stunt of color-flash, as well as the highly-protected flowerhead. Another is the silken parachute by which, in autumnal gales, next year's seed floats away. It thus founds—as do some undesirable, rapidly-breeding human immigrants—new colonies. . . This Sierran thistle had 248 seeds. Here was an annual birthrate so high that, were there no competing plants, thistles, within a few centuries, could people the entire North Temperate Zone. . . There is, however, a keen struggle for existence. The seed-cracking bills of snowbirds, of sparrows, (white-crowned, or golden-crowned) dispose of many seeds, while scattering a few. . . . This is, however, Nature's way: high birthrate then Survival-of-the-Fittest.

Even the lowly Jimson weed is the subject of experiment as to the VARIATION. Such VARIATION is an important factor in Evolution. VARIATION as shown in our Artichoke leaves' photograph enters into NATURAL SELECTION. Intelligent plant and

LEAF VARIATION ON SAME ARTICHOKE PLANT

"The wild artichokes grew unpleasantly close to the Bedouin's camels-hair tents. The snarling dogs of the none-too-friendly Bedouins disputed our Geogardener's right to collect specimens. The desert dwellers made, at first, no effort to call off their herd-dogs. However, the flash of a yellow, near-silk neckerchief opened negotiations. Soon it became possible to, not only gather the desired specimens, but to photograph their camp."

"DE JIMSON WEED, IT BLOOMS JESS' ONCE"
> *"Fo' de Jimson weed*
> *She blooms jest once,*
> *And when she's shed, she's shed.*
> *An' when yo' am dead*
> *T'aint fo' couple o' months,*
> *Fo' yo' am gwine to be*
> *Long time dead!"*   (Old plantation song.)

animal breeders, utilizing its laws, have, thru long-continued ARTIFICIAL SELECTION built up valuable strains, horses and hens,—plums, paeonies and potatoes. . . Out of such observations has come two yet-infant sciences: Genetics, Eugenics. Data is accumulating in both with ever-increasing acceleration.

At the Carnegie Institute, Cold Springs Harbor, two eugenists, the late Dr. Davenport, his associate, the late Dr. Laughlin, experimented with Jimson Weed variations. There showed an even wider variation range than in our artichoke leaf photograph. Dr. Laughlin once showed the author their experimental garden. As we

walked along the Jimson weed rows he recalled above Negro song
. . . There were tall Jimson weeds, also short ones. There were solid
leaf margins, also incised ones. Some plants matted the ground
like moisture-conservers on deserts or on alpine moraines. Others
were rangy, with leaves at four-inch intervals.

Nearby was the Genetics Laboratory. It had stacks of thousands of fruit-fly variations. "The Laird of Skibo's" steel millions,
said Dr. Laughlin "are helping solve problems in genetics, and
eugenics. Possibilities of human betterment are of infinite horizon."
. . . The learned Doctor continued: "Here are being worked out laws
paralleling those of immigration control. . . Here may be the beginnings of a technique of disease control as important as Pasteur's
discoveries in bacteriology." He concluded "We have already listed
several score inherited tendencies to disease". Once we apply the
knowledge of pure science herein to applied or medical science in
controlling disease we can end many human miseries including
haemophilia, Huntington's chorea more than a dozen types of blind-
ness.

One important result of applied eugenics will be the reversal of
the present dysgenic trend of the birthrate of The Talented. We
need, for example, more of the researcher pattern of intellect.

BEDOUINS, IN ARTICHOKE LAND, MANAGE TO REPRODUCE

An example of public good possible out of geogardening is California's roadside forestry. Same now is a fixture in Government. Our Geogardener, (this was some years before World War I broke), was making certain studies in South Germany. He observed that the trees planted along roads over which he motored were numbered. He asked a German army officer the reason. "The crops of all trees, fruit or nut, are sold." "But do not boys help themselves?" "Not in Germany. They are disciplined to respect 'Verboten'." "But the other trees, poplars, willows, birches?" "Ah! that is another story. They make good sawdust flour." "But sawdust contains no food value." "Never mind, it makes one forget the empty stomach. There will be a war in 1915. Germany's enemies will try to encircle and starve her. With such measures as roadside trees' sawdust, we will persist until victory is ours." (This was said in 1910).

CHAPTER 9

BEEF-WOOD

KANGAROOS IN ACTION, BEEFWOOD LAND

"We are the Trees
That grow for man's desire,
HEAT IN OUR FAITHFUL HEARTS.
Dwelling beneath our tents, he lightly gains
The few sufficiencies his life attains—
Shelter, and food, and fire."

(Mary Colborne-Veel.)

A DICTIONARY of Blackfellow language is not available. Hence the name of "she-oak" or "beefwood" in aboriginal-Australian cannot be given here. Sure, however, it must have been musical if it was similar to Blackfellow place names. Among the euphonious Blackfellow place names are Wooloomaloo, Warnambool, Geelong, Murumbidgee, Wollongong, Paramatta, Barcov, Pelbarra, Narribeen, Kalgoorlie, Coolgardie. Most of these probably are as descriptive as our Pioneer place christenings as Coyote Wells, Deer Creek, Bear Mountain, Stony Creek, Sucker Flat, Blue Tent, Whiskytown, Bedbug (now Ione), Hangtown, Sorefinger, Fiddletown, (can't you almost hear the musicians' "Hush now! Susannah, don't cry")— Humbug—(where they almost lynched the object of their practical (?) joke when the mint remitted almost double per ounce for the "white gold" which had proven to be platinum!)—also Missouri Flat, Michigan Bluff, Illinois Town, Rough-and-Ready, Chinese Flat, Negro Hill, Mormon Island, all in California. Compare also

Tubac, Arizona-Pima for "adobe house." Why, oh! why! did the
Colonials "Down-Under" substitute "she-oak" for the Blackfellow
name of this very popular roadside-forestry tree. Their other name,
"beefwood", is better. The latter does describe the dried-blood-
red heartwood of this unique tree. The verse above seems to picture the fire-red of the beefwood's heart.

To really understand the beefwood, one's geogardening foot-
prints should be made toward Arizona's Adamana. This is Petri-
fied-Forest town. When a geogardener there is delving into Paleo-
botany, he hears the legend that its original host, Adam, and host-
ess, Anna, gave their names to it. The Adamana Petrified Forest
records, — in its prostrate, silicified tree-trunks, — a remarkable
story of conifer efficiency. It is an efficiency tale which our intellectuals, with their EXCESSIVE birth-control, might well ponder.
Here is evolutionary evidence in permanent stone. The Southern-
Hemisphere conifers, which include the celery-leaf pine, met defeat.
They went down in the struggle with the snow-shedding, needled
pines of our North.

Our Beefwood, with its needle foliage, also is of a geologically
very-ancient flora. The colossal earth-crust-twist that split the Celebes Deep saved us beefwood evidence of Mother Nature's thru-the-
aeons experimentation. In beefwood, she "invented" one needle-
shaped leaf. That type was to be her model, later, for vast circumpolar needled-conifer forests. Imagine the Old Lady laying the
beefwood needles thriftily on her shelf. There they would remind
her when, later, she felt she should improve on the non-needled
Down-under conifers. Thus, racking her brain for the ever-better,
came her success that spread all thru the Northland.

It must have been the eucalypts and the beefwoods that constituted the "20,000 giants" the Australian Simson cleared as described in Dowell O'Reilly's verse:

> *"Simson settled in the timber,*
> *When his arms were strong and true,*
> *And his form was straight and limber;*
> *And he wrought the long day through*
> *In a struggle, single-handed,*
> *Watch the trees fall slowly back,*
> *Twenty thousand giants banded*
> *'Gainst this solitary jack."*

Australian schools use a series of exploration maps. The unexplored part of the Australian continent in each one is shown

black. The explored part is shown in contrast in yellow. The first map of Beefwood Land is dated 1788-98. The yellow speck is hardly the diameter of a knitting needle. It shows the expeditions of French, Phillips, Dawes, Hunter. These names, like their successors, are examples of Anglo Saxon daring in exploration. Then, as a melon's two seedleaves grow into a vine, the yellow expands. By 1815, resulting from the work of Blaxland, Wentworth, Lawson, the map shows the Wollondilly, the Warragamba, the Kowming, as well as the Kurrajong Range. Note again the tinkling Black-fellow place-names. By 1928, Cunningham, Evans, Oxley, Hume, Howell have increased the known area, say 5 fold. By '42 thru Sturt, Bonney, Russell 3/4 of the coast is known. By '46 Sturt has crossed halfway from Adelaide to the North Coast. By 1875 there are but 7 black islands in Beefwood Land. This final mopping up is largely the work of Giles.

BLACKFELLOW LANGUAGE IS MUSICAL

CHAPTER 10

BEGONIA

*"Old fashioned begonias . . . in pots arranged on shelves in
the Cape Cod sitting room" were enjoyed by Tenas Brad-
shaw in Joseph Lincoln's novel . . . (Cape Cod captains,
for decades, brought back from the West Indies—along
with rum and molasses—begonias, easily grown indoors,
whose color brightened gray Cape Cod winters.)*

ENGLAND'S RENOWNED Kew Gardens have one of the world's best
collections of the genus *Begonia*. It was this that sent our Geogardener wanderlusting to Martinique, to Mexico, to Guatemala, to
Colombia, to Venezuela, to Brazil to study Begonia in its native
haunts. . . . He was told that there he would find them growing
almost like weeds. As weeds he did find them in the abandoned
plantations of Martinique.

On that island were broad acres, once under brilliant Gallic
ownership. These had yielded great crops of indigo, of sugarcane.
The management of these estates was by a type of intellect that, for
centuries, had been dominant. Such folk, prolific, always had sent
forth colonies of born leaders. These included the Normans in
Sicily. Their kingdom had won the applause of all men as the
"most tolerant in Christendom." This rare type started another
colony across the Straits of Dover. It was by the company that, in
1066, was under one William, yclept "The Conqueror". This William
and his men gave England an aristocracy that was eventually to
build the far-flung British Empire. These Norman-French, grown
British, were to continue the real group that could consummate the
shift into the British Commonwealth of Nations. They gave the
world the Pax Brittanica. The same group, leading again in colonization, was to give U.S.A. one of its two dominant strains of blood
—the Tidewater-plantation Virginians. Their descendants included
Washington, Jefferson, Monroe, Madison, Jay, and, later, Robert E.
Lee. These folk have steadied our America thru many a crisis. . . .
Our Geogardener found, in Martinique—(and, on the same journey,

HUMAN LUMBER WAGON

While going down mountain toward where wild begonias grew in long blankets out of maidenhair, our Geogardener passed this human lumber-wagon coming up grade. His DAILY wage for 13 hours balanced that for 10 minutes of certain unionized U. S. A. workmen . . . Geogardening for wild begonias gave; as a by-product, profound contentment for birth under the Stars-and-Stripes.

MARKET DAY IN BEGONIA LAND

in Haiti)* the gardens, also the plantations of these Norman-French. The estates, alas, were overgrown with jungle. Their jungle-flora included numerous begonias.

Begonia, however, stimulates bright recollections as well as somber ones. Our Geogardener determined that he would follow Kew-garden advice and have a wider contact with wild, or "sauvage", Begonia. A few years later, therefore, he went a-sleuthing to Brazil. Enroute to the Golden-monkey Jungle, he found begonias blooming in profusion. Where there had been recent road work, the fresh cuts were dotted with tiny begonia plants of the small pink variety most common in our gardens. These were as numerous as the smallpox pits in Paulo Souza's face. These seedlings were rushed to bloom in that sticky hothouse atmosphere when the plants were hardly half-thumb high. Along with the attractively-colored golden-monkeys, with millions of orchids, with boa constrictors, and with *morphos*, the begonia-pink-splashed road cuts made a tropical geogardening-ensemble long to be remembered.

It was the *morphos* and Paulo Souza that deepened this exotic feeling. The *morpho* is the big "blue-silk" butterfly that is used commercially,—like the blue kingfisher feathers of Kwantung—for inlays and in jewelry. In Amazonian Brazil, the *morpho* is green. Farther South, however, it is the deep ultramarine blue that is most popular. . . .

At Otto Maier's, the German tradingpost, at the jungle-end, our Geogardener met this Paulo Souza. Maier said Souza was a *"sambo,"* as the term goes in Brazil. This meant was helf Negro, half Amerind. The trader said he was the only reliable *sambo* of the scores living in the nearby jungle. Paulo Souza's problems were simple. He had a patch of land bordering on a little stream. There were twelve bananas, three cocoanuts, four papayas. His women cultivated a small cavassa patch, that yielded the manioc which takes the place of maize of the North. Otto Maier said *sambo* fishing thereabouts consisted in tying the baited line to a bare toe, then

---

* In Haiti, was witnessed one of the most tragic of a long series of blunders of mistaken idealism that extends from the misinterpretation of the ideals of Jefferson and of Lafayette— as seen in the dropping of the guillotine in the French Revolution—to the crazy interference with our army and our navy strategists when a group of these, backed by an appreciable volume of voters compelled the abandonment of the fortification of Guam "lest it offend Japan." This was at a time when all informed folk knew that an all-out war was inevitable with a Japan that wanted to dominate ALL coasts of the Pacific including North and South America. It had been coming ever since 1914, even 1905. Japanese militarists had organized pilgrimages of school-boys, until everyone of these had felt, with his own childish fingers, the scars of Nipponese shells on the steel mast of a Russian battleship. This was erected at the sacred water tori of Miyajima and each boy repeated: "This is what the Yamoto race does to all barbarians!"

This same element in France of 1789 forced the brainy French Caribbean plantation owners into ruin. Their estates became the property of demagogic mulattos. To obtain a clear account of the atrocities, search, search, search—until you find Lathrop Stoddard's almost-forgotten "The French Revolution in San Domingo."

snoozing, back to a cocoanut-palm's trunk until the tug of a surprised fish restored wakefulness.

The sole masculine labor seemed to be a trek, about once monthly, for "blue-silk" butterflies. Otto Maier was pessimistic about Brazil's future* *"Endlich wirt Brazil ein colossal Haiti!"* Otto continued: "We Germans thought we had planned to occupy it. We selected the key area, the state of Sao Paulo. This commonwealth is so powerful it usually names Brazil's President every alternate term. We Germans had, in the Sao Paulo fortress, everything needed to eventually dominate Brazil, finally all South America. We had rare leadership combined with scientific technique. We blundered, however, in just one particular: Overwhelming surplusage of natural wealth. We would have been wiser to select poorer terrain. Sao Paulo was so amazingly fertile our immigrants from low-living standard areas like Bavaria and the Rhinepfaltz became *milreis*-crazed. Our women no longer bore 8, 10, 12 children. They stopped at 1 or 2."

"Meantime the *sambos* multiplied." Otto Maier said, "We have a German folksaying about a high birth rate *"Die vermehren sich wie Karnikle.†* We hoped our German girls, transplanted to Brazil, would reward our Pan-Germans, for their new-found release from poverty, by fruitfulness. 100,000 mothers at the 8-child rate would give us 800,000 children, 6,400,000 grandchildren, 51,200,000 great grandchildren. We thus would have, in a few generations, a Teutonic population-mass in South America comparable with U.S.A.'s or Russia's. German Weltmacht would then have been supreme! Instead, our girls went on a birth-strike!". . .

"Pure-Portuguese whites in Brazil are not numerous" said Otto Maier. He continued, "This gives the *'sambo'* his opportunity. The pure Brazilian black comes largely from just across the Atlantic. He says he is a 'Ginny-nigger.' This means his forebears come from the Guinea coast. He has the sex habits of the jungle. His birthrate is adjusted to every enemy, from muscular gorillas to charging bull elephants, from deadly snakes to swarming tse-tse flies. So wives yield a baby a year. In Brazil the "Ginny-negro," Maier rattled on, "consorted with the Amerinds. The Amerinds, again, are a most prolific strain. Study same from Quebec's habitants, thru Mexico, to Chile. Even your U.S.A. redskins are increasing. All I can see for Brazil eventually is 'ein colossal Haiti'."**

* "In the end, Brazil will become a gigantic Haiti."
† "They multiply like wild rabbits."
** In 100 years of Negro rule in Haiti—no white citizenship was permitted—nor white realty-ownership. (Readers Digest 6/44).

BUTANTAN IN BEGONIA LAND

One geogardening fascination is the ever finding of wild species that never have been utilized by plant breeders. Even with a flower cultivated for centuries like the Rose, hybridizers have not exhausted the "sauvages." Our Geogardener recalls the thrill of hearing in France, about a new yellow wild rose. The rose-breeder's collector had obtained it not far from where Kermanshaw rug-weavers fix their vegetable dyes in camel's milk. This find gave gardeners 2 popular new roses. These were named for that rose-grower's only sons. Both were trained rose experts. Both made the supreme sacrifice in World War I.

English gardens had scores of begonia creations. All, however, were based on a half-dozen "sauvages." There are hundreds of wild species that begonia-breeders had never utilized. There were repeated journeys to Begonia Land. While thus in the State of Sao Paulo, Butantan was visited. This is the Rockefeller-financed Snake-venom Institute. It is saving many lives annually throughout Latin America. It was fascinating to see the parcels-post vans unloading snakes, poisonous frogs, even deadly spiders from jungle, from pampa. Seldom does one find a more striking example of American idealism in action.

ALASKAN DOG TEAM

Alaska is both birch and spruce land. Several birch tree trunks are to the left of the dog team.

SALMON TRAP IN THE ALASKAN BIRCH AND SPRUCE AREA

CHAPTER 11

BIRCH

"Lay aside your cloak, O BIRCH TREE
Lay aside your white-skin wrapper!
For the summer-time is coming,
And the sun is warm in heaven,
And you need no white-skin wrapper."

—(Longfellow: Hiawatha.)

THE TERRIBLE power of the avalanche is recalled to our Geogardener whenever, in his strolls, he meets birches. A triumvirate of these graceful trees adorns many an American lawn, following a fashion commenced many years ago. In the gardens of yesteryear, it was the vogue to plant such a clump of 3 white-barked birches. Our Geogardener, therefore, finds these stimulate memories of a Sunday afternoon in Norway. He was sitting on a boulder, watching a peasant girl. She was dressed in the sensible, yet colorful peasant costume of her fjord. She was weaving, for nearby wild strawberries, a basket of birch-bark. 'Twas in a narrow, gorge-like valley at a fjord-head of the glacier-carved gorge. Both sides ran steeply up to the great Snowfield above. Suddenly, in front of them, there was a deafening roar. It resembled that of an iceberg snapping from a sea-lapped glacier-tongue. Down that granite slope, the avalanche crashed thru the birches. It snapped them as if they were matches. One boulder rolled within a hundred yards of the peasant maid. She later pointed out light green scars of young birches in the black-green pine forest. These were where former avalanches had roared . . .

The birch family is circumpolar. We find, therefore, its paper-like, but tough bark used over a wide area. Hence there were birchbark canoes in Redskin North America, birchbark baskets in Norway, even ancient birchbark rucksacks in early Finland. It is not strange, therefore, that our Geogardener found this lover of the northern coolth in the Himalayas. Several species grow there. The bark of the yellow birch formerly was used for tanning the famous Russian leather and for making a yellow dye. In Scandinavia, our Geogardener found its leathery bark used in the Hinterlands for shoes. In ancient Scotland, its sap was fermented to make a kind of beer. Our Geogardener learned much about the use of birch timber, birch leather, "Russian oil," a medicine made from birch wood. In France, the young branches are used for peasants' brooms.

Few areas call the Geogardener more persistently than the Himalayas and their "Back-of-Beyond." America's gardens are already enriched by its chaparral, including cotoneasters, pyrolas, buddleas. Tibet's *blue* poppies are a rare color note, and only too rarely seen in cultivation. A Texas six-footer can easily be lost in their giant Thalictrums. The tree paeonies of the mountain valleys that run up to The Snows are, at once, the delight and the despair of the gardener who likes the Different.

Our Geogardener and his wife, in their coffin-like *dandywallahs*, were borne on the calloused shoulders of the little Ghurka coolies. These swung around hairpin-turns on cliff-hugging footpaths. They chatted of how, in similar *dandywallahs*, there came down the icy passes, for English gardens, the first rootstocks of the giant Tibetan saxifragas. Their clustered pink blooms now brighten the Decembers of many a California garden.

. . . There are few passages in English literature that record the feel of the Himalayan forest with the upper fringe of BIRCHES below The Snows better than Kipling's Namgay Doola:

"His Kingdom was 11,000 feet above the sea and exactly 4 miles square, but most of the miles stood on end. . . His revenues maintained one elephant and a standing army of 5 men. . . This King would ride to Simla . . to assure the Viceroy his sword was at the service of the Queen-Empress . . . then he and his cavalry, (2 men in tatters) would trot back to their own place, *which was between the tail of a heaven-climbing glacier* AND A DARK BIRCH FOREST.

When you glimpse your trio of 3 birches in a corner at your lawn, dream, geogardeningly, of the birch forests. Close your eyes and think of the birch zone where :-

"40 miles away, untouched by cloud or storm the white shoulder of Dongo Pa—the Mountain of Council of the Gods—upheld the evening stars. The monkeys sang sorrowfully to each other. . . The last puff of the daywind brought from unseen villages the scent of damp wood smoke, hot cakes, dripping undergrowth and rotting pine cones. That smell is the true smell of the Himalayas."

Your nostrils will enjoy it, will remember it with a hound's-smell-memory, if ever you go a-geogardening thru the passes to the land of the yak and 'tsamba, to the "Roof-of-all-the-world."

"Enormously above them . . . the last of the BOLD BIRCHES stopped. Above that, in scarps and blocks upheaved, the rocks strove to fight their heads against the white smother. Above these again, changeless since the world's beginning, lay the Eternal Snows."

(Kipling: "Kim.")

"The Hallowell farm . . . I made haste to buy it . . . before the proprietor FINISHED GRUBBING UP SOME YOUNG BIRCHES which had sprung up in the pasture . . . To enjoy these advantages, etc." (Thoreau: "Walden").

> *"Give me of your bark, O BIRCH TREE!*
> *Of your yellow bark, O BIRCH TREE!*
> *Growing by the rushing river*
> *In the tall and stately valley!*
> *I a light canoe shall build me,*
> *Build a swift Chemaun for sailing,*
> *That shall float upon the river,*
> *Like a yellow leaf in Autumn,*
> *Like a yellow water lily."*—(Longfellow: Hiawatha.)

Birch fecundity is shown by the birch saplings sprouting in the sod weights on this farmstead. Fjarlands Fjord, Norway.

"Kim's . . . big toe was nigh cut off by his grass sandal string. Thru the speckled shadow of the great deodar forest, thru oak plumed with ferns, BIRCH, ilex, and rhododendron, . . the lama . . swung untiring.

(Kipling: Kim.)

PUNKAHARJU ESKER FROM THE AIR

Eskers are said to be formed by glacial action. The glacial-gouged depressions on either side of this remarkable Esker became lakes. Our photograph shows the density of tree growth which, even in Finland, supplies much of Europe's newsprint. These thick forests forced the west-trekking Finns to use waterways as highways. (See text).

You may see the white bark of a slender birch tree on a lawn as you stroll thru city streets. Remember then that it furnished paper for the young Cherokee, Sequoyah. He learned the whites had something far better than the smoke of signal fires. They had "talking leaves" or an alphabet. Hence his determination to invent an alphabet for his tribe. 'Tis said his first attempt was 153 sound-characters.

CHAPTER 12

BOTTLEBRUSH

"Where is Australia, singer? Do you know
These sordid farms and joyless factories?
She is the scroll on which we are to write
Mythologies our own and epics new:
Her crystal beams all but the eagle dazzle.
Her wind-wide ways none but the strong-winged sail:
She is Eutopia, she is Hy-Brasil,
The watchers on the tower of morning hail!"

(Bernard O'Dowd.)

The kangaroo, also the emu, of "Down-Under" have so intrigued grown-ups that Australia featured them on her coat-of-
arms and on her postage stamps. It has remained for the kiddies,
however, to grasp that Aussie's flora is equally fascinating. With
characteristic childish imagination,* they promptly dubbed the
flowers of the genus *Callistemon*: "bottlebrushes". The name is
most appropriate, for the flower arrangement does suggest a bottle-
cleaner.

The bottlebrushes are peculiarly Australian. Structurally,
they, like the wallaby, also the platypus or duckbill, are most primitive. They give a glimpse of the flora of the long, long ago... Geologists declare Australia was isolated from Asia at the time the
Celebes Deep came into being. Hence, while evolution proceeded
apace in Eurasia, it stagnated in Australia. This is fortunate for us
as it rolls up the curtain of the Long Ago. It was, indeed, but
yesteryear, that Tasmanian Man, a pure paleolith, was not yet quite
extinct.

Some day someone will collect into geographic chapters, the
world-wide childhood names of plants. Under Germany, we will
find *"stiefmutterchen,* the "little stepmother," for pansy. Kiddies'
imagination also dubbed the California wild mallow that blooms
along with the Harvest Brodieas among the yellowing grass "Fare-
well-to-Spring". Spraguea they called "Pussy Ears". One of the
Brodieas they appropriately named "firecracker lily."

---

* See Sierran Cabin . . . From Skyscraper, for children's poetical names of Californian wild
flowers.

"Last sea-thing dredged by Sailor Time from Space,
Are you a drift-Sargasso, where the West
In halcyon calm rebuilds her fatal nests?
Or Delos of a coming Sun-God's race?"

(G.W.L. Marshall-Hall "On Australia.")

A Christ-Child Day in Australia.

A copper concave of a sky
  Hangs high above my head.
The hot air faints upon the grass,
  And at its bitter breath,
Ten thousand trembling flower-souls pass,
  With fragrant sighs, to death.

These are no alien skies I know,
  Yet something in my blood
Calls sharp for breath of ice and snow
  Across the wide, salt flood.

Ethel Turner

TEMPLES AT MANEKARNKA GHAT, BENARES

Hindu pundits tell one the architecture of their temples is based upon preserving in stone the form of pine trees. These, they say, are always stretching toward God-in-the-Heavens.

Whether one hikes, day after day, thru the Sierran giant-conifer forest—or follows a trail in the densely-matted jungle of Brazil, of Venezuela, of Malaysia, of Ceylon . . . One is almost awed by the fact that each tree follows a certain urge. It is a REACH-ING-TOWARD-THE-LIGHT. It is what the great biologist Hertwig dubbed *Zeilstrebigkeit.*" Have we Occidentals, being excessively-urbanized and over-industrialized, forgotten this concept? Are we city-dwellers becoming parasitic?

BROOM

The Broom Lands are of unusual interest to students of Eugenics. Eugenists interested in the problem of EXTINCTION, should, when in France, visit Baume-les-Dames in the Doubs Valley. A small town, it is named from a Benedictine Abbey. This was founded in 763. It had a chapter of noble ladies. Only those entitled to 16 quarterings were accepted into membership.

Similar institutions drew upon the deeply-spiritual members of mediaeval noble families. The rollicking roysterers became fathers of many—including not a few with the bar sinister. Those with a deep religious urge,—often appalled at the 'sinful world,"—found solace—AND CELIBACY behind abbey walls. In their generation, the Church always gained rare leadership. This was what made Cluny feared by Rome. *BUT*, EACH GENERATION THOSE PRECIOUS GENES FAILED OF TRANSMISSION. When one studies the faces in frieze, in painting, in tapestry, one comes to grasp what happened. While geogardening, and incidentally observing biological shifts, one wonders if we are not paralleling the deadly celibacy of the "Dark Ages" today by the EXCESSIVE birth control of our Talented. Certain lands of the Broom—Spain, Portugal, their island colonies flounder about without Leadership. Their Talented failed to reproduce.

CHAPTER 13

BROOM

"Ye bright mosaics! that, with storied beauty
The floor of Nature's temple tessellate,—
What numerous emblems of instructive duty
Your forms create!"—(Horace Smith—Hymn to the Flowers.)

Few mosaics, even in stone,—as in Venice's Saint Mark's—can excel those of old Mother Nature herself. It is a rare thrill to cruise along Cornwall's sun-drenched South-coast in May. There one can see, indeed, rare mosaics. Their contrasting yellows of broom and of furze, observed against their matted greens, form color patterns never-to-be-forgotten . . .

The broom's use as to bonnetpiece* gave its name to an English royal family. The Plantagenet knight, before entering the lists, decorated his helmet with a sprig of *"Planta-genes"* or yellow broom. . .

Our garden species of broom originate in several areas of both European and North African coasts. When garden broom-bushes are bloom-clotted with molten gold, our Geogardener travels in memory to Carcassone. There, when the hills were golden with broom, he met the aged Monsieur X. His was a pathetically misdirected education. His father, in early manhood, had died at Sedan, fighting Bismarck's *Blut-und-Eisen troops*—predecessors of the Nazis. An aged, royalist grandfather, therefore, had the education of this only grandson. This ancestor belonged to the old nobility. He was unshaken in his faith that the legitimate king MUST someday regain his throne. Who, then, would remain capable of interpreting heraldic devices? Who could know "or" from "argent"— "gules", from "vert"? Who could read the quarterings? Who could relate how the first de Wolf had won knighthood in saving a kingly life? Who could recount why the Archbishop of Salzburg had an escutcheon whose device was a most plebeian turnip? Who even would remember how the sirloin, muchly desired by football players, arose from the knighting of Sir Loin-of-Beef? Who knew the mottoes of the Earls, and the obligations they imposed on every cadet? Who knew the childhood discipline that made possible man-

---

* One Scottish clan, the Murrays—with their green and blue plaid crossed with red—had the butcher's broom as their badge. This is, however, a lily, not a legume, like our garden brooms. When one studies the French origin of Caledonian names, (as "Grant," based on "le Grand—the tall fellow,") one wonders if, perchance, they borrowed the bonnet-piece-idea from the Nordic French, such as the Plantagenets.

hood deeds of valor, which bought the proud right to wear the Devices? . . There would be a demand for those learned in heraldry. Of this the tottering grandpere was sure. Did not the kings rule by Divine Right? Would not the Bon Dieu, after the nations were sufficiently chastised, end this mad rule of the *demos*—the mob? When kings once more guided the destinies of states, then would the old nobility be restored. What if their fledgelings did not know how to read coats-of-arms? Yes, little Pierre's education must be concentrated on Heraldry . . . Now, accumulated years had brought crushing problems to this Pierre. He was as silver-haired, as bent, as tottering as had been the grandpere of his youth. Grandpere slept beneath the cross-above-the-shield, on the lichen-stained stone in Carcassone's graveyard. Little dreamed he how poorly equipped was Pierre to be, with an education concentrated on a moss-covered science of Heraldry, in an age of submarines, airplanes, and radar!

Let us not forget those who made the supreme sacrifice in that heroic "First 100,000" who held massed German might in World War I. It was necessary to give gasping France time to mobilize. These Britons did it. An amazing proportion thereof was of sons of noble British families. Whether you had previously met them at Gibraltar or Singapore,—Cairo, Bermuda, or Auckland, you knew they were of a rare leadership type. Theirs were the families that thru the centuries had built the British Empire:—

A few mottoes of British nobility might be worth consideration as evidence of the high character of these men.

"Pret d'accomplir." (Ready to perform). Motto of the Earl of Shrewsbury.

"Verite sans peur." (Truth without fear). Of Lord Middleton.

"Tache sans tache" (A work without a strain). Of the Earl of Northesk.

"J'ai bonne cause." (I have a good cause). Of the Marquis of Bath.

"Fay en tout." (Faith is everything). Of the Earl of Sussex.

"Vota vita mea." (My life is devoted). Of Earl of Meath.

"Deo date." (Give to God). Of Lord Arundel.

"Fari quae senteat." (To speak what he thinks). Of the Earl of Oxford.

"In ferum pro libertate reubant." (For freedom they rushed upon the sword). Of the Earl of Leicester.

"Aymez loyante." (Love loyalty). Of Duke of Bolton.

"Au bon droit." (To the just right). Of the Earl of Egremont.

"Fay pour devoir." (Faith for duty). Of the Duke of Somerset.

HINDU FLOUR MILL

A Hindu flour mill. The contrast between the women of a nabob's zen-annah and the wife of a Hindu royot is unbelievably great. This woman's husband raised a family of 10 children on a near-famine diet on his wage of 4c per day. Americans will never think clearly internationally until they appreciate that much of the grinding poverty of the Indian masses is due to Hindu-born customs. These include child-marriages, the practically-slave labor to the Rajahs, also the superstitions, rooted in widespread ignorance under an exploiting Brahmin priesthood. Suttee, or widow-burning, has practically ended because of British pressure. It is as important to grasp this before passing thoughtless judgment on the British in India, as it is to understand that negro slavery was an institution established by and existing under negro chiefs in Africa for centuries before the first white slaver ever sailed into a West African port. Such data should be valuable to all Americans in working at eugenic population planning in U. S. A.

CHAPTER 14

BUDDLEIA

"Unclean wives of many husbands."
(Kipling's description of polyandry in the Himalayas.)

To FIND the racemed buddleia growing wild, one must climb the passes of the Himalayas. One must go to Tibet, land of Kipling's polyandrous women. Queues of red hair there were worn by the Mohammedan-Chinese coolies. These, descending, were passed by our Geogardener and his string of Ghurka coolies as they ascended a certain Himalayan pass. It was probably this same pass over which came, to our Occidental gardens, the first racemed—or Asiatic— or lavender-buddleias. Because said pass is the meeting place of caravans of Chinese Turkis, of Ghurkas, of Lepchas, of Yunnanese, the "Roof-of-all-the-World" is fascinating to the student of anthropology . . .

Our Geogardener's Ghurkas always were of absorbing interest. They are the only ones in all Hindustan whose loyalty to the British Raj has never wavered. So great is their skill in knife-throwing, they can decapitate an enemy at an almost incredible distance. World War II soldiers, back from Burma, are prone to repeat the yarn about the meeting of the Japanese and the Ghurka in the

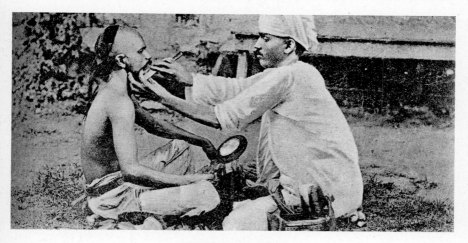

HINDU BARBER
The difference between American and Hindustani living standards is shown in this open air barber shop photographed near the Taj Mahal, Agra. The types shown in our picture probably represent descendents of the types of slave labor that built the marvelous Taj.

CAMEL CAVALRY
Camel cavalry, British Indian army. Same parallels our own Filipino con-
stabulary, includes a wonderfully well organized camel corps. The loyalty of
these men in the British Raj is described in "Kim," also in Kipling's lines
beginning "There's a widow in sleepy old Chester."

jungle:— The Nip fired. "Missed" said the Ghurka, as he spun his
knife. The Nip's piano-key teeth showed in his smile, as he exclaimed "You missed too". "You shake your head" retorted the
Ghurka. . .

The Asiatic species of buddleia, which the kiddies call "butter-
fly-bush" should be in every California garden. Not only does it
attract many butterflies, it also is a favorite feeding-ground for
hummingbirds. One thus may have the delight of watching "hum-
mer" nesting. One may also then study hummingbird behavior.
To witness even once the "wedding-dance" of Anna's hummingbird
well repays the planting of buddleia bush. If, for any reason one
postpones going-a-geogardening to Ecuador, to the jungles of the
Orinoco or the Amazon, one at least can have several species of

hummingbirds in his California garden.* When our Geogardener was in Salvador, he found the mere names of its hummingbirds pictured a flower-garden display of color. These included Mountain Gem, Rufous Saberwinged, Garnet-throated, Cinnamon, Coral-billed, Golden-tailed, Guatemalan, Emerald, Violet-eared, Blue-tailed, Azure-crowned, as well as the Star-throats.

There are hummingbirds in even greater variety as one goes a geogardening farther south into our hemisphere's deeper Tropics. There are petasphoras, and Gould's spiketails. There are white-footed racket-tails—with appendages like tennis rackets. There are jewel-throats. There are the scarlet-topazes. The feathers of these tiny winged jewels flash like all the bandana-encased gems of yesteryear's vendors in old Delhi's precious-stones mart. There is even the green-blue turquoise shades of the blue hummingbirds in Barbados' gardens.

Can one ever become tired watching the color flashes of the rufous, the purple-throated, the big Anna's,—and perhaps a passing calliope? If so, close your eyes and recall the color-flashes of the birds of Asia's Buddleia-Land. These include marvellous blues of the kingfishers, whose feathers go into Chinese inlays. There is the range of greens in the parrots. Asia is pigeon-land, too, with hues not seen in our rather drab Occidental species.

Colorful, too, are those songsters of the Middle East, the green bulbuls or fruit-thrushes. Especially fascinating is the golden-headed-green bulbul. A Geogardener also notices the orange-yellow narcissus flycatcher. These Asian flycatchers are no more cousins to our flycatchers than are Asia's golden orioles related to our American orioles. He will also see the black-and-yellow sultan-bird of the Himalayas. . . . Then there are the sun-birds. Some of these, in Hindustan, erroneously are called "hummingbirds". One is the fire-tailed yellowback. . . Yes, the road into Buddleia-Land has its avian color-feasts as satisfying as the hummingbirds that come to our California garden "butterfly-bushes." Other colors are seen in native gem-stones. Buddleia Land is, par excellence, the land of lapis-lazuli. Mediaeval artists powdered this gem stone to make their unfading blues. Here is a blue-green only to be seen in the anklets of Ghurka beauties. One may find these girls on the south slopes of the Himalayas—the long, sundrenched slopes that one slowly climbs, with the Bengal plain behind one, up toward the snow-armoured plateau of Buddleia Land—mighty Tibet.

---

* While Eastern U. S. A. has only the ruby-throated, California has, besides Anna's, the purple-throated, the Allen, the rufous, Costa's, and calliope.

LAMA

British garden-lovers, for decades, have sent plant explorers for ever-new finds. One thinks in this connection of Douglass, who discovered the Douglass false-spruce or Douglass tree. Note in any California flora how often "Douglassii" occurs. These aesthetic Britons encouraged the Colonials to comb their Hinterland (the Appalachians to the Mississippi Valley) for thrillers. It was smart to have blossoming in one's London garden something never before seen in England. Thus our early American life was enriched by expeditions based on Philadelphia. John Bull's respect for highly intelligent Jonathan, garden-connoisseurs brought charming Dr. Garden (of Charlestown) undying fame when Gardenia was named for him. Of all such, explored, probed areas the world over, none has yielded more exciting botanical finds than "The Roof of all the World," "The Back of Beyond" the mountains and valleys of Tibet.

FOREGROUND, TYPICAL BUDDLEIA TERRITORY

CHAPTER 15

CABBAGE

"Now 'tis the spring, and weeds are shallow rooted;
Suffer them now, and they'll outgrow the gardens,
And choke the herbs for want of husbandry."
(Shakespeare: Henry VI Act III, Scene I.)

"CABBAGE-HEAD" long has been a folk-term of contempt. And "cabbage-head", too, has been, in certain sections, slang for a painful boil. With our Geogardener, however, it awakens memories of the perfume-farms of Grasse, in France. It was not far from where this industry had, for centuries, been centered that our Geogardener finally found his first wild cabbage. It was in one of those deep, limestone gorges that are characteristic of Southeastern France. It grew beside a cliff-clinging highway between La Tourette and Grasse. A spindly weed, it must have taken centuries of artificial selection, and of continued discovery of occasional mutations to produce, from that unpromising green, the "headed" plant of the food gardens ringing all our cities. One can imagine Bronze-Age cabbages to have been as "stringy" as aged mustard greens.

Near where, after years of search, this find of wild cabbage was made, there commenced the domain of the Counts de Grasse. Therein was located, for many decades, the perfume-farms which, under the rare Gallic intellect, gave France a monopoly of perfumes, of "waters" for Oriental harems, of perfumed soaps. This soap industry is as naturally a by-product of perfume manufacture as is glove-making that of sheep-cheese (Roquefort) manufacture. The raw product comes from the tiny, highly- and carefully-cultivated farmlets around Grasse. These include rose- and orange-petals, also jessamine and violet flowers. Each kind is placed in its vat, over which is poured hot fat. By aging, the odors are transferred from flower to the now solidified fat. Most of the odor then can be leached out by alcohol. The remaining fat, still highly scented, becomes the base of the perfumed Parisian soaps eagerly bought the world 'round.

It will be remembered that one Count de Grasse, in our Revolution of 1776, was almost as ardent a champion of our new republic as was his fellow-country man, LaFayette. . . .

Cabbage yields, of course, the contents of Germany's sauerkraut barrel. Its newly-appreciated food values now form the basis

GRANDMOTHER

While geogardening for the wild origins of cabbage, we met on the trailside this grandmother. She had never seen a motion picture. We gave her the price of three tickets, the other two for her grandchildren. She broke her promise to thus use the money. What did she do with it? Well, as Kipling would say: "That is ANOTHER story."

WILD CABBAGE LAND

Wild Cabbage Land extends over much of the South of Europe. Here is a typical gorge village. A few doors below a habitant was fishing from his balcony. The French botanist spotted the wild cabbage below in cranny of the precipice.

of our sauerkraut-juice drinks. It is in Russia, however, that cabbage is most prized. Even *borsch,* the Russian red beet soup, carries an abundant cabbage-content.

Truly cabbage ranks high among our Geogardener's memory-stimuli. A cabbage field recalls his stay at Lake Ladoga's island monastery. A pilgrim here, Grand Duke or peasant, partakes of a diet principally cabbage in various forms. The devout monks have, as yet, not invented a cabbage dessert. However, this is the day of *ersatz.* With automobile steering-wheels appearing from soy-bean mash, and transparent, bullet-proof, fighter-plane turrets of coffee-bean plastics, with *buna* rubber from limestone plus coke, tomorrow's visitor to the cobalt-blue domes of Lake Ladoga may have a cabbage-sugar pie or gelatin. *Quien-sabe?*

At Ladoga, afterwards famous in both Russo-Finnish wars, Mr. and Mrs. Geogardener arrived one spring day. They found the pilgrim cell assigned to them had mildewy, musty, walls. The hot-water bag was extracted from the baggage. The next task was to fill the lifesaver. Hence a trip to the monastery kitchen . . . Russian orthodox monks, wisely, are not celibate. In the kitchen quarters, reeking with cabbage odors, were wives and numerous children.

To them the red rubber bag was a marvel. It was passed from hand to hand. Finally the sign language, "which ALWAYS (?) works" resulted in its being filled with COLD milk. Act II saw COLD water substituted. In Act III, sign language,—pointing to a samovar, brought HOT water. In Act IV, the scene shifts to a long midnight mass. The Geogardeners are standing, first on one foot, then another. Leaving the sanctuary, they stopped to study the anthropological evidence in the monastery's remarkable frieze. In Act V, they enter their sleeping-quarters to surprise a queue of pilgrims. These had preceded them from the mass. They were en route to their sleeping quarters beyond. The pilgrims were filing around the bed. Covers were reversed. On the lower sheet, exposed to the wintry draft, reposed that marvel of marvels, an American red-rubber hot (?) water bag.

The word "cabbage" is said by some authorities to originate in the Latin *caput,* meaning a head. Consider this when, with irritation, you would call a dunce a cabbage-head.

> *"How oats, field peas and barley grows,*
> *Nor you, nor I, nor nobody knows."*

And probably no living being knows the full history of the building up of fat garden cabbage from its spindly "sauvage" beginnings.

KANGAROO RAT TERRAIN
Cacti in lower picture are bisnaga. Many an Indian—and, in our days, a white man has been saved by bisnagas from death from thirst. The other cacti are chollas.

"Fine old man was Old Dan Tucker. Used to freight outer Winnemucca. Took his tooth pick from a wagon wheel," etc. Among his other examples of frontier resourcefulness was sung: "Took his cider from a cactus, none so good at rifle practice.

CACTI AND LLAMAS
The cacti range down the North American Backbone from Montana and Nevada, thru Arizona's Sahuaro, Mexico's Organpipes, the climbing cactus of Salvador's arid West Coast, the epiphyte cacti of Colombia and Ecuador, way down to Peru's Llama land.

CACTUS

When studying the flaming torch and other cacti in Utah's Dixie, our Geogardener heard, at a campfire, a cowboy's love song. He sang it to a tune from "Naughty Marietta." He had caught the charm of, not only the purple torch cactus, but of the yucca, the pinyon, also of the bluebird-blue mountains at dawn, of the rosy cliffs when, at sunset, blushes were heightened by sunset rays. This cowpuncher had the feeling of our great, cactus-ornamented Arid Southwest. As he rode his range, his inner urge found expression in this plaintive verse:

1.

"Where blue desert ranges stalk thru Southern Utah,
Where the rabbit-bush's arrayed in molten gold,
Where the pinyon jays are flitting thru the nut-pines
I sing to you the sweetest story ever told.

2.

"Where vermilion cliffs for miles blaze 'gainst the sky-line,
Where once red-skinned fingers plaited yucca ropes,
Where the spotted mule-tail fawns play and gamble,
I sing this love song of my growing hopes.

3.

"Where the flame lobelia blooms in the moist canyons
From thick blankets of the fragrant maidenhair,
Where the Virgin rips its way down thru the granite,
I sing this song to you, my lady fair.

4.

"Where cliffs tower almost shutting out the sky line,
To the Great Bear and up to the Northern Crown,
Where the Star Belt blazes like a million diamonds,
My song, I hope, will not call forth your frown.

5.

"Where the Scarlet Bugler thieves the hues of sunset,
Where the PURPLE TORCH lights up the desert miles,
Where the Bristle-cones march 'long the rock-ribbed ridges,
I sing to you, just hoping for your smile."

CHAPTER 16

CACTUS

*"And cactuses, a queen might don
If weary of a golden crown
And still appear as royal."*

E. B. Browning

As the cowboys of Cactus-Land declare: "The cactus is built for business". On one Arizona range, our Geogardener was studying the cacti. There came to it one day a tenderfoot from Boston. He boasted of his horsemanship. He insisted on accompanying the cowboys. On the first trip, his horse shied. It threw him a glancing blow against a sahuaro. This cactus is as corrugated as is the iron of the roof of those dwellings that Australians, out in the "Never-Never," call "fireless cookers." Moreover, about an inch apart along each corrugation is a sunburst of needles. Each thorn is about one inch long, and is as stiff as steel. Our tenderfoot, scraping these, was, on that side, as raw as a beefsteak from shoulder to ankle. No infection, however, followed. This, perhaps, because the needles, being sundrenched, were sterile.

The above range was but one of a string of ranches held by its owner. These extended from the prickly-pear-cactus areas to Texas, across New Mexico, to the sahuaro-ornamented ranges of Arizona. Having recently bought another cattle range near the Trinity Alps of Northern California, he, to conserve his time, purchased an airplane. Our cynical tenderfoot, being the butt of many jokes by the cowboys after his accident, snarled: "I suppose you soon will have your cowboys lassoing cattle from airplanes." "Not yet, quite" drawled the tall, blue-eyed Texan rancher "but, last night, our head wrangler *did* lasso the Cow that jumped over the Moon.". . .

Can any gardening be more fascinating than cactus-gardening? The most remarkable one of which our Geogardener knew was, believe-it-or-not, within a stone's threw of Manhattan's Fifth Avenue busses. It was in the old brownstone area. Its owner had an intellect like Dana, the mineralogist, with the latter's skill in measuring the flashes from microscopic crystal-faces. This rare ability our New Yorker channelled into cactus-culture. He had a remarkable collection of blooms . . . It would be difficult, too, to describe the exotic charm of a certain night-blooming-cereus hedge in Honolulu. . .

Potted cacti grow ever in popularity. One can neglect them thru a long summer vacation and they still "carry on". What most touches any geogardener, however, is to find, in Gronigen, Visby, Luebeck, or Bergen a half dozen tiny pots of cacti behind a sunny south-exposure window pane. Seldom does one see a blossom. These unique desert plants, however, have a fascination for "shut-ins."

It is the wild cactus gardens*, however, that are most fascinating. Some "pear" areas extend as far north as Montana. Our Geogardener found occasional fine blooms in the Nevada desert, even in the Pyramid Lake region. On the border between New Mexico and Colorado, he found, one midsummer day, on an arid river bar, an estimated one million silky, burned-orange optunia blooms. . . . The *bisnaga*, or barrel cactus, has often saved life of paleface, as in the case of legendary Dan Tucker, as well as of redskin from death by thirst. Decapitated, then a wooden club converted into a pestle, it will soon yield "cactus-cider". This is a life-saving drink. . . . *Bisnaga* pulp, also, is made by the Mexicans into cactus *dulces*. This is an inheritance from the Amerinds. A *bisnaga* folktale evidences a kind of eugenic selection in vogue among Indian fathers. An Indian swain was compelled to prove his I.Q., also his physical endurance. Between sunrise and sunset he was required to uproot a *bisnaga* with his bare hands. He then had to strip its skin with his teeth. Next, with his obsidian knife, he cut the pulp into cubes, so as to make it into *dulces*. These, evidence of physical strength, also mental cunning, were presented to his sweetheart's father. It was as much of a test of eugenic worth as was the bullfight for the very earliest of Spanish Kings.

Botanizing in tropical jungle, one is surprised to find epiphytic cacti. One species of Phipsales is even called "mistletoe cactus". Other mistletoe-like cacti are Weberocereus. They grow high in tropical trees, along with epiphytic members of the pineapple family. Members of another genus, Acanthocereus, are climbers. These are found almost vine-like in beach chaparral in Central America.

The cacti, side by side with certain African desert euphorbias, are curious examples of Nature's parallelism in the evolution, under pressure of aridity plus heat. These plants are as different in origin as the bear and the camel. Yet each, thru millions of years of adjustment of environment have (A) abandoned leaf-making, (B)

---

* For descriptions of Cholla, Deerhorn, Darning Needle, Beavertail, Grizzly Bear, Hedgehog, Pancake, Nipple, Beehive and other Cactus see E. C. Jaeger's "Desert Wild Flowers."

SPANISH BAYONET
Wild prickly pear, with a young yucca or "Spanish Bayonet."

evolved thick fleshy, water-storing stems, (C) created thickened
evaporation-hindering epidermis, (D) found strength in corrugation, (E) grown protective thorns. Yet our cacti are American, the
milky-juiced, cacti-like euphorbias are African.

———————

Western Hemisphere cacti have been "exported" to
North Africa, Australia, Hindustan.

"It was all pure delight—the wandering road—the
flush of the morning laid along the distant snows, the
branched *CACTI*, tier upon tier on the stony hillsides, the
chatter of monkeys, the solemn deodars, climbing one after
another with down-dropped branches, the incessant clang-
ing of tonga horns—the halts for prayers, the evening
conferences by the halting places, when camels and bul-
locks chewed solemnly together and the stolid drivers told
the news of The Road."

(Kipling: Kim.)

INCA HYMN

I.

"Gold tiled thy temples,
O! God of the Sun.
Blood-red the battles
That for thee we've won.
Here from the High-Priest Rock
The sunrise kiss we send.
Eastward to thy blood-red orb,
Rising years without end.

II.

"Ice-helmeted guardsmen,
Thy Andean peaks stand,
Ranging 'long the farflung miles
Of thy desert sand.
Morning and evening
Their rose-pink cloaks they don
Their clouds are scarfs of thy colors,
O mighty God of the Sun."

JAGUAR SKINS
Note the men wearing *"tigre"* or jaguar skin *ponchos.*

CHAPTER 17

CALCEOLARIA

*"The mechanism of inheritance in man, in Drosophila flies,
in plants, even in the unicelluars are fundamentally the
same." Prof. T. Dobzahnsky, Sci. Mo., 241, p. 162.*

The Calceolaria Belt, in places ocean-washed, climbs highest in
Inca Land. The favorite beverage of *Indios* therein is *"leche de
tigre"* or "tiger's* milk." This drink is the Peruvian equivalent of
what Kipling called "fixed bayonets" :-

*"Now, all you recruitees that's drafted today.
You shut up your rag-box and 'ark to my lay.*

   *   *   *   *   *

*First, mind you steer clear o' the grog-seller's hut.
For they sell you Fixed Bayonets wot rots out your guts,
Ay, drink that 'ud eat the live steel from your butts.
An' it's bad for the young British soldier."*

Leche de tigre is made by mixing a cocktail of milk and a very-
raw, homemade alcohol. Its effect on yarn-ing is electric. Our Geogardener was informed—the day he found his first wild calceolarias
—of 3 Indios who started to imbibe. As they sat down to drink,
Juan told of meeting, down in the jungle, an anaconda. He declared
that he had ripped another boa open with his machete, to find it
had swallowed whole a pig. Mateo, after a few more drinks of
tiger's milk, told of *his* adventure with a boa constrictor. This had
similarly disposed of a llama. Pedro, who had been imbibing before
the other arrived, had therefore, a fully-fired imagination. "You
fellows haven't begun to see things. I missed my mule the other
morning. A boa constrictor had gulped him down". . . . Balzac
wrote marvellously after a dozen cups of coffee. . . What might he
not have accomplished on *leche de tigre?* . . .

 Let the gaudy pouches of your garden calceolarias induce you
to go a-wanderlusting. Climb over the *saroche*-inflicting Andean
passes to Cuzco. Here flourished the capital of the vast Inca empire.
Cuzco's temples to the Sun God flashed sun-rays from hundreds of
tiles of solid gold. These were as yellow as the dwarf calceolarias

---

* "Tiger" was the name of Pizaro's conquistadores gave to the jaguar. There is no group
where the problem of the control-of-alcohol is more acute than the Indios of Inca Land.

that bloom in the crevices of the paving stones of certain little-used streets of Cuzco. Inside the Temple of the Sun, the gold-incrusted walls were inlaid with emeralds. These reflected the hue of calceolaria foliage. There will be seen marvels of a unique civilization. Men for centuries will regret that Conquistadors should have destroyed it so ruthlessly. Here one can glimpse, thru the fogs of history, what Incan intellects wrought. . . Cuzco is almost at the center of the Calceolaria Belt, for this attractive flower grows wild from Mexico to Chile. . .

Search both hemispheres. In neither can be found more striking examples of DYSGENIC havoc than this very Calceolaria Belt. Between the Northern and the Southern limits of this ballooned flower, there once stretched two great empires. To the North was that of the Aztecs. It had absorbed the civilization of both the Tol-

CALCEOLARIA-LAND INDIO

The Inca engineers fitted their blocks of stone so nicely that our Geo-gardener repeatedly tried unsuccessfully to insert a pocketknife blade into the interstices.

tec and the Maya. To the South ranged that of the Incas. It, in turn, rested upon the Chimu, and the pre-Chimu. The latter had been accumulating human wisdom long before Christ Jesus suffered on the Cross. . .

Before starting northward over the passes to Cuzco in search of further *sauvage* calceolarias and other garden flowers, our Geogardener discussed this problem with highly intelligent friends in Ariquipa. Said a learned Castilian-Ariquipan "My conquistador ancestors destroyed all Incan intelligensia. That is one reason why Ariquipa is a Peruvian oasis of *hidalgo* blood. They killed the Incan nobles,—most of us did not intermarry with the slaves. As you go North," he added, "watch the varied clothing coloration of the *Indios*. They were thus registered as to place-of-residence. A Quito Amerind can be immediately spotted even as far South as Juliaca. This system of registration-of-aliens was in being throughout the Inca-ruled part of your Calceolaria Belt. It had existed so long, 'twas like Chinese attitude toward the Manchu-imposed queue. They had forgotten that it originally was a mark of servitude. The Quichua or Aymara mother even now weaves cloth in the same color pattern as in preconquest days" . . .

Calceolaria's northernmost provinces include Mexico and Guatemala. Here there existed, when Cortez came, another advanced civilization. U.S.A. adopted income-taxation about the outbreak of World War I. At Anahuac, the Aztec capital, was a PERFECTED income-tax system, four centuries earlier. . . As to clothing expressing majesty, it would be difficult to excel in sheer beauty, the royal feather-cloaks. Our Geogardener, during his first attempt to trail Calceolaria to its native haunts had awakened to the marvels of bird coloring of the tropics*. . . We boast of our electric refrigerators. Montezuma's table in Mexico City offered fresh Vera Cruz red-snapper, also pompano. These were brought by Amerind runners. There is no record of ptomaine poisoning. . . . The system of tribute of hostages—of diplomacy in handling varied tribes—of religion remind one sharply of similar institutions in Rome of the centuries following immediately Remus and Romulus.

All above indicates that, thru NATURAL SELECTION, accelerated by ARTIFICIAL SELECTION, there had been built up groups, (the royal, the priestly, the warrior castes,) of high eugenic

---

* Following suggestions made by a professor in Mexico City our Geogardener tried to locate any possible Montezuman feather cloaks. He learned Cortez brought two as gifts to Charles V. That monarch was not only King of Spain but German Emperor. He deposited one in Seville, where it is said it still exists. The other our Geogardener later saw in Stuttgart Museum. . . . After a university course under a renowned Egyptologist, and several winters in Egypt, our Geogardener sensed that Calceolaria-Belt civilizations, the Maya, Toltec. Aztec also the Inca had, in many ways, paralleled the advances of that on the Nile.

worth. Because these were a menace to the Conquistadors, they were exterminated. Spanish policy was as ruthless herein as that of the French as to the Huguenots. It recalls, also, the Czech massacre at Lidice by the Nazis. The aim was security by complete elimination of all leadership stock of the eugenically-worth-while. Only the docile peon caste was permitted to live. These were needed for slave labor.

One might mention a hundred evidences of Inca intelligence. One is asphalt surfacing of military roads four centuries before its rediscovery by the Yankees. As the Ariquipa-Castilian said "Pizarro's men were a daring handful, lusty for Incan gold and emeralds. They simply HAD to eliminate all leadership castes, all you call "Eugenically-important". They conserved only the servile Indios. So completely was this type wiped out, not one Amerind leader since has arisen to overthrow our Spanish here. . . .

When, at Christmas time, you bank, afront the tall poinsettias, your pots of florist's giant, saccate calceolarias,—lean back,—close your eyes,—then dream of quetzal-plumed Aztec nobles—of Inca priests wafting the Sunrise-Kiss to the Sun God.

"Each blossom that blooms in the garden bower,
On its leaves, a mystic language bears."

(Percival—The Language of Flowers.)

MARIMBA

Perhaps calceolaria may be the test of your "G. Q." Geogardening Quotient.) As you saunter along your calceolaria borders, do you see more than brown-mottled yellows against green layers? Can you envision Calceolaria Land? Do you see a Marimba band playing on market day in the Quetzaltenago hinterland, striking, not metal tubes, but gourds, carefully selected for tone-values? . . . Do you glimpse a peon stretched out and snoozing blissfully under the meager shade of a bush calceolaria beside a Venezuelan desert trail? Do you recall many-petticoated squaws proceeding, with that walk that is almost a run, along an Inca road at 11,000 feet. (Calceolaria grows wild in the interstices of that ancient pavement) . . . Can you remember an Indian lad? He is a llama-herd, but seems more interested in flamingoes feeding in a mountain lakelet. Their nuptial plumage shows pink against the gold of the wild calceolaria on the lakelet shore . . . If such flash, like an unrolling motion picture, as you are looking at your garden's border of ageratum, then you shall be marked: "G. Q.: 100."

CHAPTER 18

CALENDULA (Marigold)

Strew thy green with flowers; the yellows, blues,
The purple violets, and marigolds.

(Pericles. Act IV. Sc. 1.)

"PLANT such stuff in your fine garden? Them's weeds back in Sicily where I came from!" A look of disgust flitted across visage of Guiseppe, our Geogardener's Sicilian gardener. It happened his first August. He had been handed packets of two kinds of calendula seeds. One was orange, one canary. He was told to start

EASTER IN CALENDULA LAND

One of Guiseppe's native Piano dei Grecci's tiny wild calendulas made an Easter morning boutonniere. Village women wear to mass on Easter Day the special costume shown in photograph.

July seedboxes, that Thanksgiving's and Christmas' outdoors, each, might be a blaze of red-gold and yellow. He opened one envelope, poured the seeds into the palm of his hand. Then followed above exclamation. . .

Later our Geogardener spent some time in Sicily, even at Piano de Grecci—Guiseppe's native village. There wild calendulas grew everywhere. They were under the blossoming almonds, on rocky cliffs near the sulphur mines, in the crevices of lichened Greek Temples at Segesta, at Girigenti. They grew, too, among the stone seats of Taromina's marvellous Greek Theatre, whose curtain's centerpiece is the smoking volcano, Aetna. One found them in the streets of Palermo near Rodger's tomb. . . They bloomed as weeds in the walls around the cathedral of Montereale, with its renowned mosaics.

Geogardening had been attempted in Sicily, since it was known, that, because of the ancient history, it was the possible place-of-origin of a number of garden plants*. The outer rim of Sicily, therefore, was circled, as well as criss-crossing the island. . . . . At Castelvetrano was observed a typical Sicilian trick: The "milk wagon" arrived in the form of a goat. Our Geogardener had been out botanizing at 5 a.m. Returning to the little inn, he saw the milking, from Nanny's teats, into a filthy, discarded mineral-water bottle. The milkman also suspiciously was pressing his elbow rhythmically to his side. Our Geogardener sprang forward, pulled back the milkman's coat. Down fell a rubber bag with a long tube suspended from his sleeve. The rascal had been holding the rubber end in his milking-hand. He squeezed infected water to dilute the milk. This was hardly assuring when one remembered every third dwelling in the village had crepe on its doors. . .

The peasants of Provance make an infusion of dried calendula flowers. They are a favorite with the old-dames for controlling the spasms of infants. One marvels at the knowledge of these herb-doctors of peasant Europe. Like our Indians, also the Chinese, they have, thru the centuries, faced many problems of disease. They therefore have experimented with practically every leaf, every flower, every root, every bark. Doubtless some who were sick, who might have recovered, died as the result of this ministrations. Then, too, there have been included in their "medicines" superstitious compounds. They have used owl-feathers, a spider shut up in a nut-shell, the powdered claw of a tiger killed on Fullmoon Night. Yet, scrape away the barnacles of superstition. Beneath you will find

---

* In addition to calendula, see also Chapter on Sweet Pea.

wisdom. Witness the transfer, into our scientific medicine, of such Californian-redskin remedies as cascara, grindela, yerba santa.

Our Geogardener collected, for his herbarium, some of these tiny wild calendulas. He later compared with his garden giants. The relative sizes were as per the circles in our diagram. These illustrate what plant-breeders accomplish by ARTIFICIAL SE-LECTION. When will men consider the genetic improvement of human strains as worthy of careful thought as those of Sicilian Guiseppe's "weed," the calendula?

We heedlessly buy seeds from seedstores, plants from nurseries. How many reflect, however, what the original plants may have cost? Sierra Club Bulletin, Aug. 1942, says: "Between the headwaters of Rogue River and Sacramento River there ran anciently an Indian hunting and trading trail. Over it came the first Hudson Bay trappers, on their way to beaver grounds in Alta California. . . The London Horticultural Society sent one man twice into Northwest America and California in quest of plants — David Douglass, an adventurous Scotchman WHO ENRICHED ENGLAND WITH NUMEROUS PACIFIC COAST ANNUALS AND BULBOUS AND WOODY PLANTS."

VILD CALENDULA
WHICH WAS A
BUTTONAIRE AT
PIANO DEI GRECCI
EASTER MASS

BY ARTIFICIAL
SELECTION, PLANT
BREEDERS HAVE
BUILT UP STRAINS
OF CALENDULAS
WITH FLOWERS OF
THIS SIZE

CHAPTER 19

CAMOMILE

"Aromatic plants bestow
No spicy fragrance while they grow,
But crush'd, or trodden to the ground,
Diffuse their balmy sweets around."
(Goldsmith . . . The Captivity)

*"*INFUSIONS: CAMOMILE, Menthe, Tilleul, Vervaine." One usually found this near the bottom of dinner menus of prewar luxury liners of *Compagnie General Transatlantique,* such as the Normandie, the Ile de France. The *maitre d'hotel* soothingly pronounced it like *"ann-fees-zee-ong"* to a table companion whose blanched visage was reminiscent of mal-de-mer. His advice was taken. A cup of steaming camomile tea DOES help a rebellious stomach . . . Gallic imagination has flowered in accurate artillery-power, in seductive millinery, in charming gown-making, in the manufacture of exquisite perfumes, in individuality of automobiles, in the decoration of rare china. It also has ever been evident in a French cookery that is not only palatable, but most wise. . . Your boulevardier knows how to lunch and to dine sensibly. He smiles cynically at American gorging of *hors d'oeuvres,* which *he* samples gingerly. And, remembering, he uses a cup of camomile tea to polish off a dinner. Dare it be hoped that seeing camomile growing as a garden weed may turn your geogardening footsteps toward this France?

Camomile is found in many American gardens. With us, it has never won patrician status. It usually is classified as of those "weeds," regarding which Shakespeare wrote:

"Nothing teems,
But hateful docks
Rough thistles, keksies, burrs,
Losing both beauty and utility."
(Henry V., Act V, Sc. 2.)

The writer's diaries' first record its growing wild between the paving stones of Athens' Acropolis. This golden-centered, white-rayed composite is, however, from Provance and Spain to the Levant, a source of slumber-inducing tea. German traders in Greek and Anatolian seaports used to accumulate profit-earning bales of dried camomile. It is a prime ingredient in the "herb teas" old women compound from the Baltic to the Black Forest.

Since, from camomile's native Mediterranean Basin, we have drawn so many plant immigrants, can we not use such biological material to aid us in studying our country's immigration-control problem. These migrating weeds illustrate how U.S.A., even today, lacks a truly biological approach toward its immigration problems.

"Weeds", (like immigrants), can be divided into (a) "valuable", (b) "neutral", (c) "noxious":

I. "VALUABLE WEEDS".

Some immigrant plants, commonly called "weeds" can be classed as worthwhile. An example of this is filaree. It is, of course, doubtful as to whether even filaree is as nutritious as the wild grasses which it displaced and which the Covered Wagon folk described as "up to a horse's belly". On one of the author's cattle ranges, nevertheless, immigrant filaree has become a prized fodder for dairy cattle. Its rosette of foliage, like the dried leaf-thatch described in the chapter on artichoke, conserves moisture. This is valuable in terrain like California's.

II. "NEUTRAL WEEDS".
Thus can be classified our camomile. In the Mediterranean Basin it has a commercial value. With us it is a real weed. As Dr. Laughlin used to assert, each applicant for admission should be evaluated as to his worth to The State. His entrance almost inevitably meant citizenship. This carries gains such as old age pensions, costly to taxpayers. Dr. Laughlin declared each immigrant must be considered as displacing, as to descendants, the old stock that created our republic. This parallels the displacement of the "belly high" grasses by filaree. Does, therefore, the immigrant represent something at least almost as good as what he displaces? Dr. Laughlin was often called by Congress for advice on immigration control. He was recognized by our lawmakers at Washington as foremost in statesmanship, in vision. Dr. Laughlin insisted the only way to really evaluate the candidate for admission is to obtain his family history. He often discussed this with our Geogardener. He declared that such a plan would pay immense dividends. One gangster, stopped overseas, would save costly items in our annual crime bill of billions.

III. "NOXIOUS* WEEDS."
Examples hereof include a dozen immigrant weeds that have penetrated into, for instance, certain

---

* Milk thistle, star thistle, spiny clotburr, all these can be classed as undesirable Mediterranean immigrants. They are like the Sicilian Blackhanders Mussolini dumped upon us. Later Il Duce sneered at "America, Land of Gangsters." Dr. Laughlin's suggestion as to immigrant family records is a revival of Sir Francis Galton's eugenic philosophy.

California alfalfa fields. One of these is foxtail. It is a grass with a barbed seedhead. Our Geogardener has often seen a year's first crop of his alfalfa sold at 30%, 50%, even 75% below a pure stand of alfalfa because of foxglove content. Such might be considered as undesirable as Sicilian gangsters of Black Hand ancestry—as those parasitic because of their operation in commercialized vice, whom our Geogardener recognized as descended from dealers in rotten-vodka.

"Medea concocts a magic brew. SHE PUT DIVERS HERBS into it, yielding color juice such as safflower and alkanet, and soapwort and fleawort to give consistency or body."

(Essay "Natural Science," Professor D'Arcy Thompson University of St. Andrews.)

ATHEN'S PARTHENON UPHILL FROM SOCRATES' TOMB

Camomile is a weed in U. S. A. It is an article of commerce where it grows wild. Our Geogardener found it being gathered by Athenian basket women from the roadside between Socrates' Tomb and the Acropolis above.

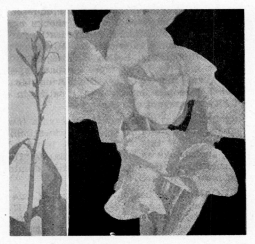

"Indian-shot" lilies developed from a skinny insignificant canna bloom (see left above) with a prickly capsule. Then Luther Burbank commenced work on canna's development. He planted tens of thousands of seeds."
Result our present day giants (right above).

WHERE CANNAS ARE WILDFLOWERS

Most canna species are "sauvage" in the Caribbean area, Central and South America. Our Geogardener, however, found them apparently wild in the Asiatic tropics, particularly on river borders. When you admire your gorgeous giant yellows and reds, remember they are a bit of the Tropics that braved the Temperate Zone. So think, too, of scenes like above as characteristic of Canna Land.

"My mouth was full of buckwheat cakes,
  A tear was in her eye,
  But all that I could say to her
  Was:
  'Susannah, don't you cry.' "

"Hush now, Susannah,
  Don't you cry,
  I'll be comin' back to Oregon
  With gold dust in my eye."

(Covered Wagon Song.)

CHAPTER 20

CANNA

If you are going 'cross The Plains
With long-eared mules to damn,
Remember beans before you start
Likewise jerked beef .. and ham.
"Song of The Covered Wagon Trail" (Hulbert)

WHEN COVERED-WAGON days were vividly fresh in memory, canna was generally called "Indian-shot lily". Its globular, black seeds were of the size of shot used in buffalo-hunting. Kiddies needed only a few feathers inserted in a red bandana headband, to become Sioux or Blackfeet. They played at shooting buffalo from plunging ponies. The Covered Wagon folk saw the vast herds of shaggy bulls, with their cows and calves. Even those who arrived later, by the recently-completed Union Pacific, told of trains delayed, sometimes for several hours. This was caused by herds migrating to or from summer or winter pasture.

"Indian-shot" lilies developed from a skinny, insignificant canna bloom with the prickly capsule. Then Luther Burbank commenced work on canna's development. He planted tens of thousands of seeds. He was happy if a few dozen thereof showed signs of improvement. He used, for canna, the same technique as with his "Shasta" daisies, his eschscholtzias. He told our Geogardener one day: "To gain in California-poppy color variety, as with Iceland poppies, I planted annually 100,000 seeds. Up and down the rows I went, watching for color-mutations. After some years I had a range of color from milk-white to red." Then he made this significant remark: "ONE CAN, IF INTELLIGENTLY ALERT, ISOLATE ALMOST ANY QUALITY ONE WANTS". What a concept for eugenists of vision!

In talks our Geogardener had with Mr. Burbank, the Plant Wizard, sometimes he seemed wistful because he was not a Methuselah, "If I had only a score of years beyond the scriptural allotment, what could I not accomplish!" He had paralleled in vision, as to furniture hardwoods, the concepts of Lumber-king Eddy as to lumber conifers*. He would speak of both the cherry and the black-walnut. "If I had sufficient years ahead, I could, by ARTIFI-

* See "Sierran Cabin . . . From Skyscraper" for data on the Institute of Forest Genetics near Placerville, Calif.

CIAL SELECTION, give mankind hardwoods that would be available in one quarter the growing time of our primeval forests." Then Mr. Burbank said, "As a business executive, translate that time-saving into compound-interest dollars. You then will grasp how future farmers could grow furniture hardwoods as a profitable crop."

At another time, Mr. Burbank asked our Geogardener, then Australia-bound, to visit Western Australia. From that area he wanted all possible seeds of bright-colored everlastings. He contemplated experimenting with producing, again by artificial selection, improvements in immortelles. These, he declared, would be as epochal as his building his giant Shasta daisies on the old garden types.

"I will not request your bringing back pineapple material" he in his later years said, "I now am too old for that. My correspondents have sent me tantalizing, hardy, frost-proof pineapples. If I could have a quarter-century longer, I could build up, by ARTIFICIAL SELECTION and careful breeding a pineapple so suitable to California there would later be plantations in the Great Valley from Red Bluff to Bakersfield, first settled by the Covered Wagon Folk.

**SUTTER'S FORT. KIDDIES PLAYED AT BUFFALO-HUNTING
WITH INDIAN SHOT SEEDS**

WILD CANNA LAND

It was a tropical river similar to above scene that our Geogardener found his first "sauvage" canna. The genus has wide distribution in the tropics. One species includes even Florida in its habitat. Jungle trees in the background, instead of being green, as in an English park of oaks, beeches, and lime trees are bizarre in coloration. . . Many tropical trees flower at the very tips of their branches. Thus forest greens are mottled with cerise, lavender, cobalt, vermilion, burnt orange. In this land of high tropical fertility, one must also expect high tropical disease rates. These are not lessened by dependence on superstition, in lieu of scientific medical care.

The Seminoles live in the heart of the Everglades, where one canna grows "sauvage."

CHAPTER 31

CARNATION

"The pink in truth we should not slight,
It is the gardener's pride."

(J. W. von Goethe—The Beauteous Flower.)

THE ORIGINAL wild carnation still grows in Savoyard meadows. Our Geogardener gathered it there. The story of its remarkable building up into our florist's varieties was told in an appendix to the author's "War Profits and Better Babies." It there was used in connection with the efforts of Papa Dachert to improve human stocks in the France whose plant-breeders had blazed the way with carnations, roses,—even California's wild mountain lilac, or ceanothus.

Read therein how "Oeillete sauvage" (wild carnation) is *"avec un leger parfum,"* (has a light perfume). The florist therein says: "neighborhood peasants' gardens contain almost all size graduations from the small wild carnation to the giant florist's varieties. These exhibit also many color-variants. Likewise there are odor-variants. From the *'leger-parfum'* of the wild pinks, it ranges to varieties heavy with perfume." One becomes sensible to a border thereof when, passing on a dark night, with no blooms visible "the air is scent-laden". . .

In Yosemite Nature Notes, (12/'44), Park Ranger Parratt writes under the heading "Nature Sense in Yosemite." He suggests that one should enjoy sensations of all five senses. . . Why not carry his suggestion into your own gardening? You plan for color. How about music, odor, taste:

MUSIC? Same can easily be obtained. In California, even a single elm will attract numerous songsters. Vines around the house provide nesting sites for the house finch. This crimson-helmeted songster furnishes the most important element in the spring Dawn-chorus. A clump of shrubbery, (escallonia, cotoneaster, pyracantha) insures charming song from October until the spring migration of the house finches. White-crown and golden-crown sparrows are secure in such shrubbery shelter.

FRAGRANCE? Some clove-pinks bloom in California every month of the year. Their heavy-odor season is April to September. These *"sauvage"* carnations are but one of many flowers yielding perfumes. In our Temperate Zone we cannot yet hope to produce heavy odors like frangipanni. We have on the other hand, hardly begun to breed for perfume. What has been accomplished by plant-breeders in producing odorless African marigolds is an example. To some, the smell of these is most offensive. If geneticists can pro-duce small nutmeg melons because they are more marketable than the old type giant muskmelons, what can not be done in isolating other plant mutations with promising perfume?

TASTE? One must go to France to grasp what can be done with cookery based upon a herb garden. Italy's *finnochi*, too, is used in many ways as a flavoring. Who can forget the *finnochi*-flavored honey of the Italian hill-towns? Geogardening there brings, as a by-product, gustatorial delights.

When, on Mother's Day, a man walks down the church aisle, he is classified by the color, (red or white), of the carnation which is his boutonniere.

You take a pink,
You dig about its roots and water it,
And so improve it to a garden pink,
BUT WILL NOT CHANGE IT TO A HELIOTROPE.

      (E. B. Browning—"Aurora Leigh.")

"In Eastern lands they talk in flowers,
And they tell in a garland their loves and cares."

    (Percival—"The Language of Flowers"*)

"In the packet was—one flower of the blood-red ahak . . .
and eleven cordamons." . . . *"The flower of the* ahak *means*
diversely 'desire', 'come', 'write' or 'danger' " according to,
etc. ("Beyond the Pale," Kipling).

---

* Mankind borrowed the Language of Flowers from the same Orient that also gave us Persian rugs, which held the first table bouquets. These Orientals, too, gave mankind such imaginative literature as "Arabian Nights".

CHAPTER 22
CATALPA

"The catalpa's blossoms flew,
Light blossoms, dropping on the grass like snow."

(Bryant—The Winds.)

IT WAS early one morning at a Western country club. One of its greens was in a grove of catalpa in full bloom. The dew on the green gave it a bluish appearance, not unlike the sky-reflecting color of some mountain lakes. There our Geogardener witnessed a conflict between two dogs, using their instinctive pursuit strategy while a jack-rabbit simultaneously fell back upon his defense mechanism of escape. The older dog was adult. The younger dog was halfway between puppyhood and maturity. Even the latter, however, had learned the value of chasing quarry in parallel lines. The rabbit started along his escape course. The 2 dogs took up the chase on lines on either side of the rabbit's line of flight. This was parallel to it, and about 40 yards distant. While they were proceeding along these straight lines, they kept the rabbit tacking between them. Eventually the rabbit must become exhausted, while they were still fresh enough for the kill. The rabbit seemed instinctively to sense that the younger dog was his less dangerous pursuer. He took advantage of dropping behind a small bush, while the younger dog continued to rush on. The older dog, some 80 yards away, also did not know about the feint. The rabbit backtracked, thus escaped.

Our Geogardener, whose attention had been distracted from the fine catalpas to the rabbit, was interested in the chase. Evidently the strategy of both pursuers and pursued involved certain principles of survival. These exist throughout both animal and plant life. As Dr. David Starr Jordan once said "evolution does not travel in a circle. It travels in the spiral. That spiral is always upward."

Dr. Jordan's quotation above is significant. Human evolution, since Pithecanthropus gluttonously crammed jackfruit into his mouth with his none-too-clean fingers, up to the days of Aristotle, Dante, Galileo, Copernicus, Linneaus, Pasteur, Edison, the Wright Brothers and Lindbergh always, unless there has been artificial interference, has been upward.

When, however, we have excessive birth control among the high powers that the tendency is not eugenic but dysgenic . . .

Catalpa is a tree of our Southeastern U. S. A. forests. It belongs, however, to a tropical family, the Bignoniaceae. It is, therefore, an example of the centripetal force of radiation. Under population pressure, any species tends to be ever radiated towards its frontiers* at all points of the compass. At such frontiers the struggle for survival is fiercest. There an individual competes with, not only others of his species, but with those of other species of his family being thrown off, from the latter's centers of radiation.

The Catalpa, one of our most beautiful flowering trees, is very popular in roadside forestation. The seed-mechanism of the Bignoniaceae is also worth notice. Pods are as protective as battleship armor. The segments thereof split slowly, too, over a long period of time. The seeds are true wanderlusters. Their sails spell wide, wind-propelled distribution. Colonies thus thrown off are as lusty as those sea-powerful Athens radiated, protected by her triremes. With a pod as strategic as an Athenian trireme or a modern battleship—with winged seeds, insuring distribution—with a time-graduated release of seeds, a few detached by gale force each windy day—the thoughtful man has, in Catalpa-of-the-Bignoniaceae, a source of wisdom. If every president of U. S. A. had been an understanding observer of catalpa, our country would have had eliminated, at birth, many immigration-control problems. Same might have prevented the coming to U. S. A. of a certain immigrant jailbird. In making his millions he corrupted tens of thousands. He then swindled our government of even the income tax on said millions. U. S. A. compromised for a mere fraction . . .

On desert washes in California is a tree with willow-like leaves. Desert rats long ago dubbed it "desert willow." The seed pods, however, proved them poor botanists. These fruits are long, narrow, with winged seeds. They show close affinity to the catalpas of our Southern streets also the Bignonia vines of our semitropical gardens. Mexican peons collected desert-willow flowers for a tea as prized by them as is the tea made from dried orange petals in Provence.

From Costa Rica to Colombia, the jungle and the brush is filled with Bignonia vines and trees. There are over twenty genera. These include the strikingly colorful Jacaranda trees. They are cultivated throughout the tropics for their showy panicles of violet flowers. Another genus is Crescentia, commonly called Calabash. Its somewhat gourd-like fruits, highly carved, are said by some to

---

* See Sierran Cabin . . . From Skyscraper for the Frontier-Struggle where Life Zones clash.

have been used when Montezuma regaled Cortes with *chocolatl* drinks. There is also a black Calabash. Its fruit was used by the natives in making a black dye. Yet another cousin of our catalpa is the candletree. Its long hanging fruits look somewhat like candles. The Catalpa of U.S.A.'s Dixie has an additional fascination because of its Asiatic cousins. It is but one of many examples of survival of trees in our South with all intervening plants blotted out until the geogardener crosses Oregon, Alaska. Not until he arrives in Manchuria, perhaps not until China, even Java or Hindustan does he find the others of the family.

The catalpa's plebeian cousin, the desert willow, grows on "washes" of our Mexican-border states. This "wash" environment insures as much underground water as can be expected in a desert. (The true willow, however, is a member of the Salicaceae.) Here is an interesting example of RADIATION into, and of occupancy of a new NICHE. Most of desert willow's cousins are tropical. Many thrive in the Rain-forest. Our species "forgets" its rain-drenched ancestral home. It invades, thrives in such dessicated area as California's Colorado desert.

One factor of desert willow's efficiency is its seed-pattern. One pod, plucked and held in the left hand as this is written, is 14 inches long. It looks like an overgrown knitting needle. It is convex on one side, concave on the other to catch the wind. Each seed also, has, at both ends, "whiskers" sails. Paper-thin, it is light in weight. It has moreover, above mentioned "whiskers" at EACH end. Both "beards" are as long as the seed itself. Said sails are as useable as those of a 1830 China Clipper. To understand their dispersion, go, some January, to the desert in a 50-mile-per-hour-gale. The above mechanical equipment is characteristic of many Bignoniaceae seeds. Watch this plant's seed skidding over the crusted wash-surface. You then will grasp how Bignoniaceae seeds can travel. In a few generations they could negotiate the miles between Honduras or Costa Rica, and California's Imperial Valley.

Consider, too, desert-willow's birthrate. One tree our Geogardener kodaked had an estimated 70,000 pods. One contained 76 seeds. This one tree's annual crop probably exceeded 500,000 seeds. This again illustrates Mother Nature's strategy. Such adequate mechanical equipment makes for efficient radiation into everwidening circles of food-producing area. Such food is essential to reproduction. High reproduction rate is yet another factor in evolutionary progress. Desert willows on this "wash" grow about 16 to the acre. This presumably is full carrying capacity, or POPULATION-SATURATION. Desert-plant root-systems are much more extensive than their leaf-systems. This is necessary to store moisture. Imagine seeds thus radiated producing 16 trees to the acre. If all sprouts lived, each tree alone could plant, ANNUAL-LY, some 500 square miles. Such figures forcibly illustrate how NATURE PRODUCES MANY INDIVIDUALS. ONLY THE FIT-TEST MAY SURVIVE.

Thus we glimpse Mother Nature's strategy for filling empty spaces. High birthrate, Resultant population-pressure, Expansion into the Open Lands. A parallel in humans* created our Atlantic-to-Pacific-nation.

---

* The Harvard undergrads in Kenneth Robert's "Northwest Passage" have "overripe" rabbit-pie dinner. This is followed by the buttered-rum affair. Later Langdon Towne must listen to Reverend Browne's statement as to the latter's family of 7. . . . Here is a birthrate already lower than that of Browne's English ancestors. A 7-child rate, however, meant, if all lived, 49 grandchildren, 343 great-grandchildren. This was adequate for what Historian-President Woodrow Wilson called "The Swarming of The English".

"And God in the woodland dwells—
We listen to notes from the million throats
*   of chorister birds on high,*
Our psalm is the breeze in the lordly trees," etc.

Henry C. Kendall.

"Shikishima no Yamato-gokoro wo,
Hito towaba, Asa-hi ni niou Yama-zakura-bana!

Above signifies "If one should ask what is the spirit of a true Japanese, point to the cherry-blossoms shining in the sun." Japanese cherry long has held in Japan the place we have given the rose. . . Poems like the above were being written when Charlemagne was welding his empire. . . In Spring, one or more tea houses with cherry trees in blossom become the objects of ten thousand pilgrimages.

It was down-mountain from a cluster of chalets like these that Monsieur Z pointed out the ancestor-type of our cultivated cherry. This Eurasian cherry seems to be a hill-lover like our own Sierran cherry shown in this chapter's inset.

"The cherry is first among flowers as the warrior is first among men."
Japanese Proverb.

CHAPTER 23

CHERRY

"She can make a cherry-pie
Quick as a cat can wink her eye.
She's a young thing,
And cannot leave her mother."

IT WAS below Mt. Blanc that our Geogardener found his first wild cherry. There he met Monsieur Z. This Frenchman had something of the wanderlusting spirit of his countrymen, Jacques Cartier, La Perouse, Bougainville, Cadillac, Iberville, Bienville. He, having lived in U. S. A., was eager to show an American his bit of France. Hence, far below the ice-encased aguilettes of Mt. Blanc, he pointed out scattered wild cherry trees, ancestors of our Bings, our Queen Annes.

The ascent yielded more, however, than the locating of the wild origins of the cherry, with its legend of the truthful and youthful Washington. It brought a glimpse of how the American leaven works in France:

"My Countrymen," said Monsieur Z., "explored North America from Quebec to Detroit, to Duluth, to Dubuque, to Saint Louis, to New Orleans. Having heard much of the *peau-rouges*, (red skins), I determined to 'Go West' as your Monsieur Greely phrased it. So I became cow-boy. Being French, which is more than being Scotch, I saved every possible sou. I bought cows. In a few years, I owned a herd. Each year they multiplied. Finally, when I had cattle which, converted into francs, meant a competence, I then sold out. I bought French *rentes* when they were depressed. Then, when they shot up, I made a "clean-up" as your Western goldminers call it. With the proceeds I bought real estate. This multiplied in value. I felt I could do something truly *a la Americaine*: To give to humanity. This dream of mine truly was not French. Our folk aim at establishing a Family—at founding an 'Establishment.' If their child be a daughter, the aim year after year, is to build up for her a Dot. The larger the Dot, the higher the climb thru marriage. I was bachelor. Why not imitate, In France, in a modest way, the Carnegies, the Rockefellers. So, out of my ever-growing surplus, I bought one chalet after another on the side of Mt. Blanc. My plan is to consolidate these into Mount Blanc National Park as a gift to France . . ."

    This was some years before World War II. Wild cherries still grow on the flanks of Mount Blanc. Our Geogardener wonders, however, what became of Monsieur Z. and of his dream of "Altruism *a la Americaine!*" . . .

    The bibulous were fond of anticipating possible rattlesnake trouble by taking daily a drought of alcoholic snake antidote. So, too, there was a time when men who lined up at the bar eased their consciences. When the barkeep said: "Name your poison, gentlemen." Some called for "bitters." One favorite bitters tonic in the California gold belt was made by steeping the native wild, or bitter cherry* into whiskey. This is not advised as a sure-cure. Some of the gold-miners also used horned-toads, similarly prepared with a whiskey liquifier. One suspected the stimulating alcohol was the real appeal.

    The California wild cherry in size is between a rice-grain and a pea. It has, however, a perfect fruit including a cherry-stone. The Eurasian "sauvage' cherry is somewhat larger. It is undoubtedly the one from which our orchard's strains were isolated by ARTIFICIAL SELECTION. Man has thereby made progress with

---

* The Wild choke cherry's inner bark was gathered in large quantities by the Indians and later by some whites for its medicinal value to check diarrhea, and to relieve nervous excitablty.

cherries, apples, peaches, poultry, sheep, racehorses. Is it not
strange that eugenics (the science of applying the principles of
genetics to improvement of human stocks) does not awaken similar interest?

Size of wild cherries in our cut is contrasted with a leadpencil.
The California bitter-cherry is, of course, not the stock upon which
our luscious orchard cherries were built. Your editor, however,
botanizing at several places in Eurasia, as at Mt. Blanc, found
said original stock growing wild. These "sauvage" cherries are
but little larger than the Sierran cherry. Our eagerly-bought market cherries, therefore, have risen from such unpromising, small,
rather bitter wild cherries thru years of ARTIFICIAL SELEC-
TION. This, undoubtedly, has been added to Mother Nature's
NATURAL SELECTION over untold ages. Thus was secured
seed-transportation by encasing the pit in a pulp that had color,
some taste, also food values.

When one contemplates the size of the wild cherry, as shown
in our photograph with that of our orchard beauties, like the Black
Tartarian, one recalls that such results were indeed of patient
growth. Then one remembers Jessie Mackay's lines:

> *"Never was a Luther*
> *But a Hus was first—*
> *A fountain unregarded*
> *In the rimal thirst.*
> *Never was a Newton*
> *Crowned and honoured well,*
> *But first a lone Galileo,"* etc.

Chamberlain writes of old Japan:

"Gardens are supposed to be capable of symbolizing ab-
stract ideas, such as peace, chasity, old age. The following
passage will show how the garden of a certain Buddhist ab-
bot is made to convey the idea of the power of Divine Truth:
"This garden consists almost entirely of stones arranged in
a fanciful and irregular manner in a small enclosure. The
sentiment expressed depends for its value upon acquaintance
with the following Buddhist legend, somewhat reminding us
of the story of Saint Francis and the birds. A certain monk,
Daita, ascending a hillock and collecting stones, began to
preach to them the secret precepts of Buddha. So miraculous
was the effect of the wondrous truths which he told that even
the lifeless stones bowed in reverend assent. Thereupon the
Saint placed them upon the ground around him, and conse-
crated them as the 'Nodding Stones.' "

JAPANESE PEASANTS ADMIRE CHERRY BLOSSOMS
Even the rudest peasant in his raincoat of thatch, will grow eloquent over
cherry blossoms, or iris, or lotus or wisteria or chrysanthemums. He will make
a "pilgrimage" of miles on foot to a teahouse that offers an attractive bit of
flower-color: The Nipponese will patiently transfer same to a sweat-towel for
the head—to a bit of cloisonne. They, for centuries, have written poems about
floral beauty. It was puzzling, while geogardening in Japan, then in Korea, to
reconcile the brutal ruthlessness toward the Koreans with this appreciation of
flowers.

SUN-DRENCHED, SUN-STARVED LEAF CONTRAST

Cinerarias grow luxuriantly in the fog belt of the California's Transition Zone. This suggested to our Geogardener that to find them sauvage he must track them to some seacoast. One could guess, as with the thimbleberries of the Avenue-of-the-Giants, Humboldt Redwoods, as to what their broad leaves indicated. These seemed evolved, with Caledonian thrift, every bit of filtered sunlight. Note in contrast with the ample leaf of shadeloving Thimbleberry, the reduced needlelike leaves of a gilia from a sunscorched, excessively drained Sierran Moraine.

CHAPTER 24

CINERARIA

"Sing away, aye, sing away,
Merry little bird,
Always gayest of the gay,
Though a woodland roundelay
You ne'er sung nor heard,
Though your life from youth to age,
Passes in a narrow cage."
(Mulock: "The Canary in His Cage.")

IT WAS in the Canary Islands that our Geogardener finally found wild cinerarias. We of today link the islands with certain little, carefully-caged, canary-colored finches*. The best songsters that we call "canaries," now come to us from Germany's Hartz Mountains . . . These feathered minstrels are additional evidence of what breeders can accomplish through ARTIFICIAL SELECTION. . .

The ancients knew that these mysterious Canary Islands existed. The Canaries, to them, were the spots of land just this side the Dropping-Off-Place. They christened the archipelago the "Dog Islands." (Latin *canis* or dog). There must have been wild dogs anciently in Canary Islands. Sailors, when blown out to the Dog Islands by unfavorable winds, brought home weird tales of gigantic canines! Yarn-spinners among these ancient skippers also told some big ones about the inhabitants of the Canaries. These had their eyes in their shoulders! They walked around, each with his head under his arm! ! . . .

Strikingly-colorful groupings of cinerarias are found in Californian gardens. Among these are those in the shade of the State Capitol at Sacramento. They also are numerous in private gardens at Carmel. There are pleasing color contrasts: cobalt against magenta, violet clustered with bougainvillea-red, purple-eyed whites next washed-out azure. Cinerarias grow luxuriantly in the fog belt of California's Transition Zone. This suggested to our Geogardener that, to find them *"sauvage,"* he must track them to some seacoast. One could guess, as with the thimbleberries of the Avenue-of-the-Giants, (Humboldt Redwoods), as to what their broad leaves in-

---

* One does find "canaries" wild, both at Teneriffe and on the Grand Canary. They are, however, more of the color of our greenbacked goldfinch.

dicated. These seemed evolved to save, with Caledonian thrift, every bit of filtered sunlight. A geogardener must be Agassiz-like* in his crystal-gazing.

Carmel folk wisely plant their cinerarias under their shady Monterey cypresses, Monterey pines . . .

One sees careless gardeners jam seedlings into cruelly-unwise environments. A vacationer had enjoyed the beauty of Carmel's cinerarias. Returning to his home in California's hot San Joaquin Valley, he bought a flat of 60. These he set out in intense sunlight. At the season's end found 4 of the three score big-leaved shade-lovers dead . . . One cannot even, in gardening, hammer "square pegs" into "round holes" and expect harmony . . . If men only could grasp that a such parallel also exists as to humans. One yester-year college president spoke of "wasting a thousand-dollar education on a ten-dollar lad" . . . Today we have progressed enuf that we are sensing that that may also mean tragic unhappiness for that boy.

Another parallel exists as to races . . . Can the blue-eyed Nordic reproduce permanently in the hot valleys of semi-tropic California? Remember, herein, what finally became of the once powerful Vandal Kingdom in North Africa.

TENERIFFE AND "EL PICO"
It was near the Canary Islands Palm (left foreground) our Geogardener found wild cinerarias.

* It was once said of Agassiz that he found fossil the imprint of a single fish scale on a fragment of shale. Upon this he built up an outline of the entire fish. Years later, a fossil of the whole fish was discovered. It verified Agassiz's prediction.

SNOWBUSH VS. LOWER SONORAN CHAPARRAL

Contrast the tiny needle-shaped leaf of the Upper Sonoran chaparral with the large, thin, juicy one of Snowbush, (*ceanothus cordulatus*). The former is evolved to exist in the fierce August temperatures of its Life Zone. The heat thereof is so intense that John Muir called its dominant pine "the most palmlike of pines" . . . The snowbush ceanothus, on the contrary, has a leaf that almost shouts of mountain coolth . . . So, too, with cineraria. If a geogardener sees but a single leaf, he knows that cineraria—like California's natives, thimbleberry and snowbush—probably is a shade-lover. He sees it evolved to conserve every momentary sunray filtering through the foliage of the trees overhead.

Now the blundering San Joaquin gardener and his flat of 60 cineraria seedlings poses this question: CAN OUR AMERICAN NORDICS, EVOLVED ON SNOWY BALTIC SHORES, COMPETE WITH AMERIND PEONS FROM MEXICO in either California's hot interior, Central Valley, or in areas like sweet grapefruit orchards of Imperial Valley California or the Gila River Valley of Arizona? One almost gasps at the speedy growth of Los Angeles. Statistics as to the Anglo-Saxon birthrate in Hindustan are not at hand. One's impression in India is that, even with the system of sending the kiddies at an early age to England, there is lacking control of factors affecting the Anglo-Saxon birthrate. Meantime the sterility of Nordics there-in is amazing. One important factor undiscovered by populationists and eugenists is: HOW MUCH STERILITY IS DELIBERATELY CONTROL-LED? HOW MUCH IS UNPREVENTABLE? Can we obtain light herein by studying the limitations of reproduction in California's pines? . . . IF PINE-TREE REPRODUCTIVE ORGANS ARE SENSITIVE TO THAT WHICH CREATES THE LIFE ZONES, so that we have belts of Sabines, Yellows, Lodgepoles, and Whitebarks, WHAT MUST WE THINK OF THE HIGHLY SENSITIVE NERVOUS SYSTEM OF HUMANS?

WATER VENDERS IN MOROCCO

Rockrose thrives in the rock-deserts on both sides of the Strait of Gibraltar whose Tarifa, with its pirates levying a tax on all passing vessels, gave us our English word "tariff". . . Go a-geogardening for rock rose in Spain or, better yet, in Morocco. You thus will accumulate, not only botanical knowledge, but mental pictures for memories for old age, or if you become bedridden, or should you be stricken blind.

GROUP OF CADETS, FROM SPAIN'S "WEST POINT"

CHAPTER 25

CISTUS

"Know ye why the Cypress tree as Freedom's tree is known?
Know ye why the Lily fair as Freedom's flower is shown?
Hundred arms the Cypress has, yet never plunder seeks;
With ten well-developed tongues, the lily never speaks."
                                        (Omar Khayyam.)

THE CISTUS, like the cypress, belongs to the Mediterrean flora. The cypress is Freedom's tree. The cistus, with its red-blotched petals, seems to Hollanders, on the contrary, to be symbolic of the bloody Spanish Inquisition. Dutch gardens often contain a cistus. This is to remind their young folks of Holland under William the Silent. Do we not again, in fighting for the Atlantic Charter, need to re-read Motley's "Rise of the Dutch Republic?" Would it not stimulate us to standing firmer for preservation of OUR liberties? The Hollanders tell their sons the cistus comes from Spain. It forms the chaparral in the very home of their oppressor, Phillip the Second. Phillip never comprehended Omar Khayyam's tribute to the cypress. Phillip, on the contrary, tried to crush Holland's freedom. He yearned to enslave the folk of the Land of Windmills. The Dutch say the rockrose's petals are indelibly stained with blood shed by orders of this bigoted king.

The cistus' other name is "rock-rose." Two rockroses grow wild on the rocky semi-desert between Madrid and the Escorial. One is white, the other pink. Both have the red blotches on their petals. During much of the year, this arid area would be classed as dreary by most Americans. Westerners, however, have learned to enjoy such landscapes. In winter, this part in Spain is bitterly cold. This is especially true when what elsewhere is called the *"tramontana"* or the *"mistral"* sweeps down from the glaciers up Spitzbergen-way. In summer, the sun is merciless in showering down his javelins.

There is a between-times, however, when Spain's arid stretches take on a rare beauty, like that of a happy bride. This is Cistus-Time. Then both the white and the magenta rockroses are in all their glory of bloom. It is worth while to have a clump in your garden to send you geogardening to Castile-of-the-Rockroses. For thus one gains, not only massed flower-beauty, but stimuli to build for oneself "castles in Spain." Castile fairly drips history as does New Zealand's pohutakawa its honey.

The pages of history contain, indeed, no more tragic story,

Spanish under "the Lions-and-Castles flag . . . succeeded in throwing
the mighty Moor back across Gibraltar's strait." . . . A "Bab" or city gate in
Morocco-of-the-Moors. BAB is Arabic but roots back in BAB-ylon and in
BAB-el. The Tower of Babel is supposed by some critics to have been named
for Bab-ilu, the Gate of God. The Babs often take the name of the highway
projected beyond the Gate, as Bab-el-Rabat, Bab-el-Fez.

than the decay of Spain. The Spanish once were dominant in
Christendom. Spain's growth in power began with the injection,
into the Iberian peninsula's population, of much Visigoth blood.
Soon thereafter Spain became Europe's leader. Such dominance
continued until the time of Columbus. The Lions-and-Castles flag
everywhere was triumphant. Legions fighting under it even succeeded in throwing the mighty Moors back across Gibraltar's
strait.

. Came, however, the time Phillip II was to ride the stony trail
to where he was to build the Convent-of-the-Escorial. The rocks
along this track are lined with rock-rose bushes. Spain in Phillip's
day held overlordship in even the Netherlands. Her flag flew over
all South America, except its East-coast Portuguese settlements.
Spain also held the Captaincy-General of Central America as well
as the Viceroyalty of Mexico. The latter even included most of
Southwestern U. S. A. This is what later became our states of
California, Arizona, New Mexico as well as what destined to become the Lone-Star republic of Texas. Into these, lines of missions

were to be extended. It took MEN to have accomplished these conquests. Spain, however, had reached its zenith. There is no more tragic page in all history than this collapse of imperial Spain.

Intolerant Phillip II persecuted his Low-Country subjects from Leeuwarden, from Gronigen, to Ghent, to Brussels. The Inquisition eliminated those who dared think. It furnished the pattern for Hitler's Gestapo, four centuries later.

Another cause of Spanish decadence was dilution of Visigoth blood thru crossings with slave concubines. Overseas conquests, too, ever sucked out more of the daring. Greedy Conquistadors, eager to return to Spain were intent on grabbing golden tiles from Incan temples. Some of these died in battle. More perished because of jungle fevers. All had left their women behind. Thus arose, from Arizona's San Xavier de Bac and the Presidios of Monterey and San Diego thru Mexico, Peru to the Rio Plata and the Chilean fortresses a *mestizo* caste. Spain-South-of-the-Pyrenees— also New Spain from Texas to Cape Horn became tragically hybridized. Spain's leadership types were bred out. The Land-of-the-Rockroses no longer was dictator of all Christendom.

The cistus has narrowed leaves characteristic of certain moisture conserving plants. Its stems, too, are sticky like a California tarweed. This is so much so that, after a wind-storm, grains of sand adhere to the foliage. Each milk-white petal has a conspicuous claret-colored spot to guide insects to its honey stores. Thus Mother Nature, fond of her rock roses, conserves moisture by her ancient devices, while she makes certain of sturdier babies by cross-pollenization.

ORANGE VENDOR IN MOROCCO

"The objects and pleasures of travel are so unintelligible
to most Orientals, they are apt to regard the European traveller as a lunatic."

(Karl Baedeeker)

"A WANDERING MINSTREL—I, A THING OF RAGS AND PATCHES"
(MIKADO).

Cistus from Spain's chaparral . . . escallonia, chaparral of
the Andes . . . cotoneasters and pyracanthus, chaparral of the
Himalayas . . . Manuka, chaparral of New Zealand . . . all these
are worth garden space to attract chaparral-loving songsters.
Our Geogardener's chaparral plantings offer protection to
winter migrants particularly white-crown and golden-crown
sparrows arriving in two streams, year after year, about the
equinox. These bird-bandings disclose they have summered in
respectively, California's High Sierras and Alaska. The white-
crowns, with the meadowlarks, furnish Californian birdsong
from the September thru to the March equinox.

CHAPTER 26

COTTONWOOD

"There's a tree by a stink-ing water-hole,
Where bil-lows on bil-lows of pam-pas grass roll,
Where the An-des 'scarp high 'gainst the sun-set sky
Where fla-min-goes fly by with ne-ver a cry,
Where os-triches flock-ing, go and come ...
I hunt them with bo-las but never with gun,
In Pat-ta-go-nee-ah.

With some twigs that drop-ped from a COT-TON-WOOD
tree.
A hot pu-cher-o I'll make for me ...
A can-ful dipped up from that stink-ing pool ...
I'll boil it first, for I am no fool.
Jerked beef I'll shave from my sad-dle-bag chunk,
It's my pil-low, too, and the ground's my bunk.
Then worn out, I'll dream of feasts to come:
Beef a ca-bal-lo and a long draft of rum.
For eggs can ride on a thick beef-steak.
Em-pan-ad-as rich my girl shall make.
'To-mor-row I'll steal an os-trich egg
I'll gorge 5 men's meals while cit-y fools beg.
For I'm in Pat-ta-go-nee-ah.
I'm in Pat-ta-go-nee-ah!

(Guacho Song: "IN PATAGONIA.")

T HE COTTONWOOD holds the same place in the hearts of those who live in the Arid west as does the POPLAR in Italy. How gripping this is can be understood when we remember "poplar" persists from the days when Romans lovingly called it the "Tree of the People", of the POPULACE.

A pioneering Kentuckian or up-state New Yorker would select his Outwest "160." This was when a still opulent Uncle Sam gave a farm to every young husband. Food was no problem, with plenty of deer, antelope, elk. Water, however, was. A spring had to be found—otherwise a wet-spot for an easily dug well. Beside the home were planted cottonwood cuttings, if the Covered Wagon's supply were still alive. If not, Mother had a bag of cotton-wood clusters. Their "grapes" already had burst, showing the silky-white fibers, or cotton, that insured wide winter-gale-dispersion. These were seed-boxed. In a few years the rapidly growing cottonwood, in its moist soil, gave welcome shadow. Here shade temperatures in August might reach 115 degrees.

The cottonwood's efficient seed-mechanism has resulted in its wide range: Canada to Patagonia. The cowboy of Montana's gaillardia-enamelled prairies, the vaquero of Texas' Llando estacado, the gaucho of Argentine—all often have no other fuel to cook their "jerky" or "chili con carne" other than the fallen twigs described in the annexed song of gaucho's boasting.

A decoction from the bark of populus fremontia is used as a wash for bruises and cuts, especially for the sores on horses caused by chafing.

THE URUGUAY'S PIONEERS' MONUMENT, MONTEVIDEO

The South Americans also pioneered into Cottonwood Land. . . If the Good Neighbor Policy is to work, we Norte-Americans need to know more than did a certain debutante. When a Uruguayan diplomat was introduced she chattered "Oh! yes. Uruguay. That's a town in South Africa, is it not?" When peace was restored, she continued with "I've learned a lot of Spanish since I came to California. "Yerba" means goat, "Buena" means Island. Oh! yes! and "Manana" is morning and "pajamas" is night."

One of the most prized escallonias of our gardens is the peerless E. montevidensis.

CHAPTER 27

CLARKIA

"CLARK-IA" ROOTS into "Lewis-and-Clark." It is, therefore, link-ed with the Maid-in-Buckskin.* She was given a place in the Hall of Fame. Her loyalty to Lewis and Clark did much to cement to our nation the upper end of the Louisiana Purchase. There is, therefore, hardly a plant in your garden that more strongly stimulates the memories of American history than Clarkia. It was named for the man President Jefferson selected to accompany Merriwether Lewis into the Oregon country. Clarkias, in different species, grow "sauvage" from the Lewis-and-Clark country up North, past Sutter's Fort, then southward to the line of Spanish missions along the California Coast.

---

* The dramatic story of the Indian girl above described has been revived. (see Readers Digest 2/44).

"BIOLOGICAL ILLITERACY"**

If we can raise a generation trained in biology, we will have a different kind of lawmaking. Let us remember only two presidents of the United States were biologically-educated: Thomas Jefferson, Theodore Roosevelt. Jefferson grasped the importance of his agents, Lewis and Clark, bringing back as much biological information as possible. Jefferson was a natural-born scientist. Another such an intellect was depicted in the remarkable film of Madam Curie, discoverer of radium.

We also have historical illiteracy.

** A term coined by the author in an effort to help mould public opinion toward demanding a sounder education in Nature Study. Mother Nature offers thousands of examples of how we could plan for happier living. (Remember, too, the author's phrase in the opening 1900s "Learn to read a trailside, as one does a book.")

CHAPTER 28

CORNFLOWER

"Not a flower
But shows some touch, in freckle, streak, or stain,
His unrivall'd pencil. (Cowper—The Task.)

E UROPE'S CHARMING blue cornflower grows in delightful color-
contrast with the tawny, ripened grain. Germans call it
"Koenig's-kreissen." This is because German royalty made it fash-
ionable for boutonnieres. It is said the first German Kaiser thus
wore one whenever obtainable.

The term *"Koenig's-kreissen"* is, however, rather inaccurate.
The blue cornflower was much more than a king-ly favorite. It
really was the symbol of victory of the Liberty-loving. It represented escape from the foreign dictator. Napoleon seems to have
felt himself quite a breaker of women's hearts. He thus hoped to
gain by diplomacy—in lieu of military force—a muchly-needed con-
cession. He called on a certain queen. Preliminary to begging the
desired favor, he presented her with a costly bouquet of orchids.
The indignant queen threw Napoleon's exotics to the oaken floor,
trampled them. As the departing Napoleon banged the door to
the right, the queen's little son, the crown prince, entered at the
left. He saw the queenmother in tears. Noticing the crushed bouquet on the floor, he rushed outdoors to the garden. Gathering
quickly a fistful of cornflowers, he ran with them to his mother.
The princelet, cornflowers and all, was pressed to the maternal
bosom. Then the queen tucked the sky-blue flowers into her cor-
sage.

The story spread. The queen's ladies-in-waiting told to their
own maids the tale of Napoleon's spurned orchids, and of the compensating cornflowers. Soon the whole city was gossiping about
the chagrined Corsican. The little crown prince's part in the yarn
lost nothing in the telling . . . From that day the cornflower became, throughout the Fatherland, the symbol of Liberty.

Is it not a strange twist of history that a cruel Nazi dictator
in that same Germany, in our day, should have crushed, not only
the very France whose armies made Napoleon's conquests possible,
but his own people under, as this is written, Gestapo terrors?

The Hohenzollern kings, who later were to become Kaisers

made a fixed policy of wearing boutonnieres of the lovely blue cornflowers. Meantime, however, they themselves already had commenced the systematic elimination of the liberty-loving from the German population. Had the "48ers" not been killed or exiled—that year before the California gold rush—Germany might have contained, within herself, the leadership that could have steered her Ship-of-State clear of the rocks of World Wars I and II.

The Hohenzollern cornflowers in one's garden therefore may serve, perhaps, to remind us that we Americans, in permitting centralization at Washington, in lieu of local self-government, may as gradually lose our liberties as did the German folk.

"There spring the wildflowers—fair as can be."

(Eliza Cook—My Grave)

CAMEL DUNG

Even your cornflowers will respond to intelligent use of fertilizer. One wonders what observant desert-dweller, back in the Neolithic, noticed that the barley around a bit of camel dung produced "40 fold" when that two feet away gave but a scrawny "20 fold." Even camel droppings, saleable for fertilizer, can yield to the head of a desert family, earnings which permit raising children. It is a far cry from such an occupation to that giving the standard of living of the average American family. Today, however, we are destroying, by DELIBERATE RACE-SUICIDE, the very precious element which has made possible the building up of our way of life compared with that pictured above.

WINDOW FLOWER BOXES, CANTERBURY, ENGLAND

This is written in a 17th-story room in a San Francisco hotel. All around are buildings 5 to 9 stories high. Their roofs show pathetic attempts at gardening . . . a pot or two, sometimes a dozen. The bird glass discloses that they are mostly geraniums. One is kerria. One a tuberous begonia, with a giant golden blossom . . . The cactus window gardens are mentioned in its chapter . . . In Sweden's Gothenburg, the street railway's trolley poles have iron collars to hold blossoming plants . . . The quaint window boxes in Canterbury in our photograph added muchly to the attraction of this **grippingly-historic** cathedral city.

CHAPTER 29

COSMOS

"They know the time to go!
The fairy clocks strike their inaudible hour
In field and woodland, and each punctual flower
Bows at the signal an obedient head
And hastens to bed." ("Time To Go"—Susan Coolidge.)

MEXICO is Cosmos' Fatherland.　Our Geogardener first found it as a wildflower in that botanist's wonderland, the semi-desert between Taxco and Acapulco.　There it grows "sauvage," near the old galleon trail to Vera Cruz.　Over this, pack-mule trains once transported cloves, nutmegs, pepper, shimmery silks.　These, at Acapulco Harbor, had been assembled.　They came from India, Cathay, the Spice Islands, even the Philippines—whose name is a monument to Spain's King Phillip.

The Spice Islands' trail ascended from Acapulco port up to Taxco of the Silver Lode, then thru Cuernavaca of the Gardens beloved by Charlotta, to Mexico City.　At that capital's Zocolo Plaza, it was continued past Orizaba and Cordoba to Vera Cruz.　Our Geogardener had descended over it from Mexico's *Tierra templada*.　He then had come down into the *Tierra Caliente*.　He was very hungry.　It had been an all-night ride under the full moon.

The party reached Cordoba at 4 a. m.　Arriving there, only one man—his mouth sombrero-guarded against "night-air miasmas"—was to be seen. "A bit to eat?" *"No se, senor."* Here it dawned upon these *Norte*-Americans they were hardly as wise as Susan Coolidge's flowers. "When are restaurants open for breakfast?" *"A la onze."* (11 o'clock). Our famished Geogardener strolled, at sunrise, into the nearby jungle. Joy of joys! A peon was approaching with a heavy bunch of bananas on his back. "How much for one dozen?" The peon grinned. *"Diez centavos"**. That meant 5 cents, American gold.　In exchange for a 10-centavos-piece, the peon, to our Geogardener's surprise, laid the whole bunch at his feet.　The bargain had been in English, for the British long had sisal factories nearby. Then he called, in Spanish, to some friends nearby, "For what do you think I soaked this sucker-of-a-

---

* Wages then, both on the haciendas and in the mines were 17¢ for a day of 12 hours, or about 1½¢ per hour.

gringo?* I actually made him pay ten centavos for a bunch of bananas." They had cost him only a slash of his machete.

Cosmos, white, pink, magenta, or yellow is a truly Mexican gift to your garden. It is as Mexican as the highpeaked *sombrero,* the colorful *serape,* the doleful bell-tolling for the too-frequent funerals, the ropy *pulque* of his *maguey.* When, therefore, oh! Gardener, you see your cosmos blossoms nodding in a late September breeze, let your fancy roam to "South-of-the-Rio-Grande" as the men of the Alamo called it. Picture tired galleons limping into Acapulco. They had run away from Sir Francis Drake's privateers, had indeed lost a third of their fleet. Imagine their great, bellying sails emblazoned with the True Cross that gave its name to Vera Cruz port. Picture their sea-weary crews swilling the fiery Aztec *tequilla* . . . the quarrels that followed. Think of the black

VULTURES IN COSMOS LAND

One Mexican trip's agenda included: "Geogarden Cosmos to its native haunts." The landing was in open ocean and by a slung basket. The fonda's bedrooms were clean. The zipolotes at the garbage cans below our window, however, made us appreciate the vast gulf between sanitation in Saxon and in Latin America. Geogardening makes for "Love-of-Country." (Incidentally, we found up-mountain our wild Cosmos).

zipolotes following the pack train thru the cactus. These gruesome vultures watched for fallen mule or muleteer, ready to pick any carrion bones. All this is COSMOS-LAND!

Because Cosmos is a lovely member of the sunflower family, there is reproduced here a cut and the explanatory note from the author's "Sierran Cabin . . . From Skyscraper." It is hoped this may, even in a very small way, stimulate pleasurable reflection as to what the composites of one's garden may remind one.

---

* "Gringo", our Geogardener learned in Chile, was a nickname applied to Scotch adventurers who fought in that nation's Independence War. The Caledonians often would sing Burns' verses about the Scottish lassies. These commence: "There's naught but care on every hand." The rollicking chorus runs "GREEN GROW the rashes! O!!". . . Since the Chileans heard this constantly, they called the red-bearded Scots "Green-grows." This later became, from Valparaiso and Buenos Aires to Vera Cruz and our own Presidios of Monterey and San Francisco: "Grin-gos".

LAKE DWELLINGS IN THE SCHWEITZER LANDESMUSEUM, ZURICH

The bridge's approaches could be quickly destroyed or even burned when enemy forces were coming. It may have been at the land-end of such an approach that the first keenwitted lakedweller started the building up, from the crabapple, towards our luscious fruits of today. It is almost amazing to trace back, not only the domestication of wild animals like the dog, the horse, the cow, also most of our cultivated food plants and to learn that nearly all the discoveries were made in the Neolithic.

CHAPTER 30

CRABAPPLE

"Blossoms, flowers and budding trees.
Thank God! we can be sure of these."

NEAR "where the Andes 'scarp high 'gainst the Western sky" is the *Pampa de Sacramento*. A sleepy old village, it is surrounded by *pampa*. Thereon is an abundance of wild pampas grass. It has, of course, a tiny church. A campanile crumbles beside the House-of-God. Said belfry, fortunately, is minus its bell, for its cross-timber has dry-rot. Same would scarcely support the tiniest of chimes. The village, too, has dry-rot. The slothful inhabitants remind one of the gravetender in O'Henry's "Cabbages and Kings."

"In Anchuria . . . President Miraflores . . . died by his own hand . . . For a real, a boy will show you his grave. . . . The head-piece is daily scrubbed with soap-bark and sand. An old halfbreed tends the grave . . . WITH THE DAWDLING MINUTENESS OF INHERITED SLOTH."

Beside that chapel in the *Pampa de Sacramento* is an aged orchard. Its appletrees have gnarled limbs, like those of one tortured with arthritis. It still bravely bears fruit. The Botany Professor told our Geogardener that the plants probably dated to the first century S. C. (i.e of the Spanish Conquest). He enlarged on what had been accomplished when Man superimposed, upon NATURAL SELECTION, a highly intelligent ARTIFICIAL SELECTION. Being an ardent member of one of the fine Eugenic Societies in the South-of-the-Rio-Grande, this Botany Professor suggested that someday we might hope humans would be similarly improved. . . .

The apples of this Andean tree were small and bitter. They were little removed from the wild crabapple. It was difficult to believe that, in a few centuries, apple breeders had developd, out of such stock, our Pippins, our Spitzbergens, our Delicious, our Bellfleurs. Simultaneously, farseeing market men had solved problems of apple distribution. Our Geogardener had found Yakima apples on sale where the Sphinx flirts with the ghost of old Cheops, who still haunts the nearby Pyramid.

Pampa de Sacramento crabapples reminded our Geogardener, too, of the charred apples from the Lake dwellings, such as those of Lake Zurich in Switzerland, of Lac Bourget in Savoy. Crab-apples* from a Lake Dwellers' village are Zurich Museum. They were recovered when a prolonged drought had lowered the *Zurich-see* below all known records.

From this charred, slag-like mess, our Geogardener tried to picture the Lake Dwellers' crude efforts at gardening. These were, perhaps, the first in that area, whence came our Anglo-Saxon for-bears. We can learn much from the creosote-preserved food from Lake Zurich's ancient mud. We know, too, that these timid folk always had a causeway behind them. They ventured out from their over-water homes to their vegetable plots. These were just be-hind the sand-beach-lapping wavelets. There they would stone-hoe, (for this was the first plow). They there would plant, culti-vate, finally harvest the barley, peas, lentils.

Picture the chance-dropping of a crabapple seed at the land-end of the trestled runway to their lake dwellings. It sprouts, grows into a tree. It blossoms. It bears agreeably-acid little ap-ples. Then some brainy chieftain passes one day. He carries on his back a young porker—a *wildschwein* or *sanglier*. . . . This might have been mankind's first roast-pork-and-apple-sauce. Later he finds, in those limestone hills, a BIGGER, A SWEETER AP-PLE. He is imaginative enuf to take a cutting from these better crabapples. This he plants beside the chance seedling at the shore end of the runway to his lake-village. In after years, he boasts about that tree. He makes wisecracks. This is a part of his leader-ship, based on his superior intelligence. It was much as a Pharoah's temple-building, with stone records of his kingly attributes. This lake-dweller chieftain's loud talks were not unlike Senator Sor-ghum, arrived home from Washington to mend his political fences. ARTIFICIAL SELECTION IN PLANT BREEDING HAS BE-GUN.

Good eugenists are careful to be exactly truthful as to what can be expected from heredity. They, therefore, consider with caution a story about the Watsonville apple man: It was said he was born in Somer-setshire, England. He lived 30 years in California without returning. He was always sure the apples of his boyhood had a better flavor than any he could raise in California. He was told this was due to cross-fertilization of apple blossoms by the English bumblebee. He imported some of these, unloosed them in his apple orchard. The bumblebees, how-ever, flew to a nearby salt marsh. There they crossed with mosquitos. The next generation, it is solemnly alleged, had stingers at both ends.

---

* The bitter crabapple of Scotland's braes were long ago adopted as the badge of Clan Lamont. Their very name was derived from Norse LAGAMADR (a law-man). Geogardening in Scotland, one hears of an early Lamont of the 1200's, a Duncan Lamont. He grants lands to the monks of Paisley.

This little book's Foreword opens with: "After all, the dominant stimulus is COLOR." Apropos of above, following is a very rough translation of a Mayan Song about vegetable dyestuffs that may be of interest:

I.

Where the deer come down to drink at Lake Atitlan,
There lives a MAYA with the blackest velvet eyes
Her re-bo-so, her hui-piel, her nag-o-a
Flash the colors of her bright native dyes.

II.

Where the petals of the wild pink tree DAHLIA,
Are scattered in the swishing tropic breeze,
She won her golds and her bright burnished yellows
From heartwood of the stout fustic trees.

III.

In a garden near an old Spanish kitchen,
Where the hammock of her baby brother swings,
Indigo stalks were boiled for the blue tints
Cer-ru-le-an as a tan-a-ger's wings.

IV.

From the thorns of the low spreading No-pal,
She picks the bodies of co-chin-neel scale.
Thus she gained brilliant, bright, gorgeous scarlets
That flash 'cross the cactus-ribbed vale.

V.

The browns that she's woven in contrast
With the reds and the blues and the gold
Came from boiling the bark of za-po-tal
Over charcoal of mangrove, I'm told.

VI.

You ask the name of this velvet-eyed maiden?
My answer is "Nun-ca, senor"
I'll not fight you with my new machete,
So! Vamos, quick, thru that open door. . . .

VII.

"Where the deer come down to drink at Atitlan
Dwells this Maya with the black velvet eyes.
She is mine by the laws of the Maya
And no gringo shall look on my prize."

CHAPTER 31

DAHLIA

"If you observe a really happy man, you will find him
building a boat, writing a symphony, educating a son, or
growing DOUBLE DAHLIAS in his garden."

(Dr. W. Beran Wolfe in Readers Digest 6-44.)

DAHL-IA is another contribution, like fuchs-ia, like agave, like cosmos, to our gardens out of Mexico's fascinating flora. Would that each of such Mexican plants could plant, in garden-owners' souls, *die wanderlust* for Mexico. If these Mexican flowers only could awaken the same interest in our Cross-the-Border republic that sent the early botanists there! Their explorations gained many new species. These they named for Fuchs, for Dahl, as others had been godfathered by Nicot, by Bougainville, by Douglass, by Menzies, by Vancouver, by both Lewis and his companion Clark. . . .

We owe much of our scientific knowledge to wanderlusting von Humboldt. Today we are forgetting our debt to the author of "Cosmos." Von Humboldt's great work was commenced when the author was 79. Vol. IV was finished when he was 89. He ranked with Linnaeus in his master-ability to radiate his zeal-for-work into the lives of his students. He discovered the Humboldt Current. He further organized public opinion toward renewing Europe's wornout soils with guano fertilizer.

Von Humboldt, on his return to Europe, planned successfully that some hundreds of his students should "carry on" further exploration of so-called "Latin America." Our Geogardener's grandfather, as a young college professor, came under von Humboldt's spell. He was one of those whom Humboldt* assigned to the Mexican area. Von Humboldt's power dominated the entire life of this young professor. The latter finally died in the same Mexico, a martyr to his devotion to that country.

There is something, however, with a deeper lesson than Pan-American travel to be learned from Dahlia. The genus is noted for a high degree of VARIABILITY. It is, therefore, always a promis-

---

* Humboldt county in California—which contains a string of State Redwood Parks—was named for the author of Cosmos. Also, when the stern Covered-Wagon Folk came to rename the Nevada River once yclept "St. Mary's," they dubbed it Humboldt River. Followed, on Nevada's map, another Humboldt County, as well as Humboldt Sink.

ing outlet for plant-breeder's energy. . . . Some day these folk will, out of their vast knowledge of plant-breeding, spearhead the campaign to awaken public opinion to the consciousness that human genetics is even more important than the genetics of dahlia, sweetpeas, carnations, of almonds, apples, peaches, of tomatoes, maize, cabbage. . .

After some 35 years of Crossing-the-Border, his dahlia blooms recall to our Geogardener many Mexican memories as of the opal mines of Quaretaro, whose flat roofs under a blazing sun are much like those of the Holy Land. . . Of hacienda life on the shore of yesteryear's Lake Chapala, with loveable peon kiddies. . . Of pink-cravated *Rurales*. These Porfirio Diaz created, by simple expedient of a uniform, plus a salary a little higher than the profits of banditry . . . Of banana plantations at steaming Tapachula—Of bantering tortilla makers, bending over their stone *metates* . . . Of orchid-hung jungles, with flocks of parrots and macaws . . . Of native artists, hand-rubbing paint on disks cut from giant gourds . . . Of Amerind smiths hammering into strange designs the silver of San Luis Potosi . . . Of obsidian knives that once cut out human hearts at the *teocalli* . . . Of Yaqui maidens, snipping with bent-stick pincers cactus fruit, driving away competing, eager, famished parrots.

Sonoran maps show Pueblo de las Vidas. (City of the Widows). Husbands once were short-lived there. The neighboring Yaqui were even more blood-thirsty than were the North-of-the-Border Apaches. This is changed now. 'Tis wise therefore, to let that Dahlia in your garden point toward Yaqui Land, toward the land of Juarez, of Maximilian, of the stern viceroy, Mendoza, of Cortes, of Montezuma . . . Dahlias in one's garden, therefore, could well stimulate the flower-lover to plan to take, next winter, that long-considered trip to Mexico's West Coast. A swollen stream of tourists to our first neighbor "South of the Rio Grande" cannot help but make for a better understanding between Saxon and Latin. Once the cold plunge is over, there will be repeated journeys there . . . It is a good habit to form early in life, as did our Geogardener. Mexico is vast. Once one's footsteps turn thither, who can forget The Beyond? There are the Guatemala Highlands, the Guatemala coastal jungles. Then, on the horizon is all that stretches even to Patagonia. There are the pampas, with its gauchos, with its wild ostriches. There is Chile's Magellan Territory, with its fuchsia-chaparral and bamboo.

LAKE IN THE TREE-DAHLIA AREA
Our Geogardener found the attractive tree dahlias growning a-down the
Cordilleras throughout Central America. They are common in gardens in the
San Francisco Bay region. One wishes their presence there might stimulate
memories of their native land . . . of Indios in dugouts of avocado—of orchid
hung trees—of brilliant macaws, of parrots nesting in holes in the soft
rhyolite lava banks, of epiphytic cacti hung high in a mahogany tree—of Indios
hunting iguanas. If one's garden flowers can thus bring pictures of the overseas, one's garden has increased value.

WATER CARRIERS ON THE DATE-PALM-LINED NILE
Drinking water, whether from foul rivers like the Nile,
the Ganges or from infected wells is a potent source of
disease. From one pilgrimage to Allahabad, Hindustan, the
Faithful, carrying bottles of the sacred water of Mother
Gunga (the Ganges) spread a devastating cholera epidemic.
They repaid hospitalities by dropping Ganges water in the
wells of village after village when returning.

CHAPTER 32

DATE PALM

THE PALM which bears edible dates can be grown as far North as Sacramento, California. One specimen, in a garden of our Geogardener's family was planted about 1868. It grew for some 50 years and until an expanding business district made the garden succumb to the advancing skyscrapers. It yielded no dates however. Sacramento is in the Lower-Sonoran Life Zone. Upper-Lower, is true, but Lower-Sonoran nevertheless. To find date orchards with long lines of trees groaning under their heavy load of Deglet Noors, however, one must journey to true Lower-Lower Sonoran as in Los Angeles "desert" hinterland, the Imperial Valley.

The Deglet Noor is the Queen of dates. *"Deglet"* is said to be Arabic for "dates" and *"noor"* is a root indicating "light" as in the *Koh-i-noor* diamond. When our Geogardener first became interested in French African oases, it was said no Deglet noor reached any Dog-of-an-Unbeliever, except a few in Paris whom it was wisdom to conciliate. It was common rumor that the Arabs

Left: Date-Harvest . . . right: Date palms swaying in a Saharan Gale . . . while kodaking in the Saharan oases, our Geogardener often found the menu was limited for days at a time, to 4 items: Camel meat (very stringy), sugar cane, dates, and usually good bread when there were French soldiers near.

DESERT FREIGHT TRAIN

The desert freight train carrying dates for U. S. A. is the camel.

would assassinate anyone attempting to smuggle out a Deglet noor shoot. As the name "Assassin" came from that of a Moslem tribe whose chief occupation was what the efficient Russians call "liquidation," there was little doubt that only a real hero, daring and resourceful, could be successful in the undertaking.

Yet a certain "Yankee" was convinced the Coachella desert's sands plus Rio Colorado water, could be welded into wealth. Last winter sales of Coachella date gardens were at prices per acre that would make Figtree John squirm in his grave. The land of horned lizards and chuckwallahs, of sidewinders and bisnagas would produce enuf dates from a "160" of sand to buy all Manhattan an orgy of firewater.

There is, of course, another "date" palm, the Phoenix canariensis, grown extensively in California and in Florida. Its woody dates must have a bit of sweet flavor, for certain large birds seem to eat them. They are an attractive element in roadside forestry.

"HEWERS OF WOOD, DRAWERS OF WATER"

An Arab folksaying describes the date palm as "head in the sun, but feet in the water." This date palm is background for "Hewers of Wood, Drawers of Water." The world's then largest pumps were installed in your editor's Reclamation District when its tule swamps were converted into asparagus and sugar beet ranches . . . Compare such with above irrigation of an Egyptian date palm oasis . . . America leaped from muzzle-loader to atomic bomb in less than one hundred years. Egypt failed to improve its technique in 30 centuries. Why? The old highpowers of the Nile became extinct. The plodding, unimaginative but highly prolific FELLAHIN persisted . . . Have we not now a similar decay starting in U.S.A. by excessive birth control of the talented? Egypt once was the world's reservoir of wisdom. The fellahin outbred the leadership type.

PYRAMIDS OF GIZEA SEEN THROUGH DATE PALMS

CHAPTER 33

DELPHINIUM

"The LARKSPUR listens, I hear, I hear,
And the lily whispers, 'I wait.' "

(*Tennyson—Maud.*)

DELPHINIUM, TO our Geogardener, always spelled "E-n-g-l-a-n-d." He made repeated journeys to track his garden plants to their *sauvage* homes. These covered various areas on the European Continent, as well as Africa and the Near East. Britain, for these, usually was the most convenient travel-center. Therefore while enroute, the Geogardener always would steal a few days to enjoy the artistry of English gardens.

The Britons, for decades, scoured the world for new garden material. Much of such early exploring they based on Philadelphia, in their American colonies. Later their collectors—including Douglass, Nuttal, Jeffreys—went to the Pacific Coast. These travelled either by the long route 'Round the Horn, or overland from Hudson's Bay. Always there was a group of keen-minded Britishers, wanting novel plants for manor-house gardens. All this was true Geogardening. . . It was in the fine British gardens, our Geogardener always found the world's best delphiniums. Tourists will recall the blue delphiniums contrasted with pink hollyhocks at Ann Hathaway's Cottage, Stratford-on-Avon.

California's native flora is rich in larkspurs. In pioneer days the Great Valley floor, from Red Bluff to Bakersfield, showed velvety purple larkspurs in color contrast with leagues upon leagues of orange eschscholtzias. There were often 12 blooms on a single stalk. All along the Coast Range, from Mendocino of the Mexican Viceroy Mendoza, to San Diego of the first Presidio, is found another species, the red delphinium. This is D. *nudicaule*. Only recently have the hybridizers commenced to experiment with it. We may expect, say in 1950 or 1960, some startling results therefrom.

Another close relative of delphinium is monkshood. Some day it may be deemed worthy of as much attention of plant breeders as delphinium has enjoyed. It, too, has a rain-shed. The French call the contraption "la para-pluie"* (the "against-rain"). The monkshood flower of California's Sierras has a most efficient "rain-

---

* This seems so much more appropriate than our "umbrella", or shade-defense which the Gauls, with their nice distinction, call "para-sol" or "against-sun."

shed." Its upper part has a hood which slopes even more than the best snow-shedding roof . . . All this is to protect the seed-making organs beneath. The monkshood blooms at high altitudes. The valleys and the piedmont below probably will be rainless from May to October. The forest below the timber line, however, may have a thunderstorm at any time. In the shade of the tamarack-pines of the upper Canadian Zone, therefore, where thunder-clouds collect among the nearby peaks—the monkshood, with its blue and white umbrella, ever makes an abundance of seeds that reproduction may proceed . . .

"In emerald tufts; flowers purple, blue and white;
Like sapphire, pearl, and rich embroidery."
(Merry Wives of Windsor, Act. V., Sc. 5)

Shakespeare thus reminds us that, even in his Elizabethan Age, those remarkably energetic Britons had taken time, while exploring nearly every coast between Baffin Bay and Botany Bay, to enjoy flowers. This seems to have had a snowball-like accumulation of fascination till we find Jeffrey sent via Hudson Bay to his desert death. Even today some of the most intelligent seed firms are British. Where can one equal the intelligent Scottish gardeners?

"You are most canny with flowers" said a Somersetshire dame to a gardener near Bobby Burns old home. His garden WAS as colorful as a brilliant sunset. "Aye" said the Scot, "Canny is the word. I DO KEN. I mark my plants. I SAVE THE SEEDS OF THE BEST." Here was applied Genetics . . . How few universities, even medical schools, have courses in Human Genetics.

REINDEER MOSS GARDENS, LAPPLAND

Geogardening in Alaska, Greenland, Iceland, Lappland brings amazing color feasts. In the Northlands, the Midnight Sun works 24 hours daily. Following the snowmelt, comes a flowerburst only comparable to our Southwest deserts after a once-in-20-years' cloudburst. The glaciated terrain in our photograph was most colorful with delphiniums blotching the orange-plus-lemon of "Iceland" poppies. The reindeer seemed to know both plants as poisonous. Perhaps they hesitated at their taste. They selected, instead, reindeer moss as food. Over large areas, reindeer are only means of converting pathetically-meager vegetation into human food. Food-paucity means sparse population.

DEODAR

Your garden Deodar stands a majestic representative of Hindustan. Beneath India's deodars there once lived when the world was young, lusty Nature Lovers. These sang the Vedic hymns: Today this breed of poet-statesmen is extinct. These Northmen crossed, recrossed their blood with prolific slave-concubines. Weaklings now live:

"Where the cholera, the cyclone
And the crow
Come and go . . .
Where the merchant deals
In indigo and tea,
Hides and ghi."   (*Kipling*)

NATIVE GIRL FROM DEODAR-CLOTHED TIBET

"One of the young men of fashion gave Kim a complete Hindu kit . . . the costume of a low-caste street-boy . . . Kim stored it at a secret place . . . in Nila Ram's timberyard, where the fragrant DEODAR logs lie seasoning." (Kipling: "Kim.)

CHAPTER 34

DEODAR

"Hundreds of dressed DEODAR logs had caught on a shag of rock . . . Then went up a shout of 'Namgay Doola' . . . A large redhaired villager hurried up, stripping off his clothes as he ran . . . "That is the rebel" said the King. "Now will the jam be cleared."
(*Kipling . . . Namgay Doola.*)

OUTSIDE HINDUSTAN, there probably are no young Deodars finer than the line thereof afront the facade of California's State Capitol at Sacramento. Not yet a century old, already the lower branches are tree-like trunks. On a hot summer day, each deodar affords shade to nursemaids and their charges, also to book-devouring lads. The latter well might read Kipling's "Namgay Doola," also that most thrilling of novels—"Kim." Under such a spreading deodar can be had dreams of Zam-Zammeh, of the Grand Trunk Road. There one also can recall The Snows, those mountains which

*"lay all day like molten silver in the
sunlight, and at night put on their
jewels again."*

II.

*"Anhasuerus Jenkins . . . took two months—at Simla
When the year was at the spring,
And underneath the DEODARS
Eternally did sing.
He warbled like a bulbul,
But par-tic-ul-ar-ly at,
Cornelia Agrippina
Who was musical,—and fat," etc. etc.*
(*Kipling: Army Headquarters*)

To enjoy the great Himalayan deodar-forest, one lands enroute at a port where the turbaned folk are thick as ants. These humans worship strange gods. These divinities include elephant-headed Ganesh, also one-eyed Kali. One then traverses the endless miles where he sees the village-centered life of the illiterate caste-bound. This has flowed on practically unchanged since perhaps long before when in the 5th century B. C., Siddartha Gautama became Buddha, or "The Enlightened." In geogardening Deodar, he hears mynahs chatter, parakeets scream. He sees jackals slink

Ganapati (The Deity of wisdom & remover of difficulties)

Ganesh, the Elephant-headed God of Wisdom, also of Good Luck, dominates the lives of millions in Hindustan. A business man before closing a deal will visit the shrine of Ganesh, will try to buy his favor with an offering. Compare the courses in Business Economics in American universities. However, while the superstitious of Hindustan multiply like rabbits, our leadership type, ignorant of the Differential Birth Rates Law—race suicide.

away much as do our Western coyotes. Then one day the northern horizon will show him a line of white against the sky-blue. One thus, at last, has one's first glimpse of the Eternal Snows . . . Camel caravans from the Back-of-Beyond are now seen. An occasional rajah's elephant shuffles along the way. His purple blanket is richly ornamented with seed-pearls. As one reaches the piedmont, one sees fierce Pathans with henna-dyed beards. One Afghan has, perhaps, whiskers in green. This proclaims to all the world his recent pilgrimage to Holy Mecca.

As one climbs higher and higher toward the Deodar forests, one soon is *"Sniffing the air of the mountains . . . breathing the morning coolth."*
Now come strange hill folk. One passes sturdy little Gurkhas, proud of their record of unbroken loyalty to the great British *raj.* They did not waver even when the Shiks faltered . . . An hour later, on the trail ahead appear shrewd red-haired, green-eyed Chinese traders. They have come from behind the Great Hump. Then, pat-

DANDYWALLAH TRAVEL, TIBET

tering barefooted in the track, come women who are living savings-banks. Their heavy silver anklets have been welded for life above their feet. This is a land where the miserly have hardly heard of banks . . . Later, and just below the deodars are encountered the first "unclean wives of many husbands." These squaw-like Tibetan women folk are from meadows among the deodars.

LEPCHA HUT, TIBET
Deodars on spur to right, above hut.

GROUP OF NATIVE BELLES, IN THE HIMALAYAN DEODAR ZONE

There yak browse among the blue poppies . . . Truly there is no better land than The Snows to which to go a-geogardening away from home-garden plants and trees. . . .

Cyclonic windstorms are rare in California. In one of these, our Geogardener had one of his deodars uprooted. Sawn into firewood, it was piled in a basement storeroom for occasional winter wood-fires. Ever thereafter that storeroom was fragrant with deodar-odor. Fragrance, such as deodar's always has been held by the Devout to be acceptable to Those Above. Occidentals offer incense to God, in Cologne Cathedral, in Notre Dame, at St. Peter's. At St. Peter's antipodes, almond-eyed Chinese burn punk before Joss . . . One reason for France's conquest of Madagascar was, the profits obtainable thru certain oils for French perfumery. Not only were Madagascar oils different and better, they also could be produced more cheaply than those from the semi-desert hills around Grasse.

Our Geogardener had gone a-geogardening to Grasse. This was the domain of a Count, one of whose ancestors had been most helpful at Yorktown in 1782. Here our Geogardener studied the gardens of jessamine. Here he viewed the orchard-yielded orange blossoms. Here he saw great beds of violets, extensive squares of roses. The latter rivalled the Oriental ones that for centuries had produced the renowned attar of roses. Here our Geogardener saw how the high-grade French perfumed-soap industry arose. It is based on a by-product of the perfumes. It parallels the glove industry of the Auvergne. This was founded on the sheep's milk cheese of Roquefort.

Perfume ranks as powerful as color at mating time, along with the old frontier jingle:
> *"Red and Yellow*
> *Catch a fellow!"*

Recall such perfumes as "My Sin," or "Tabu." The olfactory nerve is not merely an aim of highly-civilized man, it extends back to the primitives, even to insects. One of the delights of "read-a trailside as one does a book" is observation as to trailside plant scents which attract insects. Just as insects attracted by color so they, too, flock to odors. True some *are* disagreeable to humans. An example is the phallic mushroom. One of its folk names, indeed, is stinkhorn.

> *"The monkeys sang sorrowfully to each*
> *other as they hunted for dry roots in the*
> *fern-draped trees, and the last puff of the*

day wind brought from the unseen villages
the scent of damp wood smoke, hot cakes,
dripping undergrowth and rotting pine
cones. That smell is the true smell of the
Himalayas, and if it once gets into the
blood of a man, he will, at the last, forget-
ing everything else, return to the hills to
die."

(Kipling: Under the DEODARS.)

"The breath of a cool wind in DEODAR-crowned Jakko, shoul-
dering the stars." (Kipling Kim).

LOWER (BOOK MATCHES)

UPPER (FLINT)

Obsessed by age-old superstition about fire, our Tibetan
feared the match as "devil's
magic." For his own smokes,
eats, he used the flint-and-steel
sketched above. Taking the flint
out of the purse-like pouch, he
placed it in his left hand. With
his right hand grasping the
crescent-shaped steel at the top,
he struck sparks into tinder,
thus obtained fire. Contrast this
with the next cut.

The collecting instinct persists from
boyhood into second childhood. It has,
with some Americans, turned to book
match covers. It is said some rarer ones
from Russia have sold as high as $50
each . . . What progress from flint-and-
steel to book matches!

"We never harmed you! Innocent our guise,
Dainty our shining feet, our voices low;
And we were happy but a year ago.
Tonight, the moon that watched our lightsome wiles,
That dreamed upon us thru the DEODARS"
Is wan. etc. etc., (The Plea of the Simla Dancers . . . Kipling).

CHAPTER 35

ELM

IT WAS not the elm, but the cranberry, Thanksgiving-turkey's side-partner, that beckoned our Geogardener into the New England area. He had found the climate of California's Great Valley unsuitable to cranberry culture. His gardener had produced a few, but highly unsatisfactory cranberries. These stimulated the Massachusett's trip. Approaching Nantucket's cranberry bogs, he encountered his first New England town meeting. Here was an institution as typical of New Anglia's democracy as its noble elms. At said town meeting, descendants of whaler captains were voting. The issue was: Shall the automobile be permitted on Nantucket? There were those who argued that the development of the peace-destroying telephone, of the soul-enervating cinema had not been unmixed blessings. This was before the radio and the loud-speaker had come into general use. The Progressives won. The Conservatives' skippers met on the wharf the next day. Here they could escape the honk-honk of the horseless. Here they still could swap yarns of the days when there existed "no law of God or Man North of Hawaii." . . .

The magnificent elms of New England towns, also of upper-New York State, into which the Yankees spilled, were to be duplicated in a hundred communities. Even Sacramento, 3,000 miles away, was to come to be known for its elm-shaded streets. The elm is an arboreal symbol of the stern New England conscience. This has strengthened the political institutions of every state that ripened out of the territories from Ohio westward.

Elm blossoms, its "green roses," blend most agreeably with forsythia, also with Japanese quince. They are in demand for interior decorations for indoor bridge parties and teas. These green elm blossoms soon develop into tens of thousands of winged seeds.

The elm not only typified New England stability of character, it also beautifully exemplifies an ADEQUATE BIRTH RATE. It was this "swarming" that gave California such place names as: Maine Prairie, Massachusetts Bar, New York Ravine, Michigan Bar, also Michigan Bluff, Iowa Hill, Jayhawk, the New Bangor that became "Pinchemtight." There also was "New Boston." It shows on clipper captain's charts as a coming California seaport that was to out distance Sacramento. Today it is a forgotten bit of farming land. One may still finger it on maps preserved in New England garrets.

When, thru a leafless elm, one sees a post-storm sunset, may he remember the stained glass enjoyed while geogardening, the rare colorings of Notre Dame, Chartres, Bruges, LeMans, the lancets of York Minister, and of Paris' Sainte Chappelle. We are told the concept of making it first came from a gorgeous sunset seen thru winter trees, perhaps an elm.

中華文庫語說得

A CHINESE PROVERB SAYS: *"Whom Heaven has ENDOWED AS A FOOL AT HIS BIRTH it is a waste of instruction to teach."*

CHAPTER 36

ESCALLONIA

"Ice-helmeted warriors
Thy Andean peaks stand,
Ranged above a thousand miles
Of thy desert sand.
Morning and evening
Their rose-pink cloaks they don . . .
Their clouds are scarfs of thy colors
Oh! Mighty God of the Sun!"

(*Inca Hymn.*)

MACLAREN OF San Francisco's Golden Gate Park was a great geogardener. He brought this shrub of Chile's Gaucho-Land to this park, made Escallonia popular.

In Golden Gate Park is California Academy of Sciences' Museum. It has an African Hall. To reach it, you walk past hundreds of Escallonias. At a point in the African Hall the two horns of a certain antelope appear as one. The nearest totally eclipses the other. One thus has a veritable unicorn. It is as truly one-horned as the fabulous creatures seen as supporters on coats-of-arms. Thus one is reminded that even myths contain some foundation of truth. One is thus taught to listen tolerantly, to try to find the Truth beneath The False . . . As one's affection for unique Golden Gate Park grows, one becomes ever more deeply interested in these bush saxifrages. Then comes the urge to go a-geogardening to Escallonia-Land, i.e. to Southern Chile. One there finds the possible origin of another member of that fabulous zoo of the ancients. This had, in addition to its phoenix, its chimera, its mermaids, also its centaur. Remembering the veritable unicorn above, one asks himself: "Were these centaurs not merely expert horsemen?" . . . Where potbellied tropical South America tapers off to skinny Patagonian legs, one finds horsemen that indeed are almost centaurs. They would rather mount than walk a half-block. They are as superb riders as the Cossacks. Here indeed seems to be man and horse born in one biological unit.

These rollicking gauchos, themselves inordinately fond of dress, have dubbed one of their escallonias: *"Siete Camisas"* ("Seven Shirts"). It is most careful in dress. In fact, this escallonia

INDIOS, PERU

Nowhere is one more deeply impressed with the Scriptural warning not to expect "figs from thistles" than in what once was the Inca Empire. The ruling castes knew more than we Europeans at that time—in certain lines. The Conquistadors "liquidated,"—to borrow a Soviet term—all who could think. In a few years the Spaniards accomplished what had taken some decades in Athens—elimination of the Intelligensia. The Indio hates the white—yet has not, in nearly 400 years produced a leader to overthrow their master.

does wear 7 "shirts" in that its bark peels as does California's manzanita. Manzanita is, of course, rather finicky about its dress. It must have a new shirt yearly. Our Andean escallonia, however, must have a whole dresser of shirts. It is the true Beau Brummel of the Chilean chaparral.

The wanderlustings of our Geogardener prompted speculation as to the ancient wanderlustings of plants. Saxifragaceae seems a circumpolar family. Our Geogardener found its members to be numerous in Alaska, in Iceland. He found saxifrages even in Spitz-

BALSA ON LAKE TITICACA

Enroute to Lake Titicaca you may feel cold that eats through to the marrow. You may sleep under four alpaca rugs and still shiver. Even though you escape the saroche, you will move slowly because of the altitude. You may have a ride in a balsa. This is a boat made of bundled reeds, like the tules of California swamps. But cold or cramped, you are in Escallonia-land. You have plenty of evidence of how escallonia and its sister genera of saxifrages are adjusted to a cold that may make you shiver at mid-day.

bergen. As to those he observed in the Californian Sierras, in the Himalayas, in Scotland, they always flourished in shady coolth. There is, for example, the Siberian Saxifrage (saxifraga siberica) sometimes cultivated in our gardens. He found their cousins, the Hydrangeas, "sauvage" in the mountains back to Nikko's Lacquer Bridge. They are also mountain-lovers in China and in Formosa. The Deutzias are also from Yunnan and Tibet. All these can be explained as possible survivals in the North Temperate Zone. They

ARAUCANIANS, CHILE

Saxifrages are tough. They are evolved to withstand Greenland's sub-zero cold, the Himalaya's destroying winds, Andean desert's dessication. None of the family, however, are better equipped than the escallonias. These form the chaparral along hundreds of Andean miles. Urban's Botanica de las Plantas Endenicas de Chili lists "Siete Camisas," in all 25 Chilean species, some extending to Tierra del Fuego. In Chile, one finds the Araucanians. These Indios Pizarro could not conquer. They were as tough as their escallonias. In a rain storm our Geogardener found them stolidly following the trail. Each Indio had a rain coat of a giant Gunnera leaf.

were, presumably, left behind to fight rear-guard actions for the Ice King.

As to the South American escallonias, one wonders whether its members were not deserters who wandered down the Cordilleran backbone. Did they learn the habit of resin-making from the Mexican tarweeds? Further and further south they must have wandered. One finds hummingbirds feeding on the flowers of one species in the mountains of Venezuela. Farther south, the resinous branchlets fill the same fuel use as does "greasewood" in California's Gold Belt. In Peru, they are thus used by the many petticoated Amerind women.

South America's Andean backbone is indeed "Escallonia Land." It forms, along with fuchsia and a feathery, bamboo-like cane, the chaparral for long stretches of the Range. It grows ever in that territory of Far-South Chile that bears the name of the intrepid explorer, Magellan.

> *"Flowers are love's truest language; they betray*
> *Like the divining rods of Marigold,*
> *Where precious wealth lies buried, not of gold,*
> *But love—strong love, that never can decay!"*
>
> (*Park Benjamin—Sonnet: "Flowers, Love's Truest Language."*)

EUCALYPTUS

As the Tasman Sea's coastal plains shade off into the blazing Never-Never, even the eucalyptus show rainfall-lack. The trees that have made headway during a brace of rainy seasons now top-die. They, with their brownbarked dead limbs, on a full-moon night, look like ghosts, silent but menacingly waving their arms toward Destruction.

Life on the marginal sheep stations is hard. When that blasting desert wind strikes without warning, the grass blackens over night. Then the sheep are rushed, as fast as the railroad blocks can handle train after train, to the frozen-mutton plants on the coast. Amid all this discouragement the Aussie equivalent of our cowboy remains cheerful, resourceful. He insists both above characteristics extend to the 4-footed. One of his favorite songs is:

There was a man   *That goat had teeth*
Named Mick-ey Small   *Exceeding fine.*
He bought a goat   *Ate 4 shirts*
Just for a stall.   *Off Mickey's line.*
He bought that goat.   *Mick—he got mad,*
Oh, yes, he did   *Grabbed goat by back*
He bought in for   *And tied him to—*
His little kid.   *The railroad track.*

The goat was shocked,
It said "Oh! my!
Tho I seem lost,
I must not cry!
Just let me think
And use my brain."

*   *   *   *   *

Coughed up red shirts
And flagged that train!

Calm resourcefulness and quiet courage was ascribed to Mickey's goat. It was, however, dominant in the "Anzac" of World Wars I, the "Digger" of World War II. Pioneering in Eucalypt Land paralleled that of U.S.A. That, perhaps, is why the Aussies say the Yanks understand them better than do the British.

CHAPTER 37

EUCALYPTUS

*"Give us, when noontide comes
Rest in the woodland free—
Fragrant breath of the GUMS,
Cold, sweet scent of the sea."*
(*James Lister Cuthbertson.*)

T HE EUCALYPTUS, or "gum" was popularized in U. S. A. gardens
by that Giant of the Gold-Rush: "California" Taylor. This
Atlas of the Argonauts was beloved of the '49ers. He dazzled the
gold-diggers of his early life by his rare, high moral courage.

The word "eucalyptus" magically stimulates geogardening
memories! It is electric in recalling polished boomerangs, bush-
wise "blackfellows," laughing *cucaburras*, dignified emus, powerful kangaroos, flaming *warathah*, those lovely crows—the birds-of-
paradise, wise-appearing cockatoos, lonely back-blocks, duck-billed
platypus, brilliant bottle-brushes, ferocious-looking 'gwannas, rol-
ly-polly "Teddy bears"—whose diet is largely eucalypt leaves. Lovable wallaby mothers, babies peeping from their breast-pouches,
people the "gum-tree" groves. Section crews of railroads thru
the eucalypt forests, beg for your already-read "paipes." Under
the tall "gums," for miles, grow treeferns. They blanket those bluest of Blue Mountains, beyond which boils the fierce Never-Never.
It was in this Back-of-Beyond, reached thru a thousand-million
"gums" that Sturt found his desert-pea. There this hardy Scot's
diaries went unwritten because his lead-pencils fell apart from
their leads, his inks dried to powder.

One learned—long before World War II made Australia our
base against Nipponese in Papua and the Solomons—to use the ab-
breviated "Aussie." When you go geogardening Down-Under,
you'll enjoy "Aussie's" place-names. At Tom Ugly's you may find
a blackfellow or two. There, even in yesterday, you may be taught
to throw an obediently-returning boomerang. "Aussie" is only a
sniff, too, of the charming slang of our Anzac brethren. Mark
Twain might have ceased his grumbling about weather gossip had
he met with: "Oh! I say. Isn't this a bonzer day."

The main charm of Australia's biota, however, is its long-
continued HOMOGENEITY. As Celebes Deep became more pro-

found, isolation from Asia increased. This isolation made possible the evolution of most peculiar fauna and flora.

Types like the Kangaroo, the platypus, spared competition with immigrants from the Eurasian mainland. They thus were able to develop—each in its own way. One finds, therefore, among animals, a striking marsupial trend. In contrast, under the greater population pressure of Eurasia, the Tertiary, the Quarternary spelled progress along mamalian lines. Thus, with both animals and plants, one can—in a sense—imagine when, in the Australian environment, what may have occurred, say, in the Miocene in Eurasia—and, to a lesser extent in North America.

This peculiar evolution of both marsupial and of plant forms, based partly upon lack of immigrant competition, is somewhat a parallel of the development of the American pioneer. The latter, in some 10 generations of frontier life, also was modified, of course, by his environment. He was, on the other hand, able to work out the world's highest Living Standard. This occurred because he was spared competition with immigrants from areas of markedly lower economic status. From James River, from Plymouth Rock until after the Civil War, the American pioneer enjoyed herein a rare HOMOGENEITY. In geogardening in Australia we see a parallel. Herein each was like a lonely pioneer yesteryear's American frontier. All the above are a part of Australia's uniqueness, of her peculiar loveliness. Again all the above is based on her HOMOGENEITY.

Dr. Fairchild tells an instructive story of how biological ignorance may affect Government scientists. It is the attempt to introduce semi-tropical eucalypts into blizzard-swept Dakotas.*

The history of these British kinsmen parallels our own. This holds as to our adventures from Plymouth Rock and Jamestown to the Covered Wagon caravans of our Sioux-infested prairies. Australian pioneering was into the Never-Never. It resembled our own toilsome trek thru the alkali-saturated dust of what once showed white on our maps as "Unexplored—the Great American desert."

It is true our fellow-Nordics, the Dutch, did much of the very earliest work. First came Duyfken, Browers, Dirk Hartog, then the great Tasman. On this desk are some quaint Dutch maps. One labels the Baby Continent as "Java the Great." It is dated over six decades before Jamestown. The woodenshoed later coasted along what is now West Australia. They little dreamed, however,

---

* See his "The World Is My Garden."

of Queensland, New South Wales or Victoria. Another of these maps, dated a century before our first Fourth-of-July, shows the same vague "Greater Java." A later map shows Papua added as a big peninsula. All the Southern Land-mass now was labelled "New Holland." Eastern Australia, even then, was unknown.

Then came the British. Captain Cook, however, still labels this baby continent on his map "New Holland." Followed Blaxland, Flinders, Bass, Sturt. It is this parallel between Australian and American pioneering that should make us better understand these fine folk. The gradual progress, over some 2 and one-half centuries, of Australian exploration also, perhaps, may make eugenists also better understand their own uncompleted explorations. It took over 3 centuries from Duyfken's "Little Dove," sighting the low shores of "Java the Great" until the departure of the Anzacs for Gallipoli. Eugenists, therefore, must remember, the patience that followed that tracing of a hair line, with "Java der Groote" scribbled behind. This was the first hazy concept of the land that someday was to be the great Dominion of Australia. So, too, eugenists must be willing to labor with patience to complete what commenced when Sir Francis Galton drew his first faint sketch of the science of eugenics that gives such promise of a better race!

"As I rose in the early dawn,
While stars were fading white,
I saw upon a grassy slope
A camp-fire burning bright.
With tent behind and blaze before
Three loggers in a row
Sang all together joyously—
'Pull up the stakes and go!'"

(James Hebblethwaite.)

CHAPTER 38

FIG

"Does one gather . . . figs of thistles?" (*St. Matthew.* VII-16)

A WILD FIGTREE grows in the interstices of its stones, halfway up the wall of the Roman amphitheater. The fig's seeds doubtless were carried there by birds. One thus observes that both color-of-fruit and sweetness-of-pulp result in seed transportation. Seeds often pass uninjured thru the avian digestive tract . . . Birds frequently travel far for desired food.*

The Smyrna fig industry in California parallels Maeterlinck's philosophy.** He described how bee-keeper's success depends upon their observing the Law-of-the-Hive. California could raise, successfully the black Mission fig. It could not, however, produce white Smyrnas. American pioneer resourcefulness sent a Fresno grower geogardening to Anatolia. There he discovered the sugary Smyrnas were based on the pollenization of a certain wasp. The fig, after all, IS a flower. The wasp entered the fig's terminal aperture, carried the sugar-producing pollen. A supply of wasps were secured, shipped to California. We now produce U. S. A.-

WILD FIG GREW IN STONES OF ARENA WALL

---
* Witness the long flight of parrots for the luscious fruit of a cactus, the **pitahoya**, which grows in the state of Simaloa, Mexico.
** See his "Life of the Bee."

grown Smyrnas. THIS WASP WAS A "DESIRABLE" IMMI-GRANT.

When our Geogardener harvests the giant black Mission figs in his California garden, his memory runs back to his sleuthing garden plants to Palestine. While in the Holy Land, he made a pilgrimage to where was preached the Sermon on the Mount. Biblical scholars at Jerusalem seem agreed on this as one of the few authentic places of Christ's life. Our Geogardener took with him his pocket testament. In this he read, on the very spot The Master taught, the message that has come down thru the centuries. In the sermon's own environment one was struck with Christ's eugenic teachings. These are repeated again and again, both in the Sermon on the Mount and elsewhere in the Gospels as to:—

The right of a child to be born free of inherited tendencies to disease: "If thine eye be evil, thy whole body shall be full of darkness."

Morons: "Neither cast ye your pearls before swine."

The hyphenate lobby in Congress which, year after year, blocks immigration control: "Beware of false prophets, which come to you in sheep's clothing, but inwardly they are wolves."

World War I Army Tests: "Ye shall know them by their fruits."

Human Genetics: "Do men gather grapes of thorns?" also "Every good tree that bringeth forth good fruit."

Inherited tendencies to disease: "A corrupt tree bringeth forth evil fruit."

Sterilization Laws in 30 of our 48 states: "Every tree that bringeth not forth good fruit is hewn down and cast into the fire."

Desirable stocks, such as colonial New Englanders, also Virginians, also Carolinians, as well as the Huguenots, the German liberal "48ers" such as Carl Schurtz, also pioneers: "By their fruits ye shall know them."

The Flowering of New England: "Ye are the Salt of the Earth. If the salt have lost his savour,—it is thence forth good for nothing but to be cast out."

Chief Justice Holmes' Supreme Court Decision: "If thy right eye offend thee, pluck it out and cast it from thee."

Galton's Leadership Families: "Ye are the light of the World."

Dr. Gosney's Human Betterment Foundation, since carried on as "Birthright": "It is profitable for thee that one of the members should perish and not that thy whole body should be cast into hell."

CHAPTER 39

FREMONTIA

*"It was easy to say you would hire yourself out, but
it was like dying. You would be a farmer without land.
What farmer could exist without land?"*

(Otto Schraag: "The Locusts".)

MANY a California Coast-belt garden, from Monterey Peninsula
southward, contains an attractive yellow-flowered shrub. It
belongs to the only genus, within continental U.S.A.'s borders, of a
large and striking tropical family. Its family name—Sterculiaceae—is connected with that of a strange ancient Roman deity,
Sterculia. Our clansmen, the patrician-Romans, were pure Nordics. They were as land-conscious as Britain's squires. They were
as land-hungry as the westward-pushing Covered Wagon folk.
These crowded out ever to where "Uncle Sam has a free farm for
everybody." The land-loving Romans had, beside their hearth-gods
—the Lares and Penates—certain Gods of agriculture. These included a God-of-the-Manure Pile. This Sterculia held rank with
Pomona, with Ceres.

For some reason, the memory of this Fertilizer-God was revived when Linneaus named an important order of plants, mostly
tropical. This is Sterculiaceae. It is prominent in our Western
Hemisphere tropics. The word "Panama" itself is the Indian name
of one of this family's species. The "Panama" is the national tree
of the Republic of Panama. It belongs to the type genus, Sterculia.

Deification of agricultural fertility is, among primitives,
worldwide. Certain pantheons, however, reverence other peculiar
items. Just as the Romans treasure fertilizers, so the Japanese had
a God of Scarecrows. The Nipponese also worshipped Inari, the
Cat-like goddess of the rice-paddy.

Other Oriental gods and goddesses seem strange to Occidentals: It amazes the blond Anglo-Saxon to see a swarthy, sleek well-
to-do Hindu merchant, before venturing with a business deal, making sacrifice to elephant-headed Ganesh. Within a half day's journey from the Taj Mahal, our Geogardener was guest in an American Missionary's home. Monkeys are deified in his area. The big
black-and-white apes do not hesitate to enter open windows. One,
thus foraging, fought with the host's children for a morsel of

bread. The missionary chased it out. He then threw a stone at the retreating intruder. . . . Within a quarter hour a howling mob was outside his door. The fanatical Hindus were fearful that the sacrilege to Hanuman, their Monkey-God, might not go unpunished.

Such ascribing of divinity to animals, then to agricultural elements, (scarecrows and fertilizer) are manifestations of a primitive nearness to nature. Even the Egyptian pantheon contained such deities as the hippopotamus-headed God. Sekmet was the lioness-headed one. Anubis was the dog-headed deity. Hathor was cow-headed. Our alphabet is based partly upon these hieroglyphs.

There is a romantic, Love-laughs-at-locksmiths, courtship story of Fremont. His sweetheart must have been lonely after he was ordered West to break trail for American pioneering. He crossed the Nevada desert with its stinging alkali dust. He mounted the steep Eastern escarpment of the Sierras to the snow summit. Coming down the glaciated west slope he camped on Mt. Fremont. From thence he could overlook the great Sacramento Valley that, within a few decades, was to swarm with his fellow Americans.

This Mt. Fremont, near old Hangtown, is a thumb of the great Jurassic Sierran batholith. The school teacher of the district in which Mt. Fremont is situate used to declare that this peak was the type locality* of the first of the genus to be found by botanists. Our Geogardener climbed the peak many years ago. He found Fremontia Californica in bloom there. It, however, could hardly be classed as a bush. It was low-growing in the interstices of the wind-swept granodiorite, or "granite," of the summit. In later years, while trying to track the California Condor, our Geogardener again found bush-sized Fremontias in bloom in an arroyo of the Sierra Madres.

Seldom in fiction is glorification of the soil as the ultimate source of food more strikingly set forth than in Otto Schraag's novel "The Locust," with its Clara Bieber, Betsy Maxwell, Patricia Coroni, and its Mennonites. It is almost patrician-Roman in its evaluation of Pomona, of Ceres, yes even of Sterculia:

"Well, you see, God doesn't forget farmers,
and a farmer doesn't starve easily."
(Otto Schraag: "The Locusts.")

---

* Dr. Jepson credits its original discovery to "General John C. Fremont, pathfinder of the Rocky Mountains and the Sierra Nevada, and first U. S. Senator from California."

"That blue and bright-eyed floweret of the brook
Hope's gentle gem, the sweet forget-me-not."
(Coleridge: "The Keepsake.")

"The sweet foget-me-nots
That grow for happy lovers."
(Tennyson: "The Brook.")

"The heart hath its own memory like the mind
And in it are enshrined
The precious keepsakes into which is wrought
The giver's loving thought."
(Longfellow: "From My Arm Chair.")

"Memory is the only paradise from
which we cannot be turned out."
(Richter)

"To live in hearts we leave behind
Is not to die"
(Campbell: "Hallowed Ground.")

DOLOMITES, MILITARY CEMETERY, PORDUI PASS

A Tyrolese maiden . . . had a trowelful of wild forget-me-nots. These she was planting on the grave of her fallen soldier lover. "I plant Vergess-meinnichten each year" she said simply. "I cannot forget."

CHAPTER 40

FORGET-ME-NOT

"Where the ground is bright with friendship's tears,
FORGET-ME-NOTS, and violets heavenly blue,
Spring glittering with the cheerful drops like dew."

(Bryant: The Paradise of Tears)

A T PIAVE DE LAVINALONGA, landlord Himmel rubbed his hands, and smirked. "Will the *Hochwolhlgebornen* permit the addition, to the bill, of a fee for the waitress?" He named the equivalent of two cents. Then he hastened to add: "She is my daughter. She, of course, never gets the tip. She is dutiful. I keep it. It is my custom!" As the bill was paid, landlord Himmel commenced his story of the Blowoff.* . . . Said 2c-fee was characteristic of hiking the Dolomitenstrasse. Here was real geogardening—trac-

ROSENGARTENGRUPPE, DOLOMITES
Its talus slopes are typical wild forget-me-not territory.

---

* He had remarkable contrast photographs. One, dated 1906, showed a nearby mountain. The other, taken in 1922, had quite a different skyline. The entire crest had been blown off. Grass Valley, California, Cornishmen, descended from tin miners since Phoenician days of Albion— had taught Italians how to use explosives. Landlord Himmel said: "The Italians the last two days were so close, that what our camp was on, had become a mere shell of a summit. Ear-to-ground, we could hear their power drills. These tapped monotonously, like the tap-tap-tap of machine guns. I went to my colonel and begged for a furlough. The second of my 8 children was sick in the village below." He snapped 'We shoot cowards here' . . .at dusk, however, I was sent below with a package of dispatches, told to return at dawn. At midnight off blew the mountain top. A whole Austrian division, including our Colonel, died to the man."

ing to their native haunts beloved garden plants, such as Iceland-poppy, primroses, forget-me-nots, wild ancestors of our garden plants.

Windswept Pordai-Pass was gorgeous with sheets of Iceland poppies, in contrast with masses of lavender primroses. At its summit was a tiny war cemetery. It held a dozen graves of Tyrolese. They were from a ski-regiment. At one grave was a Tyrolese maiden. She had a trowelful of wild forget-me-nots. These she was planting on the grave of her fallen soldier lover. "I plant *Vergessmeinnichten* each year," she said simply. "I cannot forget . . . But the politicians that boss the wars, do they remember? Are even the common folks careful about it? They, too, alas, also have short memories!"

**TYPICAL TYROLESE VILLAGE . .
RIDGE BETWEEN VILLAGE AND
CLIFFS WAS BLUE-AND-GOLD
WITH FORGET-ME-NOTS AND
POPPIES**

TYROLESE KIDDIES

The Dolomites fascinate the Geo-gardener. In the high Alpine valleys is a flora surprisingly different from nearby Switzerland's. Where the Swiss Alps have stretches of edelweiss, of alpenrosen of gentians the Dolomites show massed "Iceland" poppies, orchids, forget-me-nots and dainty lavender primroses . . . At dawn, also dusk, the grey white Dolomite cliffs are unforgettably colorful with their alpenglow.

Foxglove is one of the "pestilent-smelling favorites of the herb-doctors."

"*The Sahiba brewed, in some mysterious Asiatic way . . . a drink that smelt pestilently and tasted worse. . . . Kim slid . . . into—slumber . . . that soaked in like rain after a drought.*"—(Kipling: Kim.)

LE CORBEAU ET LE RENARD

Maitre corbeau, sur un arbre perche,
Tenait en son bec un fromage.
Maitre RENARD, par l'odeur alleche,
Lui tint a peu pres ce langage:
"Eh! bonjour, monsieur du corbeau!
Que vous etes joli! que vous me semblez beau!
Sans mentir, si votre ramage
Se rapporte a votre plumage,
Vous etes le phenix des hotes de ces bois."
A ces mots, le corbeau ne se sent pas de joie:
Et, pour montrer sa belle voix,
Il ouvre un large bec, laisse tomber sa proie.
Le RENARD s'en saisit, et dit: "Mon bon monsieur,
Apprenez que tout flatteur
Vit aux depens de celui qui l'ecoute:
Cette lecon vaut bien un fromage, sans doute."
Le corbeau, honteux et confus,
Jura, mais un peu tard, qu'on ne l'y prendrait plus.

(La FONTAINE: "Anecdotes Faciles")

CHAPTER 41

FOXGLOVE

"Fox-glove and night-shade, side by side,
Emblems of punishment and pride,
Group'd their dark hues with every stain
The weather beaten crags retain."
                    (Scott—"The Lady of the Lake.")

HAVE YOU ever watched, at Glengariff, or Park-na-Silla, little Irish colleens cap their childish fingers with fallen foxglove blooms? Then, with inverted hand, and moving fingers, they would show how the fox wears his sound-deadening "gloves" while stalking his dinner.

Could any flower-folkname be more exquisitely poetical than "fox-glove"?* How much folklore about this highly intelligent rascal is crystallized therein! The "fox," the "todd" of North England, the "renard," our "Reynolds."† A German extension of fox, or *fuchs*, is mentioned in our chapter on "Fuchsia" . . .

From Aesop to Fontaine, the fox has been the symbol of brainpower . . . and, of trickiness. Much, too, is telescoped into the feminine of fox: "vixen." It carries a concept of a shrewd and shrewish wife. Do we not, even today, brand Xantippe, wife of Socrates, as a "vixen." Our Amerinds had an even higher opinion of the fox's canine cousin, the coyote. Always it was the shrewd coyote with whom the Great Spirit discusses His problems. Witness the legend of California's Marysville Buttes.** It is, too, the coyote that, as Elder Brother to the redskin, saves him from blunders.

The wild dog of Frontier folksong is the coyote, not his little brother, the kitfox. Pioneering means a high death rate. In what Browning called "A Male Land," not only are births few, because of the scarcity of potential mothers, but there are constant clashes, for men are "quick-on-the-trigger." The annexed miner's song, from the Nevada's yesteryear silver rushes, is a bit of doggerel of the hair-trigger gambler, the raven, and the coyote:

---

* The badge of Scotland's Ferguson clan is the Foxglove . . Lus-nam-ban-sith.
† Compare the German "hand-schuen," or hand-shoes.
** These Buttes are a Monadnock, the core of ancient volcano. They are in the center of the Great Sacramento Valley many miles from either the Coast Range or the Sierra Nevada. Because of their solitary prominence in the vast unbroken plain both to North and to South the Indians had, from the wise coyote, their tale of origin . . . The Great Spirit was in a playful mood. He mixed up a great big mud-pie. He let it ooze through his fingers as he made the Sierra Nevadas. With the batch of mud remaining, he lined out the lesser and parallel Coast Range. But there was still a residue. By this time he was tired and dumped what was left of his mudpie in the valley between his two new-made mountains—thus came into being the Marysville Buttes Monadnock.

WILD TUSCARORA.

In wild Tus-ca-ror-a,
In the Ru-by Mount-ains,
In the Ne-va-da Desert,
Above Al-ka-li Flat,
They are just rais-ing Hell now.
They keep it up all night.
All day they fight du-ells,
In Tus-ca-roar-a.

When gents sit at pok-er,
Out come shoot-ing i-rons.
You hard-ly are safe with
An ace up your sleeve.
No! it's very un-health-y
To try to be fun-ny,
If you're play-ing pok-er
In Tus-ca-roar-a.

For they're quick on the Trig-ger
In wild Tus-ca-roar-a.
A ten-der-foot even
Gets shot P.D.Q.
But they'll bur-y you neat-ly,
With a real bang-up head-board.
"He died with his boots on"
They may carve for you.

Out in the grey sage brush
They'll drive home that head-board
They'll call the sky pil-ot
There's a prayer that's sin-cere
But the bunch soon for-gets you.
They race back to their pok-er.
Just the ra-vens keep com-ing
Each day way out here.

Yes, the rav-ens keep com-ing
Keep com-ing and croak-ing
They talk to the CO-YOT'
Of num-ber-less things . . .

Of hu-mans they gos-sip,
Of wild Tus-ca-roar-a.
Yes, they croak and they
Cy-nic-ally flap their black wings.

Yes, out in the sage-brush,
They're croak-ing most sage-ly,
Of why men are fool-ish
In a po-ker game,
For men stay long bur-ied,
And af-ter a fune-ral
Was ev-er one seen back
On this earth a-gain?

Now the CO-YOT' is wag-ging
His head full of wis-dom.
He barks "now I re-call
What a dark-y here said.
They ask'd him to gam-ble."
He said "Boss, I'se skeerd to,
Fo' ma mam-my done tol' me,
I'd be long time daid!"

———————

"Mourn, little harebells o'er the lea
  Ye stately FOXGLOVES fair to see,
  Ye woodbines, hanging bonnilie
  In scented bowers.
  Ye roses on your thornly tree,
  The first of flowers."
                              (Burns: Elegy.)

———————

"The **FOXGLOVE**, *with its stately bells*
  Of purple shall adorn thy dells."
              (Moir: The Birth of the Flowers.)

———————

"O Solitude! if I must with thee dwell,
  Let it not be among the jumbled heap
  Of murky buildings . . . let me my vigils keep.
  'Mongst boughs pavilioned, where the deer's swift leap
  Startles the wild bee from the FOXGLOVE bell.
                    (Keats: Sonnet, "Solitude.")

CHAPTER 42
FUCHSIA

"I swear by Apollo the physician, etc. . . . that I will myself follow that . . . regimen . . . I consider best for my patients. With purity and holiness I will practice my art."
(From the Hippocratic Oath, about 400 B. C.), the "oldest code of medical ethics." . . ."The Golden Rule for Doctors."

THERE is much fascinating biography, also history, embalmed in the botanical names of garden flowers. You will enjoy your fuchsias more if you will recall they are a floral reminder of a beloved German physician. In a century of quacks, he lived the Hippocratic Oath. He was esteemed in his day as, later, was Pasteur. He was also as deeply religious as that illustrious Frenchman. In the days of his young professorship, he battled for the superstitious, illiterate, common folk. He fearlessly struggled against their exploitation in the name of Religion. He was one who earned the title of "Protestant," because of his systematic protesting. Life might have been made very uncomfortable for him, had it not been for his rare medical skill. He is credited with having saved the lives of many during a certain devastating plague. His mind was almost Aristotlean. In the midst of a religious

MAJESTIC OSORNO, FROM THE LAKE OF ALL-THE-SAINTS
The low hills above the water line, our Geogardener found to be clothed in Fuchsias, with millions of blooms.

SYMPHONY ON AMERICA'S "ROOF-OF-THE-WORLD"

Few garden plants have of recent years attracted more attention than fuchsias. The number of members of Fuchsia Societies evidences this. Fuchsia has indeed, rare fascination. Does it not mean more, however, when its pendants have an added geogardening meaning when they stimulate memories of inquisitive llamas, of zebra-striped ponchos, of Amerind pipes-of-pan, of many-petticoated squaws?

Reformation he was even more efficient as a Reformer in Medicine. To him can be ascribed the reawakening of physicians to the high idealism of the Hippocratic oath. His fame as a botanist, however, eclipses that of a physician, or as a religionist.

Systematic botanists would be shocked at linking together of foxglove and fuchsia. Philologically, however, they belong in the same pigeon-hole. The *"fuchs"* of fuchs-ia is German for the *"fox"* of fox-glove. Admiring, however, the colorful fuchsias of our shady gardensides, one would hardly connect them with the shrewd fox. Fuchsia apparently has little in common with Foxy Grandpa of yesteryear's comic strips, with words that suggest shrewdness, with old English surnames as "Fox," "Dodd" "Todd," "Todd-hunter" . . .

Our Geogardener was on New Zealand's South Island. He was tracking the veronicas, the tree-lilies, the New Zealand flax of our gardens back to their *sauvage* haunts. Here he asked his host one day, "Of what beautiful wood is this table made?" The answer was "Wild fuchsia!" That afternoon they strolled across the glacier-polished granite. Its interstices were colorful with dwarf veronicas. They arrived at a lake-head. There, in the lush vegetation, were tree trunks capable of yielding fair-sized boards. Their flowers were undoubtedly fuchsias. "But the genus is Andean" objected our Geogardener. "Undoubtedly," replied the New Zealand scientist-host. "It is but one of the many puzzles of this puzzling Dominion of ours. Some suggest" he continued "a land bridge from South America at some ancient day. As for me, I use the expression of the inhabitants of those Andes: *'Quien sabe'?"*

The two started to walk back to the cottage with the highly-polished fuchsiawood furniture. En route, the New Zealander gathered a few tree-fuchsia blooms. "We are disturbed about the future of our fuchsia trees" he said. "Notice that the visiting insects today are almost all that greedy and clumsy immigrant, the bumblebee. He cannot supply his wants as do our native insects. New Zealand six-footed feed DOWN-TUBE. The European bumblebee simply alights outside the flower. He then bites into its base to get its sweets. Mother Nature's device for cross-pollenization is by-passed. It is as useless as a palm leaf fan on Spitzbergen!"

"This parallels New Zealand's far-deeper worry. It is not bumblebees and fuchsias, but of immigrants from low-living standard areas, who may be as greedy and as ruthless as is the bumblebee." "And," he added—this was some 2 decades before Pearl Harbor—"we are woefully short of manpower. The whole population of our Dominion is less than one of your American cities."

There are geogardeners who revel in the *chaparral* of California, with its ceanothus, manzanita, greasewood, bears'-grape complex. Others find of absorbing interest the bush-heather, broom, strawberry-bush *maqui* of Provence, of Spain, of Morocco. To students of "elfen forests" like *chaparral*, like *maqui*, there exists a rare treat when they go a-geogardening to South Chile . . . Fuchsia, if we except this strangely-isolated occurrence at the south tip of New Zealand—is a Cordilleran, if not the Andean, genus. The real fuchsia kingdom extends from Mexico to the tail of serpent-shaped Chile. Fuchsia, then, is the floral symbol of a great mountain massif . . . of its lamas, "toteing" bricks of tin, from its yet hardly-scratched mineral wealth . . . of its balsa jungles, again an evidence of Aladdin-like forest wealth . . . of ruthlessly-destroyed civilizations, with all their intellectuals, kings, priests, warriors, eliminated and only the docile slave caste persisting—of vast public works . . . roads asphalt-lined thru some centuries during which our communications up north were foot trails or horseback paths . . . when, on the few wagonroads, the lumbering wagons raised clouds of dust in summer, stuck in the mud in winter . . . of an empire whose food-system was so efficient, there were no famines . . . of all this the fuchsia, appropriately drooping, is a symbol. It seems to ask "What of the future?" . . .

One marvel of the fuchsia is its umbrella. Thru parts of fuchsia's range, as in South Chile, are long seasons of dripping rains. In others, are repeated thunder-showers. In some Andean areas exist storm conditions similar to the Montana Rockies, and, to a lesser degree, in the Californian Sierras. In yet other sections of the fuchsia province, tropical rain-forest conditions obtain. Hence the need of an effectual umbrella.

Fuchsia in South Chile constituted one of the few million-flower masses observed in our Geogardener's wanderlusting. By counting the blooms in a given area it is possible to estimate the number in sight. Other "million" records were: (a) narcissus in the Auvergne, (b) orchids in Brazil, (c) eucalypt trees in Australia.

PUNTA GUIDA, SOUTH ANDEAN VOLCANO

The Chilean group form the tail, like the caudal vertebrae of a mammal, of a mountain backbone. This stretches from its Alaskan head, Mt. St. Elias, thru Rainier, Hood, Shasta and Lassen. In Mexico is Popocatapetl and Ixtaza-huitel. Then where the true Andes commence Cotopaxi, and the 23,000 foot giants of Ecuador, Peru with magnificent Miste. All along this giant vertebrae, from Mexico south, one finds fuschias in astronomical numbers.

CHAPTER 43

GAILLARDIA

*"Gai-llard: One who GAI-LY makes lemonade
from the lemons Life hands him."*

A BUFFALO SKULL, on a bit of prairie under the Lewis Overthrust
in Montana, was surrounded by a fringe of wild gaillardias.
Thus our Geogardener found his first *sauvage* blooms of this satis-
factorily-tough garden plant. Gaillardia can stand all kinds of
punishment. It is like the Covered Wagon folk who crossed its
native land. Gaillardia, therefore, is an ideal plant for the gardens
of folk who, away on long midsummer vacations, must let the
waterless flower-beds shift for themselves. Henshaw's "Wild Flowers of the North American Mountains" writes of the "abandon of
color" of certain Rocky Mountain meadows as "Gaillardia Land!"

Interesting was the christening of this trustworthy garden
flower. The French like the man who can see more than the hole
in the doughnut. They evaluate, with proper application, the GAY
optimist who also can see the surrounding ring, who promptly an-
nexes the latter. Jean Baptiste adores the individual who can go
to a New Orleans oyster bar, to invest his last "two-bits" in a dozen
bivalves. This gaillard is certain one of these shells will yield a
marketable pearl. . . . The French have a name for this fellow. By
"gaillard," the French mean just the opposite of Calamity Jane. . .

While geogardening in the mountains of Haut Savoie, a certain
day was cold, dreary. A drizzling rain was falling. We were hud-
dled around the fireplace. There was a knock on the door. In
came a rosy-cheeked young peasant girl. She pointed to the fire.
"C'est tres gai . . . Et vous estes gaillard, n'est-pas? She evidently
connected the cheerfulness of "gaillard" with "gai" or "gay." A
gaillard, therefore, IS a gay, cheerful fellow. Hence one dared
conclude the Gaillard from whom gaillardia was named was no
killjoy.

Of the first Frenchmen to be dubbed "Gaillard" we, however,
know nothing. When population pressure forced the use of sur-

names,* as well as of given names, one cheerful Frenchman evidently was dubbed "Gaillard." Search fails here to locate any fascinating biography of this jolly chap. It is of a descendant of his that we have knowledge. A historian, the latter ranks with other great Frenchmen among whose monuments are botanical names. These include Poinsett, Nicot, Bougainville, Godet, Boisduval, Lamarck, de Jussieu. He lived in those decades when newly discovered American plants thus were being named after European intellectuals.

This famous Monsieur Gaillard, historian, became godfather, in solemn French style, to this genus of Compositae. Little did he know of its highly variable blooms. These spangle the prairies from the Rio Grande to where Canada maps show such names as "Moose Jaw," and "Medicine Hat."

This bookish Gaillard was a native of Picardy. This Pickard or Packard—(we have "Packard" automobiles in America)—evidently failed to inherit the gaiety or gaillardness of such ancestor. His fame as a historian, however, gained him membership in The Academy. His tomes were ponderous. They were written even before the installment-novel period. London's romantic females then eagerly awaited next Saturday night's chapter of coming "best seller." Gaillard's books are, therefore, weighty in contrast with present-day history writing. One might compare the heaviest of Scott's novels with the most-abbreviated short-short of today. This ponderous Gaillard, popular in his day, won fame also as a biographer. His best biography was one of Malesherbes.

Gaillard of the gaillardias is, therefore, perhaps best known to the English-speaking world as the historian-biographer of that most noble of Frenchmen—Malesherbes. Our Geogardener stumbled across much Malesherbes' material while working on certain social problems with a French professor. He had a country home near the Malesherbes chateau. . .

---

* Hyatt is High Gate . . . Many names are tree names as Nash or "At an ash" . . . Braddock means Broad Oak . . . Kennedy means Ugly Head . . . Chandler was a candlemaker . . . Cameron, Crooked Nose . . . Fletcher an arrow-smith . . . Campbell, Twisted Mouth . . . the names of some American Presidents are fascinating: Grover Cleveland (or Cleave-Land) is significant. Jack-son, John-son and the 2 Harri-sons or Harry's son go back to those days when a second name was necessary. Also Jeffer-son, or Jeffry's son, really, Geoffrey's or Gottfried's son . . . Madi-son or Mathew's son, and Wil-son or Will's son. "Son" names are common. Compare these with Fitz-hugh, the "fils" or "Fis's of Hugh, Mac-Donald, which we also have as Donald-son, O'Brien, at first, son of King Brian, Welsh "ap" Madoc for the "ap," or son, of Chief Madoc. There are some Welshmen who insist that Applegate was not a man who lived at a gate with an apple tree, but was ap Legate, the illegitimate son of a legate who reveled in "wine, women and song." Polk or Pollock, was a "pollock" or native of Poland, just as Janeway was a Genoese. Among movie stars, Gable is a Saint's name (Gabriel) as Seymour is St. Maur. Grant is le grand or tall man, Grace is a Saint's name. So, too, Senator Leland Stanford who founded that University sprang from an ancestor named from his home at the "Stan" or "Stony" ford. Sandhurst, another common English name was the "hurst" or grove in a sandy terrain. The gambling Earl of Sand-wich, whose love of poker stimulated the invention of the sandwich is another example. His domain was "Sandwich," the "wich" or village at The Sands.

Malesherbes, Chancellor of France, statesman, lawyer and botanist, was a fearless liberal. Gaillard lived for years with Malesherbes. Gaillard, of all men, understood how Malesherbes was always prompt to champion the cause of the Downtrodden. Malesherbes did not hesitate even when the oppressed was the once all-powerful, altho ungrateful, king! Nor did he hesitate to confront his monarch. French kings had a habit of granting, to flattering courtiers, blank *lettres de cachet*. The holder could fill in an enemy's name. Such a completed order could send the victim to Bastile, to torture, even to execution.

One of the mistresses of Louis XV regularly sold such *lettres de cachet* to anyone who would pay money for them . . .Malesherbes, during Gaillard's stay at the former's chateau, assumed leadership in the attempt to end royal grants of *lettres de cachet*. Malesherbes' term as prime minister, as a result, came to an abrupt end. Meantime his scientific honors continued to accumulate.

Ungrateful Louis XVI also had never forgiven Malesherbes having forced civil recognition for Protestant marriages. . . . Finally the French Revolution broke. Thereupon the King recalled Malesherbes from Switzerland to become Royal Defender. Malesherbes heroically left the security of Switzerland. Came the day when Malesherbes was compelled to witness the guillotining of all his family, even his grandchildren. . . .

Gaillard, god-father to your garden gaillardias, preserved many such stories in the Malesherbes biography. When, therefore, you gather a bouquet of gaillardias hereafter, think of their homeland, of their sponsor. Recall Blackfeet hunting buffalo. Remember the herds of Texas longhorns roaming over Gaillardia Belt. Picture, too, back in France, the first Gaillard, the gai-llard,—the merrymaking cheerful optimist who could see something better than the pessimistic hole in the doughnut. Let Memory vision, too, Gaillard's friend: Malesherbes. Think of this aristocrat's rare idealism. It shines even today thru the befogged thinking of an ignorant, blundering guillotining mob.

WHEN YOU CONTEMPLATE YOUR BED OF GAILLARDIAS, DO NOT FORGET THAT THE MOB CAN THOUGHTLESSLY SNUFF OUT LIFE. THIS HAPPENED EVEN TO HIM WHO HAD ENDED THE FLOW OF CRUEL LETTRES-DE-CACHET.

Gaillardia, too, stimulates memories of Mimicry. The plant breeders, some years ago, had concentrated on Gaillardia—had isolated a wide color range of mutations. It seemed a good time to go a-geogardening for Gaillardia on the prairie toe of the Rockies from Montana's Lewis' Overthrust to the blue-bonnetted stretches of West Texas.

Geogardening thus for Gaillardia brought the usual by-products. One was finding the long-sought for Viceroy butterfly. This mimics the Monarch. The Viceroy's cousins run to orange, whites, and blacks. It is smaller than the brick-red Monarch. Otherwise, it mimics that powerful flyer wonderfully. We found it numerous on an Eocene river terrace. Same was covered with opuntias. There must have been a million silky, burnt-orange blooms in that one mass. Above these fluttered the viceroys, for whom we had hunted for years.

Long afterwards a single stray viceroy honored our home garden with a visit. At home, however, we had other mimics. There was one bee-fly, a true Diptera. It so closely mimicked the bees that after studying him for two decades, our geogardener could not summon courage to pick him from a scabiosa or a coreopsis, fearing the bee sting.

It is, however, when one goes a-geogardening into the Jungle that one finds the best mimicry. Java, Ceylon, Malaysia are rare hunting grounds for the student of mimicry. There is a wide range from huge walking sticks to fascinating green leaf butterflies.

AFRICAN LIONS

The genus geranium extends over a wide area. It was named by Linneaus. Its American range is from the Carolina coast to California. The Humboldt redwoods shelter both it and its cousin, Oxalis. The most prized garden "geraniums," however, belong to the sister genus, Pelargonium. This is South African. If, for these, you go geogardening you will see giraffes, zebras and lions.

CHAPTER 44

GERANIUM

"It is the old fight
Of the seeds against the weeds."

AMERICA NOW blunderingly sneers at pride-in-family. One once heard such expressions as "The baby has the Merrill nose" or "she has the Randolph forehead." Among flower-families, one can also observe family traits. In few among these can one recognize relationships more quickly, more accurately, than in the Geraniaceae. The seed organs in all genera known to our Geogardener have the typical "storksbill" that gives its name to the genus *Erodium*.

Our Geogardener sleuthed several of the Geranium clan to their native haunts. One of these was a forage-geranium of his cattle ranges, the filaree. The filaree is what might be called a desirable immigrant from the Mediterranean basin. Like many Europeans, it has been inured to hardship, to making the most of

MONARCH OF PELARGONIUM LAND

its forbidden environment.

The humans of its Mediterranean environment have a low living standard. Our Geogardener, in 1912, found Neapolitans as happy over a Sunday banquet of macaroni as are Americans when the well-browned Thanksgiving turkey arrives. In 1915, he found Spanish lads whose parents never had been rich enuf to give them one meat meal in all their 18 years. The filaree of their Mediterranean Basin also had to practice thrift. Water ever is scarce. The filaree therefore evolved dense, matted foliage. This is a true parasol against the sun-scorching heat. It makes the filaree a valuable forage plant. Spanish kiddies play that they stitch dollclothes with its needle-shaped seeds. In fact, the Spanish name of this wild geranium is *alfileria,* or needle. Greek children, at the other end of the Mediterranean, call it "crane's bill."

This wild geranium may teach us wisdom we today sadly lack in immigration control. We fail to discriminate as to immigrants.

The "filaree" of the California cattle ranges, the *"alfileria* of the Mission Padres, is one of GOOD plant immigrants that came tc U.S.A. from the Mediterranean Basin along with the fig, the olive, the artichoke.

That area, on the other hand, has given us some most troublesome weeds. These include the milk thistle, which is a pest particularly on California bottom lands. Even worse is the star thistle. Regularly certain Reclamation Districts in which some of our Geogardener's ranches are situated render bills for "elimination of star thistle." Another undesirable is the spiny clot burr. All three of above are protected with abundant bayonets. Yet another is the foxtail. This barbed grass injures the mucous membrane of horses and dairy cows. It sometimes halves the market value of the first crop of alfalfa from the Sacramento river bottoms. A return of $500 from a shipment worth, if free from foxtail $1,000, means loss of that much pure profit. The cost of raising is the same in both instances. This same Mediterranean Basin likewise has sent us desirable and undesirable human immigrants. The same area that produced the valuable filaree and certain equally valuable immigrants gave us the Blackhanders that Mussolini systematically, and cynically dumped upon gullible U.S.A.

When will U.S.A. learn the same Selection of Immigrants as it maintains for insect and plant pests? DR. H. H. LAUGHLIN, IMMIGRANT EXPERT, OFTEN CALLED BY CONGRESS, INSISTS WE SHOULD ADMIT NO ONE WITHOUT DETAILED STUDY OF RECORDS OF 20 OF HIS FAMILY!

CHAPTER 45

GLADIOLUS

". . . a sword of flashing lilies
Holden ready for the fight."
(Browning)

"GLADI-OLUS" or "little sword" is cognate with "gladi-ator", or the swordsman of the Roman circus. When, long ago, the genus was christened, the spectacled botanist, with his stern emphasis on the classics, was thinking in Latin. Its leaves *are* sword-shaped. He named it therefore from Latin *gladius* (a sword).

Our Geogardener found his first "sauvage" glads near an old Roman arena. Old bronze swords had been unearthed near it. Such a sword, laid beside a gladiolus leaf, made plain how gladiolus of today has, because of its foliage, the name of the Roman weapon. . . . The two hand weapons used by Caesar's legions were the *pilum* or javelin and the *gladius Hispanus*. The latter was a two-edged sword about 2 feet long. It was well adapted for thrusting or striking. . . . While geogardening in the old Roman empire, it is fascinating there to read the classics. This is particularly true of Caesar's Commentaries. Read of siege-use of the *turris ambulatory*, the *testude*, the *onager*, and the *ballista*. . . . Read of his struggles with the Seubi, the Helvetii, the Germani, the Belgae, the Aquitani, the Britanneae and, finally, of his expedition against the Parisii. Caesar's bridging the Rhine, his "campaign interrupted by violent rains," the "army in panic of Caesar," his preparing to invade Britain, his "preparing to carry the war into Germany" . . . all this reads like, not 50 B.C., but A.D. 1944.

Gladiolus, like pelargonium, also agapanthus, is another of the South-African genera that have enriched our gardens. It thus recalls zebra-eating lions, rubber-necked giraffes, charging rhinos, grinning hippos, yes, and "elefunts" and the other circus African animals. The Gladiolus-Province extends from Capetown thru Africa to the Mediterranean Basin. In fact, its cousins of the Irids, Ixia, Sparaxis, Tritonia, Crocosmia, Watsonia and Freesia, all are represented in South Africa's flora . . . Bulbs of some of the South African gladioli are converted by the natives into a starchy food. Those of the Mediterranean littoral are valued me-

Gladiolus, like Pelargonium and the 7 other genera listed in our text are gifts to our gardens from South Africa. Go a-geogardening there for all 9 of the above. Then you will have some of the deepest thrills of all your geo-gardening. South Africa also is the land of dear old blundering, bewhiskered, devoted Oom Paul and his obstinate Boers, of the Rand and gold like unto dreams about the Queen of Sheba, of glittering diamonds galore, of Zulus. Do you remember that Kipling, in his "Fuzzy-Wuzzy," wrote: "A Zulu impi dished us up in style."

If 100,000 Americans could annually go a-geogardening to that fascinating Dominion, they would do much in cementing the best kind of Internationalism. We know them as the bravest, the most resourceful of fighting men. Most of us do not know enough of their peacetime problems. They have an appalling heterogeneity. Their blacks' problem is two-fold. They have the negroes, from Bushmen and Hottentots up to the Zulu. They have the "colored people." These are proud hybrids of Dutch x native-Negro. They are cross-ings of the days when Holland's skippers paused at the Cape of Storms—later of Good Hope while discovering Java and Sumatra and Tasman's Sea and Van Diemens Land.

Our South African allies have a double "white" problem, too. Only too few of the Boers have Jan Smut's vision. They are a stubborn, bullheaded stock. They had to be, to win from Nature, the Veldt. They respect Americans as much as they suspect the British. They know we have a wilderness-conquering complex akin to theirs. They lack Canada's asset—130,000,000 blood kin across an Erased Border. Canada can hope to solve the problem of her Quebec slackers persistent thru both world wars. Canada has us to whisper "Courage"! in her life-and-death struggle with Habitants who brazenly shout "You cannot compete with our fecundity!" We of the U. S. A. are just over a neighborly fence to help them if the trouble becomes acute. Our South Africans lack that comfort. They are, because of their 4-fold heterogeneity, in as serious a situation as Finland with Swedish-Finnish-Karelian-Lapp heterogeneity—as Czechoslovakia with her Czechish-Slovak-Sudetangau-Ruthenian antagonists. Truly, 100,000 Americans annually going a-geogardening to the Land of Giraffes, Zebras, Lions would be a valuable contribution to World Peace, if our strategy be "hold U. S. A. and the British commonwealth together."

dicinally. One evening our Geogardener was only guest at a little inn.* It was in the semi-desert. Below this, our Geogardener next day found his first wild gladioli.

It was in our own America that our Geogardener found some very early cultivated glads. This was on an abandoned Oregon backwoods homestead. It was in the hinterland behind Tillamook Point, southernmost station reached by the Lewis-and-Clark Expedition. The homestead must have been located soon after the first Methodist missionaries broke trail into the Oregon Country. Some flower lover evidently had brought a few glad bulbs into this lonely wilderness. They had continued to multiply. They gave our Geogardener a startling contrast as against the magnificent blooms of today.

Eugenists sometimes want supporting evidence for their theories of what can be done to improve human stocks. They need only lay our Geogardener's finds in North Africa, or even the Oregon type, side by side, with gladiolus-show specimens. That contrast illustrates what can be accomplished when we top Natural Selection with highly-intelligent Artificial Selection. . .

In our gardening we accept ever-better strains of gladioli, roses, sweet-corn, tomatoes with scarce a thought of what they cost in human effort. Dr. Jepson, sage in University of California of Botany Department once gave our Geogardener an insight into that cost of obtaining the new. The doctor spoke of the tragic life of John Jeffrey.

John Jeffrey was sent by the Botanical Committee of Edinburgh to discover possible new garden treasures. He landed at Hudson Bay. He went overland to the H. B. C. station at Vancouver. Travelling thence southward, he discovered in the Siskiyous, the remarkable high-montane Murray's pine. It was named for a fellow Caledonian. He also found white-bark pine. In the Shasta country, he located another new pine, later named for him "Pinus Jeffrey." Finally working his way to the Colorado Desert, he attempted to cross it alone. There he died of thirst. Enroute, however, he had discovered many new plants. These he systematically had sent back to the land which still produces the world's most intelligent gardeners, old Scotia!

Thus men are martyred that we may enjoy gardening. On an August day in California's Canadian Zone, you may sniff the bal-

* The proprietor said: "You wonder how I keep proficient in the many languages useful to a hotelkeeper? There is the answer. My very good radio gives me, any evening, even such tongues as Arabic, Finnish, Flemish, Turkish."

samic vanillin boiling out of Jeffrey pine bark.   Think, then, of how this intrepid botanist suffered the tortures of a desert death by thirst, that we might have better gardens.

CHAPTER 46

HEATHER

"I love a lassie,
A bonnie, bonnie lassie.
She's as fair as the
Lily in the Vale.
She's as bright as the HEATHER,
The bonnie, blooming HEATHER,
Etc., etc."   (As sung by Sir Harry Lauder.)

NORTHWEST EUROPE'S HEART is entwined with heather sprigs. 'Tis not only in Scotland. Killarney's Purple Mountain takes its name from heather-color. When our Geogardener, yesteryear, went wanderlusting, via jaunting-car, in the Connemara highlands, he found their colleens skirted in flaming-red homespun. Such brilliant dye was gained by boiling heather in outdoor kettles. The Heath is the badge of four Scottish clans: The MacAlisters, the MacDonalds, the MacIntyres, the MacDougals.

 "The bonny heather-bell,
  O they're the flowers of Scotland
  All others they excel!" (Hogg—The Flower of Scotland)

Dartmoor and Lorna-Doone-Land are undescribedly colorful when the heather is in purple. On the Continent, Holland's moors, with an occasional gray menhir rising from the sea of red-purple, are a sight never-to-be forgotten. Down France-way, the limestone belts, as near Cro-magnon, similarly are ablaze in early autumn. Well, heatherbells are co-extensive with the Nordic broodlands.

The shrub heathers of our gardens are largely of Mediterranean Basin origin. One finds them on Provence, and on Algerian littorals. It is, however, in California that the Ericaceae, or Heather family, reaches its maximum growth. The Golden State's manzanitas, and particularly its madronas become tree-like. What are underfoot perennials in Scotland, in California became truly arborescent. Manzanita's waxy pink flowers, heatherbell shaped, bloom in January. These are followed in deep cool canyons, by the Madrona, whose blooms again proclaim their heather ancestry.

And, on tropic seas, off Siam and Indo-China, our Geogardener—enroute to trace garden shrubs to their native Himalayan fastness in the days before World War I broke—heard homesick German sailor lads singing: *"Roselein auf der HAIDE."*

DYEING WOOL IN AN OUTDOOR KETTLE, LEENAWE, CONNEMARA

Someday someone will collect into one volume data about extracting dyes from plants. This will include those of the Guatemalan Indios and those of Inca Peru . . . the ages-old dye technique of the Persian carpets (madder etc., fixed in Camel's milk) . . . the coloring of Kashmir shawls . . . even the use of hickory in our Civil War blockade (when grey was no longer obtainable and the soldiers of one Alabama regiment were called "The Yellowhammers"). Our Geogardener was fascinated by the boiling of Heather to making a bright red dye in Connemara hills of West Ireland.

WASHING THE TWEED, CONNEMARA, IRELAND

The delightful folk song of the heath folk, "The Little Rose of the Heather-Moors," recalls the purple distances that stretch across Germany, from that part of Holland where the language is more English than German, to the Eastern frontiers, where Teuton meets the "Slav" that for centuries meant "Slav-e."

Where this Baltic-heather runs into the scrub-forest like a hound's tongue protruding on a hot day, was the estate of a certain General. Far to the south was his hunting-lodge. There, for some weeks, our Geogardener was guest. The "library" contained a few shelves of books. Its walls, however, were decorated with several hundred hunting trophies. Of only one book therein seemed this mighty hunter proud. It was his guestbook. It contained names historical, fascinating. Three Caesars, two dubbed "Kaiser," one yclept "Czar" had hunted there. There were the autographs of several score minor monarchs, from king, thru *Grossherzogen,* to the bosses of the dinky little principalities whose corroding jealousies had made it possible, under adroit, systematic, ever-persistent, ultramontane plotting, to postpone the welding of the German-speaking Volk into a real nation until ruthless *"Blut-and-eisen"* Bismarck did the job.

The General, let us call him "von Sternwald", was a perfect host. His staff of servants were incredibly efficient. "Must be," he declared one day, "when it is not Kings, but Kaisers, one entertains." The first night in his library he said "So you like *rehbuck?* Very well! Tomorrow morning at 6, you and I go *rehbucking.*" When he heard that our Geogardener disliked killing, there was just the suspicion of lines of contempt at the corners of his mouth. He shrugged his shoulders. . . . At 6 a.m., however, there was a noise below our Geogardener's window. In a dog cart below was von Sternwald, and his driver. Another manservant was offering him the hunting equipment for inspection. . . .

The saddle of *rehbuck* was duly appreciated. "Have you ever tasted stag?" "No! On my hunting preserves is some of the best stag-hunting in all Europe." . . . We then had a stag dinner, but with the ladies present. . . . Followed heath-hen (the equivalent of our wild turkey in the European avifauna) . . . Partridge, later pike . . . carp from one of his baker's dozen of carp ponds. ('Tis said carp cooked in beer is the equivalent, in parts of Eastern Europe, of our Christmas turkey).

One day, toward the end of the visit, the General asked "Is there anything else in the wild game line you would like?" "Well," responded our Geogardener, "I have always heard that wild-boar hunting has been considered, thru the centuries, the sport royal. I have never tasted wild pork, except with pig-sticking Britishers in Hindustan." . . . "Royal, (*koeniglich*) sport?" he countered. "Here it is truly imperial, (*kaiserlich*) . . . Tomorrow, at 6, I go for *wildschweine*." We soon saw wild boar on the table.

The above story is related because those weeks in that unusual environment included evening after evening in which this shrewd, highly-intellectual, passionately-royalist General bantered, with the American, arguments about the relative survival values of autocracy and that republicism we erroneously call "democracy." Those evenings in that library, surrounded on all four walls with heads of rehbuck, stag and wild boar, gave rare glimpses of the philosophy of remarkable group, the German General Staff.

Should we not be willing to study them? They are arch- enemies of our American way-of-life. They believe passionately in goose-stepping regimentation. Are we wise to shut our eyes to them? Is it not more sensible to try to evaluate the forces which have built up such a powerful, such a persisting group?

For they DO persist. They root back in the old Teutonic Knights. Founded in the Third Crusade, they still were strong when Fredrick I disciplined his crown prince by beheading his devoted friend, Lieutenant Kattle, in his presence. Simultaneous was the admonition that his son would meet the same fate if he continued disobedience.

Von Sternwald's peacetime hobbies were killing wild animals and bossing everybody from Frau von Sternwald and their children to his numerous staff of servants. His God was, not Mars, but

MANZANITA BELLS, NEW YEAR'S DAY, CALIFORNIA'S YELLOW PINE BELT
Bushes in foreground were a mass of pink heather-like bells. Bees had promptly commenced the year's harvest.

a truly Northern Thor. In manners, however, he was a polished gentleman and the most perfect host imaginable. A guest had no wish that had not been anticipated and satisfied. And yet . . . and yet . . . and yet! Our Geogardener and his host were, in their ultimate aims, as far apart as Arctic and Antarctic.

Nevertheless, to the student of sociology, there was something worth reflection in his philosophy. His contempt for the low-born Hitler was profound. . . . He was Junker to his marrow. He believed in his army . . . in its destiny to rule all mankind by force. It was HIS Junker philosophy, not the Kaiser's, that made World War I. It was his Junker philosophy, not Hitler's, that made World War II.

Yet there were items therein that seems worth the thoughtful attention of all Liberty-loving folk.

PERHAPS THE MOST IMPORTANT OF THESE WAS THE CONSERVATION OF LEADERSHIP TYPES THRU AVOIDANCE OF EXCESSIVE BIRTH CONTROL. General von Sternwald estimated the Junker group contained some thousands of families. There is probably a considerably larger number descended from the similar group in Britain, if we include the F.F.V. type of families in our country which have, for nearly 2 centuries, kept the American Ship-of-State on an even keel. A student of sociology wonders how this number would compare with Britain's aristocracy, with the group France lost under the guillotine, with the *razon de gente* of Castile?

In any event the Junker system is: Keep the leadership type homogeneous. Their daughters MUST marry within the officer caste. It always must be safely above the maintenance level.* Parents MUST have at least 4 children. These biologically should —with both parents talented—be of the leadership stock.

Was not von Sternwald really biologically correct? However, Americans may detest the whole Junker scheme, would we not be wise to study its Father-rule, of war-worship, of goose-stepping and heel-clicking regimentation? It DID produce a group that (1) persisted for the centuries since the Teutonic Knights held East Prussia against the Slavs (2) intelligently created a war-machine that could have created, even for a few years, *Festung Europa,* while enslaving all peoples from North Cape to Palermo, from Brest to Kiev. Had it not been for the miracle of American industrialist's super-production, this group might have made *Weltmacht* permanent. CAN WE NOT, IN U. S. A., BY BEING BIO-

---

* See Sierran Cabin . . . From Skyscraper, story of enactment of Code de la Famille.

LOGICALLY WISE, CREATE AN EQUALLY EFFICIENT OR-
GANIZATION, YET WITH THE REPUBLICAN IDEAL OF
PEACE AND GOOD WILL IN LIEU OF WELTMACHT? At this
writing, when D-day is less than a week past, one wonders whether
U.S.A. will not be forced, in order to preserve our liberties—to
backfire their conflagration with something as efficient as this one
in the Eastern frontier of the Heather Province.

Some California heathers are aboreal: the manzanita, the ma-
dron. Their flowers, nevertheless, are true heather-bells.

THE MADRONA

Captain of the Western Wood,
Thou that apest Robin Hood!
Green above thy scarlet hose,
How thy velvet mantle shows;
Never tree like thee arrayed,
O thou gallant of the glade!
   When the fervid August sun
   Scorches all it looks upon,
   And the balsam of the pine
   Drips from stem to needle fine,
   Round thy compact shade arranged,
   Not a leaf of thee is changed!
When the yellow autumn sun
Saddens all it looks upon,
Spreads its sackcloth on the hills,
Strews its ashes in the rills,
Thou thy scarlet hose dost doff,
And in limbs of purest buff
Challengest the somber glade
   For a sylvan masquerade.
   Where, oh where shall he begin
   Who would paint thee, Harlequin?
   With thy waxen, burnished leaf,
   With thy branches' red relief,
   With thy poly-tinted fruit,
   In thy spring or autumn suit,—
   Where begins, and oh, where end,—
   Thou whose charms all art transcend?—Bret Harte

CHAPTER 47

HYDRANGEA

*"Waga kuni no Yamato shima
Ne ni dizuru hi wa.
Morokoshi hito mo,
Awoga zaramepa.** (Ancient Japanese Poem:)

> * "In the ancient Yamato island,
> My native land—the sun rises.
> Must not even the Western foreigner
> There be reverent?"

IN TRYING to Sherlock-Holmes cultivated flowers back to their na·tive habitats, our Geogardener found HYDRANGEA of the Saxifragaceae most elusive. Finally he went to China, then to Nippon. With an English botanist, he was hiking in Japan's Nikko mountains. A half-dozen miles behind them they had left the famous Red Lacquer Bridge. Pointing up a mountain ravine, the keen-eyed man of herbs said: "Let's climb there. It looks like HYDRANGEA territory."

They climbed a narrow trail. All the peasants they passed were under oiled-paper umbrellas. On these were printed Japanese "good-luck" characters. The girls who wore red petticoats were said to be those yet unmarried. All met our hydrangea-seekers with the bow from the waist, the ritual smile. All this had persisted from Samuri days. Near the head of the gorge, at the base of a cold, shady cliff was a thicket of wild hydrangeas. The botanist, exiled in Japan, exclaimed, "these are the originals of your garden hydrangeas."

As they traced their way back to Nikko, the Englishman described the lacquering process used at its Lacquer Bridge. The lacquer is made from the sap of a *rhus*, cousin to both California's poison oak and Eastern U.S.A.'s poison ivy. It is the basis of some of the world's finest carved Lacquer, as at Nikko shrine. It was used in ornamenting Nikko's Mikado's Bridge. When our Geogardener was there, the then-heir to the Japanese throne crossed on it. Our Geogardener noticed that his retinue, however, used the nearby unlacquered bridge. The Briton also spoke admiringly of Grant's visit there. This Sacred Bridge is reserved for the imperial family. The Mikado, at the time of General Grant's visit, motioned for him to follow. Grant's response was truly worthy

(CORMORANTS) TRAINED TO FISH, JAPAN

Excessive birth control had plummeted France below the reproduction line a few months before World War II. This blocked natural selection, which, unhindered, works unceasingly in China's population mass. One element is chronic food shortages. Cormorants, common also on the California coast, are trained in China and Japan to fish. Their necks are so ringed they must disgorge a certain catch of fish before they are allowed to swallow their dinner. Such Oriental patience built up over centuries, our paeonies, chrysanthemums, wisteria.

THE DIABUTSU GARDEN, KAMAKURA, JAPAN

of an American! "I am but an ordinary citizen." He used the plebeian structure.

Our Geogardener was at Kamakura when a worshipper at the colossal Dai Butsu was pointed out to him as one poisoned by lacquer-rhus. It was at the inn near the Lacquer Bridge our Geogardener was told by a bamboo grower: "There were two Japanese misers: Kato and Ishimura. Kato boasted he was cautious about waste. Even in hot weather, he never used a fully opened fan, opened but one segment thereof. 'I still maintain,' responded Ishimura, 'you are most extravagant. . . I open my fan, but do not wear it out fanning. I wave my face!'"

Our neglect of the history of Japan since Peary's visit cost us the bloody corpses of our marines on Tarawa Atoll—our fallen sea-infantry on Iwo Jima's volcanic slopes. We had knowledge of what Herbert Spencer had given the Nipponese,—not to be divulged till after his death. We had the testimony of disappointed Lafacadio Hearne,* who had yearned "to become a Japanese."

When our Geogardener was botanizing on Japan's Inland Sea, he saw pilgrimage after pilgrimage of schoolboys to the water Torii of Miyajima. On the beach behind the sacred Torii had been set up a monument. It was a mast from a Russian battleship — (How history repeated itself on the two treacherous attacks — the one on the Russian fleet, the other at Pearl Harbor) — Each lad was required to rub his fingers around the scars of the Japanese shells. Then he repeated: "This is what the Yamoto Race does to Caucasians". Such Indoctrination, for 3 decades before Pearl Harbor, produced the "suicide deaths" of the Nipponese.

Hydrangea Land is China and Japan. American gardens should exhibit more of the curious Sargent's Hydrangea from Central China. One can almost imagine some publicity firm adopting its bloom for a trademarked device. Probably no flower better demonstrates the wisdom of investing in publicity. The seed-making flowers at the center of this attractive saxifrage are most inconspicuous. There hangs around its perimeter, however, a circle of sterile flowers as showy as a line of illuminated Chinese lanterns.

Side by side with Sargent's hydrangea grow the teaplant and its cousin, the camellia. It is tragically characteristic of Samuri rule that the common people of Japan hold the camellia to the

---

* "Besides the devilish treatment I received in the Government service, I have been obliged to recognize the fact that I can never become a Japanese, or find real sympathy from the Japanese as a whole. I am obliged to acknowledge that at last my isolation became too much for me. I felt the need of being again among men of my own race, who, with all their faults, have sympathy and kindness, and who have the same color of soul as myself. How foolish the foreigner who believes that he can understand the Japanese!" (New Lafacadio Hearn letters.)

unlucky. This is because its red blossoms fall off whole in a way which reminds the Japanese of decapitated heads! Visitors to Old Japan were impressed with the ever present greeting of a smile. Then it would develop that he who failed to smile when meeting a Samuri might be decapitated!

NIKKO BRIDGE

Chamberlain writes about LACQUER. Many kinds of material admit of being lacquered. On metal, in particular, very pleasing results have been obtained. But the favourite material is wood, and the best kinds of wood for the purpose are the Camellia. A powder formed of calcined deer's horn serves in most cases to give the final polish, with a very fine brush made of rat's hair.

The pattern thus traced out is then filled in with ground-work lacquer, with a brush made of hare's hair, great care being taken not to touch or paint out the original tracing line. The article is then gently dusted with a very soft brush made from the long winter coat of a white horse, to remove any loose metal dust that might adhere to the article, and to slightly smoothe the surface. When the portion which has received the second coat of lacquer over the gold dust is quite hard, it is rubbed smooth with a piece of hard charcoal made from camellia wood or honoki, until the whole is level with the surrounding parts.

GEOGARDENING IN HYDRANGEA LAND

At the time our Geogardener found Hydrangea in Nikko's hinterland, travel in the backcountry was by kago. There were 4 coolies to each kago. Wages were 10 cents daily. This was, however, over double the wage of Chinese wheelbarrow coolies at that time. Even the Japanese pay was a monthly wage equal to six hours common laborer's earnings in U. S. A. at that time.

In considering the eugenic aspects of Japanese immigration, let us remember one cause of the present war was the determination of the Japanese militarists to possess the Pacific Coast of Canada and U. S. A. In economic warfare Japan's militarists had a powerful weapon in Japan's low wages compared to U. S. A.'s When above photograph was taken, even rickshaw coolies paid an income tax. The wage for ricepaddy coolies was about 5 cents a day. Rickshaw men earned several times this amount because most of them were known to be doomed to an early death through tuberculosis. . . It is no mere accident that dual citizenship is law in the three fascists nations, Germany, Italy, Japan.

One wonders why the Occident is so far behind the Orient in planting perfume-yielding gardens. Of course, some of U.S.A. cannot grow jessamine, gardenias and frangipanni. There are, however, hardy plants. These include clove pinks, Nice stocks, honeysuckle, belladonna lilies. These add to the charm of a full moon garden. They make more pleasing the barbecue party. Some trees, like magnolia, should be mentioned . . . If once our plant breeders were convinced there was a demand for plants with pleasing odors, they would accelerate the isolation of mutations that promise increased fragrance. The recent successes in breeding African Marigolds without an odor offensive to some is an example of what can be hoped for in the decades to come . . . In this connection it should be remembered the remarkable progress of the gardens around Grasse, the great French perfume center.

CHAPTER 48
HONEYSUCKLE

"Skeeter am a-buzzin'
In de hon-ey-suck-el-vine
Run, yo' little pick-a-nin-nies,
Run-run-run-."

At full-honeysuckle bloom, our Geogardener was tracing Honey Locust, Persimmon, Pawpaw, Catalpa, Hickory, Black-Walnut, the various American Magnolias, Dogwood, also a whole series of herbaceous plants of California gardens, such as Coreopsis and Pink Oenothera, back to "The spots from whence they sprung." He one day was climbing a Southern mountain. The "chaparral," to use a Californian term, was about shoulder-high. It was covered, for miles, with honeysuckle flowers, cream-colored and milk-white. Their odor was irresistible to millions of honey-feeders, like the bees. Here was an odor as characteristic of Dixie as that of the yellow jessamines, or of the garden-ias named for dear old Doctor Garden of Charlestown.

It was while working on this fascinating native Southern flora that our Geogardener saw much, during one spring, of Pompey MacAlpine. Both his names were queer. Both harked back to slave days. Pompey's father had been a trusted slave. He was butler to a plantation owner, Andrew MacAlpine. This transplanted Scot, like many of his caste, both here and in Britain, was a deep student of the classics. Hence his slaves were given such names as "Cato", "Julius Cæsar", or "Pompey". Being also a stern Covenanter, he usually added a scriptural cognomen. His plantation house recalled the old darky song about the slave whose weight of cognomens was almost as impressive as those of a Prince of Wales:

"Mah name am Obi-di-ah
Julius Caeser Jer-ri-mi-ah
George Wash'n-ton, Andrew Jackson Jones.
Ah's a sho- nuf black buck-nigger
White folk's says ah cuts a figger
In the minstrel show
While playing on de bones,
Ah was raised on massah's bounty
'Way down in Beaufort County
Yes, way down near de Georgia line,
Whar de watermelons ripen
And de Cherokee's a-climbing
De palmetto and
De tur-pen-tine pine."

Pompey was an old man when our Geogardener was South. He told many tales of Honeysuckle Land. He recalled how his childhood supper often was sweet potatoes and a gourdful of persimmon beer. He related stories of moonlight possum-hunting. These made a Yank understand why Dixie Land loves its "houn'-dawgs". . . He gave an insight into our waste of game. He detailed how he caught quail in a figure-4 trap. These he sold at a dime a dozen at the village store.

The fine Southern aristocracy, cruelly decimated in the tragic Civil War, left us some of U.S.A.'s most wonderfully planned gardens. Conspicuous among these are Charleston's Azalea Gardens, also those of Natchez, Mississippi.

> *Bid her steal into the pleached bower,*
> *Where honeysuckles, ripen'd by the sun,*
> *Forbid the sun to enter;—like favorites,*
> *Made proud by princes, that advance their pride*
> *Against that power that bred it.*
>   (Much Ado About Nothing, Act III, Sc. 1.)

IN HONEYSUCKLELAND, OLD DUELLING GROUND, NATCHEZ
Brave men, from a false sense of "honor," once killed each other on the duelling ground. At Natchez, they point out their old duelling ground. Public opinion has outlawed duelling. It was highly dysgenic, since it eliminated the idealistic, the courageous—our best. Is it too much to hope that by also consolidating Public Opinion, to now outlaw war? It also is very dysgenic. The draft SELECTS the best, leaves the weaklings behind to father coming generations.

IVY, QUIMPER

"Walls must get the weather stain
Before they grow the IVY"

(Browning: Aurora Leigh)

Just as a smile makes a baby's face doubly kissable, so Ivy adds to the charm of Old World buildings. How much the Ivy adds to the attractiveness of this wall near the Port Medard, in Britanny's quaint old Quimper.

CHAPTER 49

IVY

"IVY climbs the crumbling hall
To decorate decay."

(Bailey: "Festus")

IVY, TO our Geogardener's mind, is forever inseparably linked to a certain Fourth-of-July. Its memories are of the Lafayette Escadrille. Our Geogardener was working on the French birthrate's fall. His mother being of French descent, he felt an unusual interest in this problem. He was determined to contribute his modest bit toward its solution. While in Paris, a friend, a certain French professor, took him, on the Declaration-of-Independence anniversary, to the monument to those Americans who, as airmen of the Lafayette Escadrille, gave their lives to France. In the nearby park was an enormous ivy. It was really itself a tree. Its trunk was the diameter of a tall man's thigh!

Let there be no decay of memory as to the names on above named monument, even tho ivy-decorated. Said record is significant, since names are embalmed history. These 34 made the supreme sacrifice. One could dream of the ancestors of those who pioneered in air combat. Theirs was as much another advance guard as those who dared the skies. These forbears dared the fevers of the Virginia and Carolina tidelands. They, too, "carried on" in crisis. They heard redskin arrows whizzing from ambush on the James, the Rappahannock.

The monument's names included: Chapman, Davis, Rockwell, McDonnell, Campbell, Palmer, Lee, Ely, Stone, Woodard, Wolcott. Here was a roll of the British-as-colonials, "swarming" in America-to use Woodrow Wilson's expression. Their ancestors had pushed ever forward the frontiers. They poured over the Appalachians to the Mississippi. They crossed the prairies, streaked with buffalo herds. They ventured into the mysterious Rockies, that the old maps vaguely showed as the "Stony Mountains." They dared the broad white space beyond, labelled "Great American Desert." The Lafayette birdmen, who early made the supreme sacrifice, had the same high courage as Bible-Toter Jedediah Smith who went into that mysterious white area on the map. He was to ascertain what really was behind the coast called "New Albion," also "CALIFOR-

NIA." Was it all sage-brush, alkali, horned-toads and rattlesnakes, as the Spanish described it? Was there, on the contrary, enuf land to anchor a completely transcontinental U.S.A.? Our government then did not know what was behind the line of Franciscan missions, behind the Fort of the Russians that, north of those missions, protected the Romanoff sea-otter hunters.

The Lafayette Escadrille's names could well be considered in connection with the history of German General staff. Study parentage-possibilities of our group of courageous, idealistic aviators in the light of the Differential Birthrate Law. Compare, say 25 of these with 25 Prussian Knights of the 1200s. In 7 centuries, suppose there were born, say, even as few as 20 generations. Project that backwards, or forwards. If each father averaged 4 children, the total of his descendants would be even by the fifth generation 1,056. By the 20th generation, they almost would seem to use the words of Holy Writ, "numberless as the sands of the seashore." Picture how a couple of dozen Prussian Knights ancestored the present brilliant German General Staff. With all their Nazi poison, we must admit their power of leadership in that organization. Then peer forward another 7 centuries. Picture what U.S.A. has lost in the potential offspring of the aviators whose names are recorded in stone in that ivy-festooned park in Paris suburbs.

"Wait till the laurel bursts its buds, and creeping
IVY flings its graces about the lichen'd rocks, and floods
of sunshine fill the shady place."
(Margaret J. Preston—Through the Pass.)

Ivy is the badge of Clan Gordon, with its blue-and-green plaid threaded with yellow. At the time of Robert the Bruce, the Lord of Gordon, Sir Adam, was granted a Lordship in Aberdeenshire. . . . One must go a geogardening to Scotland and study names on gravestones there to come to appreciate how large a share the Scots have had in making American history.

"With roses musky-breathed,
And drooping daffodilly,
And silverleaved lily,
And IVY darkly-wreathed,
I wove a crown before her,
For her I love so dearly." (Tennyson)

CHAPTER 50

IRIS

"IRIS of all hues, roses and jessamine."
(Milton—Paradise Lost.)

THIS IRIS CHAPTER will be limited, because of space, to the so-called "Spanish" iris. It will record but one of several thrilling adventures our Geogardener had in "sauvaging" iris species. He had, in his garden, the kinds called "German" iris, "Dutch" iris, "Japanese" iris, "English" iris, "Florentine" iris, "Dalmatian" iris, also some rare types from Persia.

Several springtime excursions had been made into the Iberian peninsula. These were aimed to track "Spanish" iris to its native haunts. The earlier of these visits, confined to Spain, were unsuccessful. They covered that then-kingdom from Algeciras, Granada, Ronda, and Seville thru Cordoba, Saragossa to Barcelona, Search, also, both eastward and westward from the Madrid base was unsuccessful. Then the south slopes of the Pyrenees were combed.

Finally it was decided to spend a bit of one spring in covering an elliptical motor trip thru Portugal, commencing at Lisbon. It was when returning down-coast and almost back at Tagus' mouth that the "Spanish" iris was found in all its glory. Wild blue, also yellow "Spanish" iris spangled the spring green of Portugal's rolling hills. The "Spanish" species occurred in great stretches of apparently little-cultivated grazing. There one can watch the tired swallows reach land after their migration overseas from Africa.

This Portuguese trip included some interesting contacts: One was the Iberian "quintas." Especially fascinating was one, north of Lisbon labelled the *Quinta* of Albuquerque. (Thru all lands that have come under Iberian influence, one stumbles across delightful little *"Quintas"**.)

This one north of Lisbon was labelled "At this *Quinta* was born Albuquerque." Another charming "quinta" was the castle

---

* Who can forget Quinta Bates in Peru's Ariquipa. Its garden is heavy, on a full-moon night with the odors of plants that, in sunshine hours, attract rare hummingbirds. Who can forget its square-headed Inca idols . . . its lazy Indio boys . . . its green papaya flower for one's boutonniere, and above all Tia Bates herself, who mothered all the blonde Panagra aviators entering there from the North, the South and the Argentine routes.

It was in Portugal that our Geogardener found the blue also yellow "Spanish" Iris. These brightened the mesa against the background skyline above with color. Foreground: Sardine packing for U. S. trade. . . On the same day was seen the Convento dos Jeronomos at Belen in the photograph below. It was built as a native offering on the spot whence Vasco de Gama sailed on his historic voyage. Eugenists are interested because of the fierce SELECTION at work in crews at that time. Of every three that started with de Gama, two died. Only the toughest physically, the mentally most alert, survived.

of **Tomar**. Americans, at least before World War II, seldom visited out-of-the-way Portugal. Seldom, too, did they delve into the history of Portugal. All these are worth study, if one wants to evaluate certain forces at work in our nation. Prince Henry the Navigator, a little-appreciated character, is inseparable from the *quinta* at Tomar. The great Albuquerque is recalled by that family *quinta* north of Lisbon. That was before Portugal had diluted her Visigoth blood with that of Negro slave concubines.

We are fascinated by the pages of history wherein the iris-flag of the Bourbons waved over France, with its golden fleur-de-lis. We can with profit study that tiny bit of Western Iberia—that Portugal once so important the Pope divided the New World between her and her neighbor Spain. If we study understandingly the *quintas* of Portugal, we may glimpse some of the causes of the rotting of its great colonial empire. For in that land lived the empire-building leaders whose type is now extinct. If, after geo-gardening in Portuguese *quintas,* one continues on to Angola, to Mozambique to badly-hybridized Goa, finally on to Macao with its highly organized commercial vice,—one may be able to evaluate accurately some forces also at work within our American population-mass.

It could be stated with: Portugal once was great. The old Visigoth aristocracy still ruled the land with intelligence. Five centuries back descendants of these West Goths (Visigoths), still were dominant. They had, however, the old urge to battle. They had, too, the Viking yearning for colonization, the ashes of which are Angola, Mozambique, Goa, Macao. They were too much like their fearless cousins, the Franks who named France. Being also "frank," they died, often early in the reproduction age at the Inquisition's stake. They were as rollicking as were their ancestors who drank their mead from cowhorns (called "tumblers" because they were not to be set down), that were drunk at one draft. These Falstaffs of the Iberian peninsula did not hesitate to cross their blood with fecund girls of their slave castes. Hence came many "natural" sons, those with the "bar sinister," nevertheless hybrids. The Differential Birthrate Law works as unceasingly as Ocean's tides. Hence, while geogardening in Portugal, for the Spanish Iris that had not been found "sauvage" in Spain, it was observed that the southern part of Portugal, i.e. the province of Algarve and the southern parts of Almentjo and Estramadura were drenched with

The Iris rival in color the obi of this Japanese girl. Not all Japanese gardens, however, show such massed bloom. Of old Japan, Chamberlain wrote: A garden without flowers may sound like a contradiction in terms. But it is a fact that many Japanese gardens are of that kind, the object which the Japanese landscape-gardener sets before him being to produce something pap-like—to suggest some famous natural scene, in which flowers may or may not appear, according to the circumstances of the case. When they do, they are generally grouped together in beds or under shelter, and removed as soon as their season of bloom is over, more after the manner of a European flower-show. In this way are obtained horticultural triumphs, such as dwarfing. Thus you may see a pine-tree or a maple, 60 years old, and perfect in every part, but not more than a foot high.

slave-caste blood. Now this was far different from the Moors of Ferdinand and Isabella, Spain. The Moors included many of the intelligensia. They were indeed of those Arabs that gave us our "Arabic" numerals, also such words as al-cohol, and such star names as Al-deberan.

There is a lesson in Eugenics in all this. The tip of Portugal nearest Africa was what received the slave trade from the dregs of the Dark Continent. It is paralleled in Sicily and Calabria, in contrast with Italy's Piedmonte and Lombardy.

Portugal at that time still could produce poets like Camoens and his "Lusidad," explorers like Prince Henry the Navigator, could have a bit of hallowed ground which even now bears the copper-plate:

"In this Quinta was born Albuquerque."

Is it not significant that the Portuguese of that day thought of a "Quinta" or "garden" instead of a "home." They were passionately fond of flowers. The followers of Prince Henry the Navigator, of Albuquerque, of Cabral brought home seeds and roots from Brazil, from both West and East Africa, from the Hindustan of Goa, from China's rich flora of paeonies, and wisteria, lotus and asters. Their descendants were radiated into the gardens of Europe, and consequently of America.

Our very word *"Tapioca"* is Brazilian-native. It was used there before the Portuguese Pedro Alvores Cabral was blown off Vasco da Gama's African sea route over to Brazil. Our word "tea" comes likewise, from a Chinese dialect, the Amoy, in which it is called *"te"*. Our knowledge of tea reached Europe following trade of Portugal with China begun in the early 1500s. . . . Martin Lopez, searching for a Northeast Passage to Cathay, discovered Nova Zembla. . . . Magellan was first to break into the Pacific. Vasca da Gama is the real hero of a Homeric poem. Camoens, about 1570, wrote the great Portuguese epic "Os Lusidas".

The colonizers left their wives behind. They crossed blood with weakling natives. Today, in Rio de Janeiro or Sao Paulo, the pure whites wail "Brazil is becoming a gigantic Haiti." Already, of the Goanese, Kipling has written:

"Miss Vezzis—wore cotton-print gowns and bulged shoes . . . lost her temper with the children and abused them in the language of the Borderline, which is part English, part Portuguese and part Native. . . . Every

Sunday she went to see her mamma who lived for the
most part in an old cane chair, in a greasy tussur-silk
dressing gown in a big rabbit worren of a house FULL
OF VEZZIES, PEREIRAS, RIBIERAS, LISBOAS, AND
CONSALVESAS." (Kipling: "His Chance in Life.")

"Flower of light! Who knows if fables old
First gave Olympus' messenger thy name
Or gave thee hers;—but this I know—there came
Down the arch'd bow in multicoloured flame
To star out Earth with purple and with gold
Thy beauty;—for a breath of heaven yet clings
About thy robes, and thy translucent stillness brings
Faint Seraph songs, half heard, and winnowing of wings."

BLISS: Iris, Fleur de Lis.

"Jove descending shook the Idaean hills,
And down their summits pour'd a hundred rills,
The unkindled lightning in his hand he took,
And thus the many-colour'd maid bespoke:
'Iris with haste thy golden wings display,
To godlike Hector this our word convey—'
He spoke, and Iris at his word obey'd;
On wings of winds descends the various maid."

HOMER: Iliad.

"And thus the child of Thaumas speaks
Heaven's beauty flushing in her cheeks:
E'en as she spoke, her wings she spread,
And skyward on her rainbow fled."

VIRGIL: Aeneid.

"There's crimson buds, and white and blue—
The very rainbow showers
Have turned to blossoms where they fell,
And sown the earth with flowers."

HOOD: Song—O Lady.

(Four iris quotations above supplied by Mr. Lloyd Austin,
Rainbow Hybridizing Gardens, Placerville, Calif.)

CHAPTER 51

LAUREL

"Wait till the laurel bursts its buds,
And creeping ivy flings its graces
About the lichened rocks, and floods
Of sunshine fill the shady places."
(Preston: Thru the Pass.)

R EACTION between humans and the laurel of your garden has persisted thru the centuries. . . . Laurel appreciation is, even today, worldwide. The classic Greeks crowned winners at the Olympic games with laurel wreaths. England made Tennyson one of her Poets Laure-ate. No Japanese temple is truly complete without its camphor-laurel. Southern California now has vast orchards of avocado-laurel. Gourmets in Paris boulevards—in American luxury hotels—sup potages flavored with Caribbean bay-laurel. The German *hausfrausen* sprinkle their *apfelkuchen* with the ground bark of cinnamon-laurel from Ceylon. A California packer of dried black Mission figs inserts a leaf of the aromatic California native laurel atop each carton.

The Laurel family includes the true laurels of the Mediterranean Basin. One cinnamon laurel is fossil in California.

Where the *Indios* still make their dugouts from avocado trunks, there was, a third century ago, a far-flung *hacienda*. The Geogardeners were guests there. Hiking along a trail one morning, they encountered a peon funeral. There was no hearse, no coffin. The corpse, a baby's, was wrapped in a tattered serape. It was carried on the father's shoulders.

Returning, the *Norte-Americanos* saw the grandmother sitting outside their adobe. Her grief at the burial had been profound. The Geogardeners attempted a few words of comfort. The old squaw smiled thru her tears. She pointed to one of those unforgettable desert sunsets. "But, senor y senora, every evening I still will have the sunset." . . .

Norte-Americanos would describe that family as tragically poor. The beds in their adobe were *petates,* mats woven of coarse rushes. Flour for the *tortillas* that formed their mainstay food was ground in the *metate* at the door. The unshelled corn was hung from rafters of avocado-laurel wood. One cannot buy silks or diamonds on a 17 cent daily wage. Yet the ashen-haired dame HAD wealth. She not only had the sunsets . . . she knew how to enjoy them . . . Was not her way wiser than "Keeping up with the Joneses?"

STREET FORESTRY, PARIS

Latin-speaking nations, (particularly Italy—and to a lesser degree France) run to stern formality in gardening, including street forestry. This, perhaps, is a natural sequence of the Roman passion for Law. Note tiny formal gardens, also street trees at the Arc d'Triomphe in Paris. It was built to glorify Napoleon's lust for conquest. At the beginning of World War II the Nazis boasted they had out-Napoleoned Napoleon. They had studied all the Napoleonic failures. These never should prevent a Nazi victory. Wars of conquest by those who are obsessed with ambition such as Napoleon, the Kaiser, Hitler, and Tojo, have cost their subjects also the peace-loving people tragically in treasure and in blood. The Napoleonic wars for example, reduced the French stature several inches. It was the tall men, descendants of the old Gauls, who died in battle. What a witty Frenchman called "the meter-high folk" remained to breed.

"At the head of the British rode Marshal Haig, behind him more generals than I had ever seen. The massed standards . . . moved by, each CROWNED WITH LAUREL."—(Briscom: "Diplomatically Speaking.")

THE ABBEY OF ST. DENIS NEAR PARIS CONTAINING MANY ROYAL TOMBS

Formality in gardening, the observance of Rules of Law and Order continually impresses Americans in Italy or France. Same is paralleled in Gothic architecture. The Abbey of St. Denis near Paris illustrates this. It contains many royal tombs. The type of leadership in France that could produce architecture, such as seen in their outstanding cathedrals and abbeys, has been largely eliminated from the French population mass. Among the causes were the religious wars, the wars of conquest, the French Revolution, excessive birth control. This latter often has a tendency in France to restrict the family to a single child. This is in order that increased inheritance might result in social advancement . . . Since U. S. A. will probably within a few decades, witness the same phenomena seen in France when the League of Nation's announcements came in 1939, should not eugenists organize public opinion looking toward that coming census which will jolt Americans into an understanding of what is happening."

Dugout canoes made of avocado, (alligator pear), tree trunks. As this was snapped, the regular U. S. A. passenger plane roared overhead. In a third canoe of avocado laurel a peon groaned with malarial chills.

Of the Camphor-Laurel in old Japan Chamberlain once wrote: Japan's new colony of Formosa is the greatest camphor-producing district in the world, Japan proper comes next, though the ruthless deforestation that has disgraced the present epoch bids fair to ruin this source of national income before the lapse of many more years. Unfortunately, camphor cannot, like lacquer or maple-sugar, be extracted by tapping. The tree must be felled and cut into chips, which are steamed in a vat, the vapour being made to carry off the fumes into a cooling apparatus, where condensation takes place and the camphor and camphor-oil are afterward skimmed off. Cabinets made of camphor-wood are much esteemed, not only for the fine grain and silky sheen of the wood, but for its efficacy against the attacks of insects.

The camphor-LAUREL ranks among the stateliest of trees, frequently attaining to an enormous height and girth,—thirty, forty, and even fifty feet in circumference. Grand specimens may be seen at Atami, at Atsuta, and at Dazaifu,—all places on or near the ordinary lines of travel. Such giant trees are often worshipped by the simple country folk, who hang ropes of straw or paper round them in token of reverence.

THE PLACE De La CONCORDE IN PARIS

French gardens, such as those in the Tullieries, show Formalism. This, to a geogardening Californian, shows a rigidity as remarkable as the uniform skyline of the old "hotels" or houses of the nobility in the Rue de Rivoli and facing the Place de la Concorde. The latter was the site of the guillotine of the French Revolution. Despite the fact that the moral training of some of the French aristocracy was regrettable, some of the clearest thinkers since then have pointed out that the dropping of the guillotine in the French Revolution ranked with France's long series of wars of conquest in eliminating from the French population-mass many of the leadership type.

A LAVENDER FARM IN SOUTHERN FRANCE

*"God Almightie first Planted a Garden ... There ought
to be Gardens, for all the Monthes in the Yeare: In December, and January, and the Latter Part of November:
Green all Winter:—Holly, Bayes, Juniper, Rose-Mary,
LAUVENDER, Sweet Morjoram warme set."*

(Essays of Bacon, p. 187.)

CHAPTER 52

LAVENDER

"DERRINGER DICK, Daredevil of The Da-ko-tah's". . . . Remember the time Skinnay loaned you his dime novel of the sagebrush? Skinnay was propaganda-wise. Derringer's biography would bolster morale. Skinnay then was in need of manpower. His proposed scalping expedition was to be against the Blackfeet. Their reservation was only 2,000 miles away, across the sagebrush. To defray expenses for the foray, Skinnay had planned a few sagebrush holdups en route. These were, too, to be thrillingly heroic. (The Bad Man Bandit always has had a ready-for-use halo, especially luminous, in his baggage. Gold robbed from the Bloated Rich was to be shared with the Penurious, Poverty-stricken Poor!) . . .

In place of our desert "sagebrush", Southwestern Europe has its *maqui*. In Provencal, they tell you this word originally meant the Corsican undergrowth. It corresponds to what is called "the brush" in parts of South Africa, "the bush" in Australia, and "chaparral" when applied to the manzanita-greasewood-ceanothus complex of California. One botanist, in fact, uses the term *"maqui"* occasionally for the California chaparral. This is to denote its resemblance to the *maqui* of, not only Corsica, but the entire Mediterranean Basin. . . . As World War II swung into 1944, we commenced to often hear, with a new meaning, that Corsican word *maqui*. It then was used to designate the French underground. Its men operated from caves in *maqui*-covered hillsides in France's great limestone belt. Said belt extends from the Jura Mountains, down thru Haute Savoy, to the limestone deserts of Provance. The name *"maqui"* even previously had a double meaning. It also had meant an escaped criminal who hid in the *maqui*. Such a one practiced brigandage, such as was proposed by our Skinnay. . .

Our Geogardener once was botanizing in Corsica's Ajaccio-hinterland. He was searching particularly for plants with bulbs or *"onions"* to use the French term. He was amidst this bulb-spotted *maqui* when he came upon a *sanglier,* or wildboar, hunt. The tusker already had been wounded. It was plunging thru the *maqui*. The dogs were at its heels. The boar ripped one hound the entire length of the dog's body just before the death-stroke. An observer could understand why the boar-hunt was such a test of mediaeval royal skill. Such kingly forays were made with only sword or lance as weapons. They ranked with the earliest bullfights in Spain, at which matador often was of the blood royal. . . .

This Mediterranean *maqui* has a delightful and characteristic member: lavender. It, like the other *maqui* plants, is fascinating in its adjustment to prolonged drought plus high temperatures. Herein its evolution has been as successful as that of our arid Southwest's cacti, of Australia's acacias. Some *maqui* plants have thickened leaves. Others have foliage reduced in size. Yet others secrete aromatic resins or oils. All these devices seem to protect against diffusion of moisture as effectually as the resin-plants of California's tarweeds.

Your garden lavender, therefore, is as characteristic a *maqui* plant as your rosemary, your leafless brooms. . . It grows wild throughout the territory of Tartaran of Tarrascon, of Pere Gaucher and his famous elixir,* of Daudet's Mill. At wayside peasant stands are sold bags of that time-honored perfume, lavender. It has become inseparable from Old Lace. To really know Lavender, go then a-geogardening to the semi-deserts of Provance. It is the land that saw developed, under good King Rene, the Courts-of-Love with their troubadors. In this limestone semi-desert, where grow mats of wild lavender, are also oases of cultivated roses. Some such contain the Count de Grasse's fertile perfume farms.

We Americans have a "lavender" in the fragrant Desert Lavender of our arid Southwest. On some desert "fans" it becomes almost a small tree. The writer measured one some 9 feet high. This was where a cowboy was grumbling that the last 12 months had registered less than one inch of rain. . . . The desert lavender will, some years, after a soaking rain, flaunt ten thousand tiny purple flowers. It shows a marvellous adjustment to summer shade temperatures, just about the world's highest. Such efficiency illustrates how Mother Nature has accomplished, in countless "experiments" by Natural Selection, by ever continued improvement of her BEST STOCK.

It has remained for our vaunted Occidental civilization to reverse this Natural Selection by excessive birth control of our talented. There remains only a few years to organize. World War II diverted attention from the startling 1940 figures. By 1960, there may be national hysteria. There then may develop a demand for "More babies and we don't care what kind!"

* Any geogardener who specializes in herbs, medical or culinary, should read and reread Daudet's highly amusing "The Elixir."

CHAPTER 53

LOCUST

"Breathes there a man
With soul so dead
Who never to himself
Hath said:
'This is my own,
My native land.'"

(Scott: Lay of the Last Minstrel.)

NO ONE today knows what the dog looked like. It's a safe bet he was mongrel Indian Ki-yi. He probably was one of the kind Digger aborigines utilize as an animated alarm clock until the time arrives for a feast. He was probably half coyote, half anything else from greyhound or bull terrier to just plain mutt-dog. Anyhow Dog Bar, named for that dog, was one of the richest "bars" on the river. At the entrance to the settlement stood the Stage House. It was at a hairpin in the grade from the mountain above the Bar in the river-scoured canyon below.

Dog Bar today is the most ghostly of Gold Rush ghost towns. . . . Its Stage House is also of the realm of wraiths. Where bearded, redshirted, booted miners traded nuggets for "1, 2 or 3 fingers of rotgut," there is more than a few scattered stones of the old chimney place. Dog Bar still, however, boasts of exactly 100 locust trees. On each side of the road toward the sunrise are 25—toward the sunset, the same. At their spring bloom one could close his eyes, sniff the perfume and imagine himself in the Ohio River's bottoms—in the Ozarks—in Shenandoah Valley or on Mobile Bay.

The locust is the Gold Belt's ghost-town tree. From Whiskeytown to Chinese Camp, from Cheese Marie to You Bet, from Murderers' Bar to Jimtown, "Main Street" always is locust-lined. As a certain advertisement used to proclaim: "There's a reason!"

You will understand it when you recall how you weighed every ounce of what Caesar called *"impedimenta"* in his Commentaries. You were leaving for a 30 days' hike in the untracked wilderness. The carrying capacity of your one packmule was definitely known. The reason was the same when Covered-Wagon folks outfitted at St. Jo. Every ounce again was evaluated. Sunbonnetted Mother, however, could slip into a wee envelope seed of the beloved honey-locust. It meant the one tie to "back South." Pioneer women, following their men on Prairie Schooner expeditions, left their native land with pangs. It was a comfort to rattle, in pocket, a paper of tiny locust seeds. Grumbling males could be placated with "You may be mighty glad to have good fence-post timber some day."

An Amador County pioneer used to tell of his return, in the 1840s, from trapping for Bible-Toter Jedediah Smith's Fur Company. This trapper had been away from civilization 3 years. There being no money Outwest, his wages were paid in coonskin currency. These pelts were in demand for masculine millinery. Arriving at a trading post en route home, he wearily threw down his pack of furs. Then he pulled loose one coonskin. He threw it on the bar. He called on all present to "name their poison." As he started to leave, the barkeep called "Hold on. You forgot your change." The whiskey-dispenser went out to the fur-house, tugged back TWO bales of squirrel pelts. These the trapper wisely refused. He could not "tote" them in addition to his load of coonskins.

Thus, despite journeys on which freight was estimated down to ounces, locust seeds were found in many a Prairie Schooner. Hence from the Shasta mines on the North, past the rich "diggings" at Grass Valley, thence down the Mother Lode to the southernmost of the Southern mines, gnarled locust trees each May are hung with bee-visited panicles of white bloom. Each December they rattle their dried seedpods in the whining gales.

中華諺語說得

A CHINESE PROVERB SAYS: *"Out of an indigo vat, you can't draw white calico."*

RICE PADDY
The lotus is like rice, is always thirsty. Another rice-paddy bloom is a small flowered amaryillis. It manages to maintain a foothold along the narrow paths between the rice basins. Its bright red contrasting with the rice-green makes a pleasing color effect.

———————

When our Geogardener's train of Gurkha coolies was mounting Himalayan passes, they had a trail-song which an Englishman translated. It is given below. It reveals a strange mingling of reference for Buddha with the contempt of the Gurkha (bred in the deodar forests under mighty Kungenjanga), for the miserable Bengalis below. You will enjoy Kipling's story of the Gurkha regiment fighting beside one of Presbyterian Scots in his "Drums of the Fore and Aft." The Gurkhas are proud of their record,— which even the Shiks do not possess—of unbroken loyalty to the British Raj.

"OM MANU PADME OM"*
(Gurkha Trail Song!)

Om manu padme om!
From the spreading plain beneath us
Flash the Moslem's colored domes,

———————

* The ever-repeated Buddhist prayer is "Om Manu Padme Om," "The Jewel in the Lotus Amen." It is spoken orally. It is ground out by "prayer wheels in a mountain cascade. It is whispered by prayer rags fluttering from a deobar tree. . . . (To the uncultured Christian said prayer rags look like the identification tags of California Chinese laundries of goldmining days with "No ketchee tickee, no ketchee laund'ly." In 1849-50, miners' shirts actually were shipped from San Francisco to laundries over in Hong Kong.)

But—om manu padme om.
The prayer wheels are a-spinning
Where the mountain cascade foams.

Om manu padme om!
Amongst the weakling plainsmen
Moslem scimitars swing free,
But—om manu padme om.
Ten thousand prayer rags flutter
From the Deodar Tree.

Om manu padme om!
Building Islam's jewelled palaces,
Ten thousand plainsmen toil,
But—om manu padme om,—
We freely drive our herds of yak
Where Buddha guards our soil.

Om manu padme om!
Down there Akbar and Shah Jahan
Seem great, gigantic men,
But—om manu padme om,
They're dwarfed to midget stature
In our Himalayan fen.

Om manu padme om!
Let the weakling plainsmen coolie
Gulp his dahl and his rice,
But—om manu padme om.
Our Buddha-given tsamba
Hardens muscles in a thrice.

Om manu padme om!
Stagnant water must suffice
The plainsmen coolie and his ilk,
But—om manu padme om.
Midst blooming mountain meadows
Draw we the yak's health-giving milk.

Om manu padme om!
Never forget to tie the prayer-rag;
Nor to spin the wheel around,
For—om manu padme om,—
Gua-ta-ma, the Buddha, listens
For each windborne, prayerful sound.

CHAPTER 54

LOTUS

"Om Manu Padme Om."
(The Jewel in the Lotus. Amen.)

Above was the benediction of a Buddhist priest from Kandy's Temple-of-the-Tooth. He was carrying his begging-bowl from door to door . . . Rangoon's "Om Manu Padme Om" was the blessing of another yellow-robed ecclesiastic. He was attached to Schwe Dagon Pagoda. He, too, gave opportunity to "acquire merit" by dropping a few grains of rice into an exactly similar begging bowl.

These saffron-toga'd men often are versed in the technique of disputation. Do you recall the yarn about the darky preacher? Having outworn his usefulness, he had been hauled before his deacons. "Didn't ah argufy?" "Yeh, yo' done argufied!" "Din't ah 'sputify?" "Yeh, yo' done 'sputified; but 'yo din't show Wherein" . . . Buddhist priests enjoy attempting a quarrel with you as to the relative merits of Buddhism versus Christianity. They excel in having a hot Hell and a cold Hell. The Buddhist also will challenge you with: "Which is the more beautiful symbol of Immortality . . . The sanguinary statue of Christ-on-the-Cross in a Spanish Cathedral, or the Buddha seated in the sacred Lotus?"

The ecclesiastic, in his burnt-orange shroud, will grow eloquent about the poetry of Buddhism. He will dwell upon the concept of the lotus-sprout. It arises from the stinking, black muck of a stagnant Far Eastern pool. He explains the appearance of the plant above water—the bursting of the bud into the magnificent pinkish bloom. Our shaven-headed clergyman has been carefully trained in Oriental logic. The Christian must be alert not to be hoodwinked by his saffroned sophistry. He must maintain that, after all, the Faith based on the Cross does, when pure, offer a heartening optimism. Buddhist tendency, on the other hand, is toward superstitious pessimism. It was thus so corroded that it was easy for the War Lords of Japan to blow it away, like the dust of the decadent. This they did when wanting to substitute for the Buddhism their *Sei-sai uchi*. This most-convenient Neo-Shintoism was a welding of Church and State. It was done so cleverly that conscripts, trained therein, welcome suicide-deaths in battle.

If you did not, in discouragement, rip out your water garden on its 2nd birthday . . . if you succeeded in maintaining the delicate balance between minnows and the numerous larvae of anopheles or of culex . . . you may, some day, start geogardening with water-plants as your dominant stimulus.

Your deepest water-lily thrill will be the final tracking of the lotus back to Asia. You probably will not locate it as a wildflower. You will, however, gradually come to grasp why it has become the center theme of Buddhist prayer. This petition is repeated ten million times daily. It arises from prayer-rags fluttering from Nepalese deodars, from prayer-wheels spinning under Tibetan waterfalls. It floats heavenward from teak temples in Ceylon, Siam, from others in China with lotus ponds. Still farther East, it exudes from shrines in Japan. There, tucked away in the shade of the camphor laurels, beside the lotus pond, one hears: "Om manu, padme om!" . . .

The white water lily, with waxy petals, in Eastern U.S.A., is Castalia. Its specific name, *odorata,* records its pleasant scent.

California has a yellow wild water lily. "Digger" Indians there roasted its seeds, then ate them as we do popcorn. A Swedish folkname for their yellow water lily leaves is "Lapp's gloves." It is this lily's circular leaf of which Drummond wrote, in his Quebec-habitant verse: "Little Lac-Greiner, quit calling me"—

> *"I'll try that trout*
> *Neath yon lily pad."*

By-products result from geogardening aquatics. The geo-gardener may not acquire the remarkable efficiency of Chicago pork packers . . . (Remember how they save everything but piggy's squeal?) . . . One by-product, however, of searching jungle for water flowers is introduction to the jacana. This remarkable bird is a striking example of population pressure forcing radiation into a new niche. Note the use of his long fingernails in swiftly moving over water lily pads. To water lily leaves he is nicely adjusted as to loads. A bird with heavy feet, such as in an Irishman's brogans, would sink. The jacana's toenails are as long as yester-year's Chinese belles'. It is expected she is to live in luxury,—to avoid coolie house-labor. Hence her attenuated fingernails sometimes are incased in silver. The jacana's nails are far more useful. In fact, without such highly specialized ones, he would have difficulty keeping his tummy comfortably full.

Chamberlain wrote of the Lotus: "Japanese Buddhists compare a virtuous man dwelling in this wicked world to a lotus-flower growing out of the mud." Sir Monier Williams says that "Its constant use as an emblem seems to result from the wheel-like form of the flower,—the petals taking the place of spokes, and thus typifying the doctrine of perpetual cycles of existence." In any case, the connection between the lotus and Buddhism is very close. Buddha is figured seated on a lotus. Gold and silver paper lotuses are carried at funerals. Tombstones are often set on an inverted lotus-flower of stone as their base. Lotus-beds often surround shrines built on islets. Lotus pips and roots are used as a common article of diet.

THE BUDDHA CARVED IN LIVING STONE AT HAKONE

The revamped Shintoism was a most convenient War-cult. It centered in the divine Mikado, descended directly from the Sun Goddess. Buddhist temples were continued, however. New ones, even, were opened at various points on U. S. A.'s Pacific Coast. They were not as suspect as centers of Fifth Columnism as would have been Shinto Temples with their war cult. It is to militarism - dominated immigrants as deceitful as these that we permit dual citizenship.

CHAPTER 55

LOVE-IN-A-MIST

"Liberty, Liberty!
How many crimes
are committed in thy name."
(Madam Roland: At the Guillotine.)

THERE IS, in geogardening, something of the excitement of trailing an escaping stage robber. One cultivates a plant in his garden for a decade—enjoys cut-flowers therefrom in the home. Then, someday, comes suddenly the urge to track it down to its wildflower beginnings. The task may require all the resourcefulness of a Western sheriff in tracking a highwayman and his loot into out-of-the-way places.

Geogardening for attractive Love-in-a-mist was one such. Its skyblue color, in contrast with the compensating green of its involucre of almost needle-narrow bracts, brought its entry to the overseas list as a MUST. There were only two clues. The specific name *"damascena"* suggested the wild deserts surrounding Damascus. The other was a rather indefinite:—"Habitat: Warmer Europe." Sherlock Holmes would therefore, of course, first have eliminated the North Cape, Archangel, and the harbor of Helsinki, with its ice-breakers. Searches in Greece* then nearby Anatolia, also the Gran Leban failed to locate any wild Love-in-a-mist.

Italy, Sicily, Spain, Portugal . . . all these might have had wild Love-in-a-mist. Our Geogardener, however, found none.

Then, in following the strategy of elimination, came the concept:—why not try the limestoney semi-deserts of Southern France. After almost a dozen different years' hunt, success came. It was on the rocky, well-drained slopes of a small, walled, French hilltown. Yes,—tho Italy is Europe's hilltown area,—France still has a few. Climbing down the steep escarpment our Geogardener one day found his first "sauvage" Love-in-a-mist. . .

He was awaiting dinner at an ancient little inn—one of those surprises found occasionally in France. It sometimes happens some tiny, unpretentious restaurant in Paris or in the Provinces truthfully can boast of having once enjoyed the patronage of, say Louis XIV, or Napoleon Bonaparte. . . . So, too, in this tiny still-walled citylet there was a single inn. It too, was proud of a discriminating clientele since before the time of Marie Antoinette. It

---

*Sea beaches in the Peleponesus, however, did reward our Geogardener with wild static. There it seems to have a value as a sand-binder along with acanthus.

still served delicious meals on unchanged pewter. Its wine list was a muchly-thumbed bit of parchment. This hilltown, almost never visited by Americans, has the charm of Todi, of Perugia, of San Giminagno. On a summer evening, if rainless, one may dine beneath its "Liberty Tree." This linden was planted when the millenium had miraculously arrived with its "Libertie, Egalite, Fraternite."

Of the aims of pre-revolutionary France probably none was ravished more than that of "Egalitie." All men suddenly became "equal", whether clodhoppers with an I.Q. of 40, or savants with one of, say 150. Nowhere was this distortion more tragic than in Haiti. The net results of the spread of the French Revolution to that island were massacres of all whites." This ended in their complete extermination. The black leader tore the white section from the French tricolor. He declared "Nothing white in Haiti." The red-and-blue flag, minus the white, has remained the flag of Haiti to this day. Since the delayed end of the French Revolution era in Haiti, no white man has ever been admitted to citizenship. No Caucasian has been permitted to hold land.*

If Love-in-a-mist, carpeting the escarped sides of the feudal hilltown can, because of said Liberty Tree, awaken our nation to the menace of mis-understanding the Egalite c o n c e p t, these pages will not have been written in vain.

SABOTS ON MARKET DAY
Near where Love-in-a-mist grew wild.

France, like Italy, also distant Hindustan has Hilltowns. France's are not as numerous as Italy's. When, however, one goes a-geogardening for Love-in-a-mist, one may stumble across a French hilltown. On Market Day its pile of sabots may remind you of the jumble of ice at a retreating glacier's front. Tarry that night at the village inn, enjoy the frogs' legs. If he be in the mood, the sabot-maker can be a rare raconteur. You'll be repaid for all hours spent studying French. You'll rejoice in the by-products of Geogardening.

*U. S. A.'s negro problem today, seems almost unsolvable. In this connection, it might be illuminating to reread a remarkably well documented work: "The French Revolution in San Domingo" by Dr. T. Lothrop Stoddard. It should be remembered in this connection that our unnecessary and tragically costly Civil War was forced by a group of blundering idealists, the Abolitionists. They, blind as John Brown of Ottawassomie, tried to settle a question that was on its way to peaceful solution. Ignorantly they demanded war . . . In our own way we had the equally emotional demand "Do not fortify Guam lest it offend Japan." These unreasoning folk were silent about Japanese fortification of nearby Truk. They blocked our military experts' plan to make Guam a Pacific Gibraltar. Are they not responsible for the corpses of our Marines on the Nipponese barbedwire - entanglements on Tarawa Atoll? (Read also Dr. Stoddard's "Revolt Against Civilization.")

MAMMOTH GROTTO AT CRO-MAGNON

On a side-trip en route to CroMagnon our Geogardener finally discovered "sauvage" Love-in-a-mist. When studying overseas origins of gardening, one finds CroMagnon convenient to much Southern France material. A few days spent lunching al fresco on goosemeat sausage, haircot verts, and a morsel of pate de fois gras-served with a leaf of lettuce, of course—can well give a respite from strenuous geogardening. In CroMagnon's underground art galleries, one grasps how recent is the art of flower gardening compared with drawing, painting, even cooking.

CHAPTER 56

MAGNOLIA

"Majestic flower! How purely beautiful
Thou art, as, rising from thy bower of green
Those dark and glossy leaves so thick and full,
Thou standest like a high-born forest queen,
Among thy maidens clustering round so fair;—
I breathe the perfume, delicate and strong,
That comes like incense from thy petal-bower;
My fancy roams those southern woods along.

(Christopher Pearse Cranch—
"Poem to Magnolia Grandiflora.")

THE WEDDING DAY of a Louisiana-born bride found her parents' home decorated with magnolia blooms. Even the black walnut-staircase's balustrades were blanketed with the giant, cream-colored blossoms. She had come to California on the first train to pass over the newly-driven golden spike. . . . Strong had been the magnolia-love of the first Dixie Argonauts. Sacramento could yield, therefore, from their almost-immediate plantings above indicated wealth of magnolia flowers.

To go a geogardening for magnolia, one must journey to South of the Mason-and-Dixon Line. In bits of swamp in Alabama, Mississippi, Louisiana, one can still find remnants of primeval forest with giant magnolias. While geogardening there, do not fail to visit Natchez when its gardens are at their best. Enjoy the charming Southern hospitality. Absorb Dixie gardenlore, as a sponge absorbs water. The world nowhere has more intelligent gardener-folk than these Southern women. Eugenically, they have inherited the genes upon which are based the rare abilities that built the British Empire. Nearly all these folk are of Cavalier blood. There is, too, a dash of Huguenot. Such ancestry carries with it the peerless Gallic imagination.

Magnolia seeds were co-travellers in Covered-Wagons with locust pods. Our chapter on Locust relates how pioneer folk planted back-home trees in what today are ghost towns. Such locusts and magnolias are reminders of a great Hardwood Forest. Its locust belt stretched from Virginia's Blue Mountains to Missouri's Ozarks. Magnolias similarly stimulate memories of that warmer part of said Forest that occupied the Gulf-Coastal-Plain from moss-garlanded Tallahassee to creole New Orleans. Magnolias recall, too, the singing of mockingbirds in the moonlight. . . . The heavy scent of magnolia blossoms mingled with jassamine.

Magnolia's giant flowers, therefore, stimulate memories of the charming Southern speech heard on verandas behind white two-story colonial columns. There always is an instinctive courtesy of "quality" folks. Such courtliness was inherited from centuries of aristocratic British ancestors. Flitting along such porches are ghostly shadows of girls in hoop-skirts, of Cavalier-descended warriors in grey uniform. As noiseless as owl-flight, these steal back from Lookout Mountain, from Chancellorsville, from Appomattox Courthouse. As the soft, gentle breezes sway the great magnolia blooms, these wraiths of antebellum plantation-days seem straining to tell us something. They would warn us of any recurrence of the awful tragedy of that blundering Yankee idealism that avalanched on our nation that awful and needless Civil War.

Fanatics* like John Brown of Ottawassomie, like Harriet Beecher Stowe were responsible for thousands of lives lost in 1861-65 to "free the slaves." This was an issue that, without unreasoning interference from ignorant "reformers," could have been settled peacefully. Virginia, Massachusetts came away from Appomattox Courthouse, both bereft of their eugenically finest strains. In some Dixie counties, also some Yankee townships the leadership type is almost as extinct as is the Dodo, the Moa, the Mammoth. Of ten score Southern counties, one might exclaim with Kipling:

> "Poor beggars,
> It's blue with their bones."

In our generation, the descendants of the same unwise blunderes prevented our making Guam a Pacific Gibraltar. These seemed unconscious that, a few hours' bomber flight away, the Japanese were building the same kind of a bastion that THEY WERE OBJECTING TO OUR CONSTRUCTING. CAN ANYONE FIND A RECORD OF SHINTO PRIESTS SO CLEVERLY ORGANIZING JAPANESE PUBLIC OPINION THAT THE JAPANESE DIET WAS COMPELLED TO VOTE DOWN ANY FORTIFICATION OF TRUK, FOR FEAR OF OFFENDING U.S.A.?

*Our Geogardener was studying up-Nile palms. A cynical British statesman there told him: In order to be independent of American cotton, it seemed expedient war should be declared against the Sudanese. It was known current public opinion would not tolerate a campaign. The plotters then said: "Let's arouse the Church folk in a campaign to end the remnants of Negro slavery!" The Manchester spinners were successful. The Tommies soon met Fuzzy. "He was the only man that ever bruk a British square." Misguided churchfolk of Britain sent their sons against him. Outside Kartoom, the sands were reddened with their dying blood.

. . . ON THE CONTRARY, JAPAN'S QUARTER CENTURY'S FORTIFICATION OF THESE "MANDATED" ISLANDS BROUGHT US CORREGIDOR, BATAAN, ALSO TARAWA ATOLL. Ranking with the Pearl Harbor deceit was the use, by the Tokyo militarists, of these hoodwinked Americans, shouting so loudly "Don't fortify Guam, lest you offend Japan," that Congress yielded.

Well might Americans, paraphrasing Madam Roland at the guillotine, exclaim: "Blundering idealism! How many crimes are committed in Thy Name!" . . .

At Sucker Flat the bedrock was, in '49er's slang, "lousy with nuggets." Above the ancient river sandbars were millions of tons of pink rhyolite lava. As this was "hydraulicked" away under powerful streams from the nozzles, there were exposed strata of ancient river born clays. These, in spots, had preserved as fossils, leaves of the ancient Tertiary forest. These were markedly different from those of the woods of today. They included an avocado, a cinnamon . . . and a MAGNOLIA. Such trees indicate a more-nearly-moist, semi-tropical climate than the present one. Today has, instead, sequoias, the sugar pines, the Douglass trees of the Gold Belt. Transition Life-zone. From such fossil floras, in California, Oregon, Kansas, Pennsylvania, we know that a great forest once may have stretched from Manchuria and Siberia across Alaska and Pacific-coast Canada. It continued thru the present Rockies and Great Plains to the Atlantic seaboard. Indeed the scientific name of the California tanbark oak is perhaps the only instance of a Malay word Latinized into a genus-name.

The above might be called the Manchurian-Virginia Hardwood Forest. It has dissolved into several remnants. Our Geogardener traversed a remnant of it by dugout in Manchuria. It is the land of the wild silkworm moth. The Japanese utilized the coarse silk of their cocoons for the heavy contrast thread of pongee silk.

In U.S.A. there persisted another considerable remnant of this Manchurian-Virginian forest. Its black walnuts and oaks were girdled by the 1790's pioneers to gain a quick crop of maize. This would grow among the trees once their leaves withered. Then came Industrialism. Grand Rapids furniture saws gulped down county after county of Michigan forest. The timber-gluttons, the furniture makers sucked more and more of this hardwood until only 2 remnants persist.

The conservationists of Michigan succeeded in acquiring the Porcupine Mountain stand as a Michigan State Park. . . . On the edge of the Gulf Magnolia Belt other conservationists are battling, as this is written, to secure what the furniture saws have spared of the Tensas Swamp hardwoods. In a few isolated spots are clumps of primitive Magnolia grandiflora. Our Geogardener found one of these across the Mississippi River from the Tensas Swamp Forest. In the North Carolina highlands still grow wild other species of Magnolias. They are, however, timid, modest species of the hill-billy country. It is the giant flowered tree of the Far South that is as typical of ante-bellum days as is the goateed colonel and his mint julep. When one sees a Magnolia blooming in a garden, memories are stimulated of the fanatics of the 1850s who howled for a tragically needless Civil War.

> *"If you can keep your head,*
> *When all about you*
> *Are losing theirs*
> *And blaming it on you."*
>
>   (Kipling*)

---

* It is rather illuminating to note in our day of another kind of fanaticism that Kipling's lines above were quoted by a student in a U. S. A. Communist college. He gave them as his answer to an examination question: "What do you consider the most detestable verse ever written in the English language?"

CHAPTER 57

MANUKA

"In dark wild woods, where the lone owl broods
And the dingoes nightly yell—
Where the curlew's cry goes floating by,
We splitters of shingles dwell.
And all day through, from the time of the dew
To the hour when the mopoke calls,
Our mallets ring where the woodbirds sing
Sweet hymns by the waterfalls."

Henry C. Kendall

"Where sticks sink, and stones float," the native name for owl as above, is *"mopoke."* When seen in print there is little to suggest the hoot of any owl. But hear a Maori pronounce* that word. It is a perfect imitation of the wise old bird.

New Zealand is the native land of the manuka. It is, however, also grown generally in California. It was extensively planted when San Francisco's Golden Gate Park was won from the sand dunes. There its characteristic as New Zealand chaparral as is, in California, manzanita or ceanothus. In full bloom it is most attractive. Occasionally one finds rose-red blossoms, in lieu of the usual white.

The graduations between very-English Auckland and very-Scottish Invercargil are illustrated by a yarn Christchurch folk are fond of telling: A San Francisco woman, visiting Auckland

---

* "Mopoke" is a Maori parallel to much of our own bird-naming. As this is written under the Jeffrey pines, unseen siskins are calling "sis-kin" in the pine tops. The peewee is up there, too, flycatching between calls of pee-wee. Many of our own bird names are mimetic. Bob-White recalls this quail calling as our Geogardener was tracing the "sauvage" beginnings of certain garden plants along the old Buffalo Trail from Virginia into the Ohio Valley. At night, in this same spot, he heard the "whip-poor-will" call of that bird. In California its cousin is dubbed rightly according to its call "poor-will" . . . In the Ozarks and Ouchitas the kiddies call the ovenbird for its call note of "teech-er" the "teacher-bird." . . . The rain forest of Gippsland in Victoria, where our Geogardener saw the "nuptial dance" of the lyrebird, the "laughter" of the "laughing jackass" is much more accurately rendered into human speech by the blackfellow name "cu-ca-bur-ra." The call of the European shrike goes back to the Anglo-Saxon "scrie" which is, indeed cognate with the German schrecklich (of Nazi schrecklichkeit and think of how a grasshopper must feel when a desert shrike is impaling him on a mesquite-thorn). The shrike has at least an excuse—food hoarding . . . Our word "owl" had a similar Anglo-Saxon origin, ule, (pronounced like an owl call). The French geai, which has become our "jay," is almost the exact cry of their handsome brown, blue streaked jaybird, whether one finds him disputing the cider fruit in the apple orchards of Normandy or the dates in an Algerian oasis . . . Also mynah. Another of the jay family, the crow, has a gossiping "cr-aw" which is almost his name in English. The phoebe, as it nests on a rock in midcurrent, calls "phe-bee". One of our thrushes, the veery, similarly acquired its name as anyone can testify who has heard it calling in the Adirondacks. In Alaska, where the Thlingits use its red feathers for war-gear, our Geogardener heard a "flick-ker" note that may have given the flicker its common name on the Pacific Coast, though its Eastern yellow-feathered cousin is generally called "yellowhammer." The yellowthroat is dubbed by boys who hunt its nests in the willows; "the whitchety" bird, an exact rendition of its call note. . . . One bit of the Bullock's oriole song as can be rendered "or-re-ool."

the first time, acquired the afternoon-tea habit. Having brought her "sweet tooth" from California, she would ask for more sugar. English Auckland handed her the sugarbowl. At Wellington, half English, half Scottish, they gave her one cube of sugar. In South Island at Invercargil,—so Caledonian they allegedly buy their thermometers in summer so as to get a wee bit more mercury in the tube—her request was countered with "stir-r-r the cup!"

Manuka is but one of our garden debts to New Zealand. From thence we also obtain our New Zealand flax, our New Zealand, tree-lilies and those few we cultivate of New Zealand's many veronicas. If your geogardening stimulates your wanderlusting to that Dominion, it will open to you chests of undreamed of wealth, botanically, ornithologically, ethnologically. The unique sheep-killing, hawkbilled parrot, the kea, is but one of several score fascinating birds. The Maoris, too, ever are of absorbing interest. And botanically let there be listed these: The world's largest buttercup . . . A forgetmenot with leaves as large as a rhubarb . . .

MAORI HOUSE
Manuka was the chaparral wherein was made the clearing for this Maori structure. The houses are often elaborately carved, frequently ornamented with abalone pearl. Success of Maori racial adjustment after the whites' coming was remarkable. It is in sharp contrast with Europe's race-frictions. Continental color differences are far less than in N. Z. Instinctive Maori statesmanship may have resulted from centuries of Natural Selection. Under South Seas' pioneering, migrations probably paralleled those in U.S.A.'s generations since Jamestown and Plymouth Rock. As Americans noticed with our Northern redskins, ability in orations, diplomacy had as high a survival value as courage in conflict. The headstrong, the boastful, the obstinate tended toward elimination, extinction. He who wisely advocated adjustment, cooperation, survived to father many sons.

Tree fuchsias . . . The celery-leaved pine . . . A speedwell 40 feet high . . . Vegetable sheep . . . The world's smallest pine. (It is almost mosslike) . . . Plants of the parsley family whose leaves are like the "Spanish bayonet," or yucca, of our Southwestern deserts . . . Lilies, also daisies, growing to the height of trees . . . Mosses 2 feet high.

It will be, however, the transplanted British that will awaken your most lasting interest. There are no finer citizens anywhere.

The welcome they extended to Americans is almost embarrassing. They have inherited, too, some of the excessive modesty of the English.

The manuka produces (1) yearly its wealth of snowy flowers in the greatest abundance. (2) Their white colour renders them exceedingly conspicuous. (3) They are more or less bisexual, even on the same branch, and so depend to no small extent for pollination upon insects in search of their honey and pollen. (4) The seeds are minute, (5) produced in great profusion, (6) readily germinate, and (7) so light that they are easily blown up from the ground along with the dust. (8) Fire does not destroy to any extent the seeds not yet released. They are enclosed in their stout horny capsules. If the above facts are borne in mind, it would seem remarkable indeed if the manuka did not form a most widespread plant-association of its own. Same has been not only capable of holding its place against the attacks of man, his grazing-animals, and fires, but could increase and become extremely hard to get rid of.

MAORI HAKA

Manuka flowers whitened the chaparral around this settlement until the brush looked like Californian ceanothus in a once-in-20 years' snowstorm. Note the fine physical development of these warriors. Runts died early. Maori life has been highly selective even since the Long Ago, when their canoes ventured, Viking--like, from Samoa into the Unknown Southland. Their folklore tells of navigating by wooden pegs. These were inserted into squares of pandanus matting. Thus the nightly change of star-position was recorded. With meagre supplies of breadfruit added to fish caught from the canoes, one can imagine that only the best equipped physically, mentally survived. Eugenics works when Mother Nature need not contend with civilization's interference.

CHAPTER 58

MAPLE

THE "SWEET TOOTH" existed aeons ago. This was before men made chocolate creams, peanut brittle, the 5c candy-package that brought a fortune to its inventor. A wanderlusting Geogardener learns something eventually about this primitive human yearning for sweets, whether maple sugar or otherwise. Before cane-sugar was obtainable, our forest-dwelling Teutonic ancestors used honey. This was to such an extent that later, when towns were built, some became famous for their honey-cakes. These included Nuremberg's *lebekuchen,* also Dijon's *pain d'espice.* The latter was enjoyed more for its honey than its spices. . . .

In Saharan oases, dates filled the primitive need for sweets. . . . In Hindustan, toddy-sugar was made from the sap of the toddy palm. From this toddy sugar, fermented, came the very-alcoholic native drink called "toddy". Its name, transplanted to the Occident, gave us the expression "hot toddy." Our Geogardener's elephant used to "go on strike" at certain elephant-path stops pending his allowance of toddy-sugar cakes.

Your own garden maple may stimulate memories of maple-sugaring in Vermont. It may remind you of gorgeous Octobers in Eastern U.S.A. It may recall the singing, at a Canadian Rockies' campfire of their hymn, "The Maple Leaf Forever."

To our Geogardener came memories of wanderlustings all over Canada. These also covered journeys in northern Quebec. There men said "the next settlement has Eskimos." There one wondered what would be the future of that Dominion. Two books of yesteryear, each throw an illuminating ray into the fog-hung future. Madison Grant's "Passing of the Great Race" covered the Great Northwest, Canada's and ours of U.S.A. He felt it might become a new broodland for Nordics, as once was Scandinavia. The "Tragedy of Quebec," almost now unobtainable, records almost forgotten Anglo-Saxon data about the Lost Counties of South Quebec.

Will not future of Canada be determined largely by the workings of the Differential Birthrates Law? There are two competing groups. The cleavage between them is evident along linguistic lines. The English-speaking folk have the smallest percentages in Quebec. Theirs at present are largest from Ontario west to

British Columbia, also Nova Scotia. The French-speaking group is dominant in Quebec. In World Wars I and II the French-Canadians avoided sacrifices. They openly boasted their aim was eventually control of the Dominion by "letting the English-speaking Canadians bleed pale in Flanders and France" . . . Time Magazine (3/4 '45) carries a disturbing story about the riots at Drummondville. The very Scottish name of this factory-town spells DISPLACEMENT. The former Caledonian settlers had a comparatively low birthrate. At present this element in Quebec probably averages about the same number of children per marriage as in U.S.A., say, plus 3.

Our Geogardener, botanizing in Quebec, was pointed out one French-Canadian at the village general merchandise store. This

**JAPANESE FORESTRY OFFICER
USING HUMAN TAXICAB**

Enroute to study Japanese forest trees (maple, pine, etc.) in Korea, our Geogardener saw human taxicabs. The picture is almost allegorical. The Korean chair-coolie carries a young Japanese. When photograph was made, there still was much interlocking of U.S.A. and Korea business. The railroad from Fusan port to the capital, Seoul, was built by American engineers. It used rails from Pennsylvania, Pullmans from Illinois. Its stream of profits,—which went largely to American labor, — was diverted from U.S.A. to Japan.

habitant was whittling a stick. He was honored as the father of 24
living children. The 25th was *"en route."* French-Canadians declared a village monument ought to be erected to him. They insisted he was the personification of Habitant Fatherhood. He em-
bodied that which eventually would make the English-speaking
Canadians a hopeless minority. There were rumors of a secret
society to accelerate this end. . . .

To see maple beauty at its best, one must visit autumnal
Manchuko. Our Geogardener had been delayed in trailing wild
paeonies and other "sauvage" garden flowers. As a result his return southward from the Siberian border thru Manchuko was late.
In the higher mountains, the maples were in their full glory. The
Manchurian maple leaves are finely-divided, as in Japan. They
present therefore that pleasing, almost fern-like foliage one sees
in the Japanese maples in one's garden. When these delicately-
leaved maples don their autumnal shades, one is almost breathless.

The delay of the wild paeony expedition brought, besides the
Manchu-maple color riot, another compensation. It was in 1911.
The return to South Manchuria was too late for the masses of wild
paeonies, of Oriental poppies that summer would have flashed. Thus
came the thrill of the birth of the Chinese Republic. . . . The Manchu revolution meant despotism of centuries displaced by a republic. Thus was witnessed the overthrow of the Manchu warlords. Their rule of many decades had been most complete. The
conquered Chinese even had forgotten the queue was a badge
of servitude. Whole villages then were devoted to the manufacture
of red queue-silk. The silver-haired, aged men fought valiantly
against queue-cutting. Our Geogardener witnessed the queue-
cutting riots. University-student types, with scissors, roamed the
streets. They clipped every remaining queue. One heard the olsters
complaining they felt naked when queueless!

Thus extending up into the broodland of the Manchus, brilliant
with ample-color, swept the Revolution. Sun Yat Sin was to
become the Washington of China. It is said he drafted the coming
Chinese Republic plans, when living as an exile in Sacramento's
chinatown.

Chamberlain wrote charmingly of Maple-color Time or *Ko-
haru,* ("the Little Spring") : "This is the Japanese name for Indian
Summer. Then the oppressive heat is past. Then the sky is constantly blue, the atmosphere golden—*Ko-haru* is when the maple-
trees (to borrow a favorite expression of the Japanese poets) put
on their damask robes."

KOREAN DEFORESTRATION

The original forests of Korea, maple, walnut, camphor-laurel, ginko, pine long ago have disappeared. It was by photographs of such Far Eastern deforestration that American public opinion was consolidated behind our first National Forest laws.

Imperial Korea was poorly governed. Official corruption was widespread. The tax-gathering privilege was auctioned. An example of Korean backwardness is the deforested hill behind this poultry market. This hill once was colorful each autumn with scarlet maples. It was partly to study the world's farthest-advanced erosion that took our Geogardener to Korea. Rice fields were at starvation production because deforested hills were eroded to the bare rock.

THE MAPLE LEAF FOREVER
Popular Canadian Song

(NOTE: "God Save the King" is Canada's Anthem, except in Quebec, where "O, Canada," a French religious hymn, is substituted.)

In days of yore, from Bri-tain's shore,
Wolfe the daunt-less he-ro came,
And plant-ed firm Bri-tan-nia's flag,
On Ca-na-da's fair do-main.
Here may it wave, our boast, our pride,
And joined in love to-geth-er,
The This-tle, Sham-rock, Rose en-twine
The Ma-ple Leaf for ev-er!

The Ma-ple Leaf, our em-blem dear,
The Ma-ple Leaf for ev-er!
God save our King, and Hea-ven bless
The Ma-ple Leaf for ev-er!

**WHOLESALE HANGINGS MARKED JAPANESE ATTEMPTS AT MASS
EXTERMINATION OF KOREANS**

Autumnal maple color deepens as one proceeds from Japan northwestward
in Korea. One's enjoyment thereof was, however, lessened by the cruelty of
Japan's warlords. Their strategy of extermination included systematic execu-
tions. Even teaching children Korean fairytales brought hanging. One honors
U. S. A.'s loyal Japanese. One dares wonder, however, after having witnessed
the ruthlessness that followed Japan's violation of Korea: How many of our
nativeborn *keibei* are loyal? These *keibei* were sent to Japan to be educated.
Thru childhood, adolescence, they were taught loyalty to the Mikado. A large
proportion of them did not forswear allegiance required under Japan's dual
citizenship law to their overseas Emperor. . . Let us not forget our own deluded
who persisted in: "Do not fortify Guam, lest we offend Japan." These blunder-
ers ignored Japan's having made Truk, near Guam, a Pacific Gibraltar. Truk
did not fall until about Atomic Bomb Day. This group of our citizens, Caucasian by birth, also always have demanded, as another appeasement, an Immigration Quota for Japan. Current history has few examples of such insolence
as the interference by Japan in this, a purely domestic matter of ours. Japan
conducted propaganda in U.S.A. for weakening the Johnson Immigration
Quota Acts of 1921-2-4, America's "Second Declaration of Independence." Such
propaganda was gulped down by Americans as to Guam and to Truk, as to our
immigration control. If there is one lesson Korea's maples of the early 1900s
tell, it is: "Beware Nipponese Neo-Shintoists."

ELEPHANT COACH

Marigolds, the big "African" kind, to the Hindu, are what heather is to the Scot, Christmas holly to the English, shamrock to the Irish. This Rewa elephant coach contained a score of wives, concubines of a certain Rajah. Elephant trappings are embroidered in seed-pearls. A Rajah's power is estimated by the number of his elephants. A Rajah's guest may be given free use of an elephant. Tips (T.I.P.S.: "To Insure Prompt Service") sometimes are more than cost of a hired elephant, if obtainable.

CHAPTER 59
MARIGOLD

Flowers have an expression of countenance as much as men or animals. Some seem to smile; some have a sad expression; some are pensive and different; others again are plain, honest and upright, like the broadfaced SUN-FLOWER and the hollyhock.

(Henry Ward Beecher—"Discourse of Flowers")

MARIGOLDS, "African" marigolds, cousins to Dr. Beecher's honest, upright, broadfaced sunflower, ornamented the Sacred Bull. They were strung, lei-like, into his necklace. He walked leisurely thru Benares' Bazaar. He munched lettuce here, carrots there. He evidently found satisfaction in poking his blunt, slobbering muzzle into a container of the lentil-like legume the Hindus call *dahl.* In that city of fanaticism, stall-owners dared not even rap the brute's nose. Too many of The Faithful were watching.

Beyond was the Street-of-the-Flower-vendors. Here, for a few copper *pice,* those whose homes were disease-stricken, came. They bought small bunches of, again, golden "African" marigolds. They were to be dropped down the stinking Holy Well. This was sacred to the one-eyed Goddess-of-Hate, Kali. Such an offering usually was followed by a pitiful gift of some miserably-small coins. These, untied from a ragged kerchief, went to a fat, oily, squatting, half-naked *fakir.** Both sacrifices were supposed to placate the dread Goddess who personified Hatred. She it was who sent disease to destroy those who had neglected her worship.

"On the Stock Exchanges, yours in New York, ours in London, the value of shares fluctuates according to the varying income of the years." The speaker was our Geogardener's host in Benares. He continued: "If you want to see ecclesiasticism at its worst, study Hindu-priest exploitation of Indian's illiterate poor." During years of epidemics, shrine income soars. The *babu* with his veneer of Occidental education, gambles in temple shares. Even the Mohammedan, who snarls "Dog of Unbeliever" at the Hindu, finds the profit-motive tempting. He will venture to speculate in the securities of some Hindu temple. This, tho he would be horrified at any suggestion of his worshipping there, in lieu of his mosque.

Gather "African" marigolds in your garden. Then may they

---

* Note that our words "faker" and "fake" root into the Hindu language.

be symbols of better cooperation with your Anglo-Saxon brethren in India. The latter struggle, decade after decade, to spread knowledge of modern medical science. They leave to fight superstitions of the ignorant and their exploiters, a swarm of crafty rascals.

> *"Where some dusky heathen smothers us with MARI-GOLDS in lieu of English grass."*
> (Kipling: "The Undertaker's Horse") *
>
> *"This place smelt MARIGOLD FLOWERS and bad water, and wanst somethin' alive came and blew heavy at the chink on the shutter."*

Kipling makes Krishna Mulvaney thus describe his involuntary pilgrimage to the Temple of Prithi-Devi. He describes incidently the casting of Marigold flowers into the Sacred Well at Benares.

* Why not reread Kipling? Dare we suggest: (a) Wee Willie Winkie, (b) By Word of Mouth, (c) The Head of the District, (d) Wressley of the Foreign Office, (e) "If", (f) Kipling's masterpiece, his novel "Kim."—Also, "A Temple of Hate" by the author.

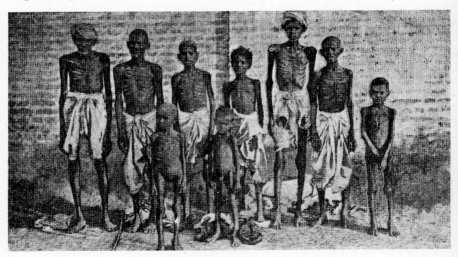

FAMINE VICTIMS IN HINDUSTAN

Marigolds are bought even more heavily when Famine stalks. "Kali, one-eyed Goddess of Hate, sent the food shortage because she felt neglected." Goats for her sacrifice no longer are available. Marigolds, however, always can be had. Blessed by mercenary fakirs, a wreath may soften Kalis' baneful gaze. For centuries, until the British came, famines annually killed millions. Now some progress is being made. Railroads make food transport possible. Hindustan's indebtedness is not so much to all Britain as to its small leadership group. These mostly are Oxford, Cambridge graduates. That famines have come over some two thousand years, the Famine Budda in Lahore Museum shows with protruding ribs like our cuts. This sculpture dates back to Alexander the Great.

BURNING GHAT OF BENARES

Millions of marigolds annually are sold in the flowerstalls uphill from Benares' ghats. Every devout Hindu hopes to die on Mother Gunga's banks. The family often is too poor to buy fuel to fully consume the body. Then the only-partially-charred remains are committed to Ganges' sacred waters. . . . Our Geogardener saw 1,000,000 pilgrims congregated at one time on Ganges' banks. Its water reeked with disease-causing bacteria. Pilgrims to the Holy River habitually return with bottles of the supposedly-Divine water. They drop small portions of this polluted water in, say, 20 wells surrounding their native village. Thus to use Buddhist term, they "acquire merit." In this way there is laid the foundation for tragic outbreaks of cholera, amoebic dysentery, intermittent fevers. Epidemics thus started have spread to Europe; to U. S. A. The Covered Wagon cholera epidemic originated thusly. Against such marrow-deep superstitions, biologists, medical men from Edinburgh, Cambridge universities struggle.

BATIK-MAKERS, JAVA

The true morningglories are natives of the tropics, both Asiatic and American. Our Java photograph below illustrates the kind of terrain in which our Geogardener found his Asiatic wild morningglories . . . The batik-makers in a village en route used two colors of native dyes—brown and blue. One had tucked, a tiny wild blue morningglory in his turban. He indicated in the sign language. "Same color."

MORNING IN JAVA

CHAPTER 60
MORNINGGLORY

IT WOULD BE INTERESTING to know who christened these characteristically funnelform flowers: "morning-glory" also to know when it was named. The expression smacks of early England. The brightly colored species of our gardens, however, are from warmer lands. The big magentas, the royal-purples, the sky-blues are not Northern. The common European sort that mediaeval kiddies, with their facile imaginations, must have known was the bindweed.

Some of the most charming of the tropical morningglories are, however, as small as bindweed . . . California has native two good-sized flowers. Puerto Rico has pretty little sky blue morningglories which the children call "*Ojitos azules*" or "little blue eyes." Most of the family are climbers. Hence arose use for cordage by natives who had no better fibers.

A cousin to our morningglory is the bright-yellow Tevoli vine of tropical gardens. The vine of another species, native to Central America, is used by the fishermen there to thread their fish. The moonflower is mentioned by la Senorita in the Pulque Song.

Along Central America's Mosquito coast the kiddies have a folkname for the tiny morningglories as charming as ours. It is "*campanilla*" or tiny bell." One of the type genus Ipomoea is Caribbean. Its Carib name was "*batata*." Our word "*potato*" is derived from this. Said wild sweet potato of Cuba is not the true potato of the Peruvian highland. Latter belongs to the Solanaceae. 'Tis interesting to note the names of the potato in other languages. Dutch call it *aardapfel*, like the French *pomme de terre*. In Spanish it is *patato*, Italian, *patate*. In Norwegian-Danish they are called *patater*, also *kartofler*. In Swedish, it is *potater*. In German it is *Karkoffel*, basis of *Karkoffelsalad*, *Kartoffelpfannenkuchen*.

An interesting cousin to the morning glory is dodder. It is a leafless parasite. It appears as stringy yellow masses in alfalfa fields, also in salt marshes. It is so efficiently parasitic that, once it is attached to its host plant, its root dies. Why not sluff off what no longer is useful? It is as ruthless as the strangler fig of Florida south to the Orinoco. There also is a giant dodder in Afganistan that lives on trees. It is said it actually preys upon itself as well as its host.

In one far corner of Geogardener's flowerbeds, was planted

some giant azure morningglories. They made a pleasing contrast with the green of the pinkflowered escallonias behind them. It was a bit of blue that would have pleased Murillio. . . During our Geogardener's vacation, the Sicilian gardener, Guiseppe, decided to inject a sowing of the vulgar, scrubby magenta variety. Next year there was a discordant color-clash of two-thirds azure, one-third magenta. In 4 years, the tough magentas had displaced the lovely azures. Our Geogardener used to insist that some day the children, who later would become the lawmakers, would learn by such gardening the working of the Differential Birth Rates Law.

CHAPTER 61

MYRTLE

"The MYRTLE now idly entwin'd with his crown
Like the wreath of Harmodius, should cover his sword."
(Moore—"O! Blame Not the Bard").

IN NORWAY, our Geogardener was tracking down the *sauvage* origins of certain herbaceous garden flowers. These included the violas, the garnet-colored scabiosas, the so-called "Iceland" poppies. He also was similarly sleuthing certain evergreens. On one of these trips he was surprised, while using the facilities of Bergen* Museum, to see therein a myrtle wreath. . . .

This Bergen wreath was of myrtle leaves, as at the ancient Greek contests. Said leaves, however, were of solid gold. Skillfully-matched pearls formed its blossoms. It had been forwarded to Ole Bull after his remarkable performance in pioneer San Francisco Opera House. This was when one, two, three strings of his violin snapped. The virtuoso, however, continued the performance on the remaining fourth. A Bergen letter, sent home, after the museum visits, brought this reply from Geogardener's parents: "Didn't you know we contributed toward buying that myrtle wreath?"

The myrtle crown was awarded the winner of certain Greek games. It ranked, as crown-material, with the laurel at the Pythian Games, the wild olive at the Olympian Games, the wild celery at the Nemean Games. Moore sings of the charming arrangement of the pearl-like myrtle flowers among their green leaves:

"The wreaths of brightest MYRTLE wove
With sunlit drops of bliss among it."

The myrtle, however, is, of course, not a Norwegian, but a Mediterranean-Basin plant. It probably would not have its delightful odor were it not a member of a flora adjusted to semi-desert conditions. 'Tis wonderful how adversity, in plant or in human, tends to bring out sweetness.

The Anatolian myrtle-chaparral stimulates, in our Geogardener, fond memories of the Near East. He there was tracking, to their origins, certain of his garden's bulb-bearing species: nar-

---

* Bergen is where 'tis said it rains every hour of every day, and where the inhabitants used to beg the stranger not to venture out without an umbrella, because an umbrellaless man caused horses to run away.

cissus, ranunculus, anemone, cyclamen, tulip. One day he was on a coasting vessel from Beirut to Symrna. He then found, from home-accumulated notes, that the freighter's given loading time might permit a short inland excursion to the site of Biblical Antioch. It was late winter. The wind off the Steppes to the North froze one to the marrow. Every few miles one arrived at another Turkish police station. This meant unbuttoning the heavy mountain overcoat, thus letting in more cold, to get out the precious passport. Then our Geogardener discovered, in the overcoat pocket, an old menu card. It had crossed Turkish and British flags. He offered this as passport. None of the police could read. There was a few moments discussion at the first station. Then they struck their rubber stamp over "Soup d'Ognion" on the card. They then waved an "O.K." Thereafter followed a succession of police stamps. When the journey to Antioch was ended—much of it over hills covered with myrtle chaparral—that menu card was utterly covered with visa stamps of the illiterate Turkish police.

What impressed our Geogardener most deeply on this Antioch excursion was, not the stretches of myrtle-scrub,—not myrtle's aromatic oil, sweetening the camel-stink, not the wealth of bulb-plants of both the Ranunculaceae and the Liliaceae . . . but the destruction of Antioch's ancient glory thru malaria. . . .

The study of garden insects, including those responsible for insect-borne diseases, is fascinating. Our Geogardener utilized a section of his toolhouse to raise insects. Butterfly and moth cocoons sometimes produced in lieu of their normal lepidoptera, fascinating, parasitic diptera. A gardener really cannot gain all obtainable joys of gardening unless he, like Fabre, studies his garden's birds, its snakes and frogs, its insects, even its spiders. Even the Prophet Cemos used the grasshoppers as an example. Any contribution to mankind's knowledge-heap, however small, is worthwhile. Hence, as our Geogardener crossed those dreary marshes between the Coast and the site of Antioch, he could not help contrasting the miserable inhabitants with even the Negro laborers at Panama. The latter, drawn from places like Honduras' Mosquito Coast, are loud in their praises of U. S. Army's mosquito control . . . Meantime, over in the Near-East there are great stretches, once with the world's then highest civilization, now abandoned to the bloodsucking Anopheles.

> *"To leafless shrubs the flowering palm succeed,*
> *And odorous MYRTLE to the noisesome weed."*
> (Pope: Messiah)

CHAPTER 62

NARCISSUS

*"The sweet narcissus closed
Its eye, with passion pressed."*

(Hafiz)

BEFORE ARRIVING at the Sand-dunes of the Sahara, one must cross the rock desert of the Southern Atlas. This bleak territory is inhabited by Bedouin nomads. These travel with their flocks from sparse pasture to sparse pasture. Their tents are often of camel's-hair wool. In addition to pasture grasses, one finds in this forbidding land an unusual flora. It fascinated our Geogardener because of the adjustment of its species to high summer temperatures, with simultaneous drought.

ARABS IN NARCISSUS LAND

In Algeria our Geogardener was hunting for (and found) wild poet's narcissus. Where the rock desert (habitat of narcissus) borders the sand desert, he kodaked this group of Arab gamblers. Like the narcissus (with its bulb-storage mechanism), these Arabs are nicely adjusted to desert conditions. Note how head and neck are protected from blistering sun-rays. One finds almost no "fallen arches" here. Their feet are as efficient as a camel's foot pads . . . The poet's narcissus of our garden is almost identical with sauvage specimens. . . Plant breeders have not changed its stock though they have produced pleasing "Poetaz" hybrids (Poeticus x tazetta).

Into such semi-deserts as these, the lilies have successfully radiated the world over, because of their bulbs.* These are highly-efficient, underground-storage plants. Here their food-materials are as secure as were the Nazi submarine nests at San Nazaire because of thick, reinforced-concrete coverings. Many lilies rush thru their bloom plus reproduction in the short winter rains. Then during the intense midsummer heat, it matters not that foliage withers and dies. Below the sun-parched soil-surface is everything necessary for next year's growth. Then, too, many liliales reproduce by bulblets, that split off (again underground, of course), from the main bulb.

The narcissus element of the African rock desert flora parallels that of the tulip in Anatolia and Persia. When, next Spring, you enjoy the red-margined cup of poet's narcissus, why not imagine you are travelling to where the Bedouins couch in the sandstorm's blast?

---

* So efficient is this mode of carrying on that, on one of our Geogardener's California ranches, a furrow plowed in the uplands will sometimes slice so many liliaceous bulbs—such as brodiaeas, calachortus, and soaproot—that they are proportionately as numerous as the raisins in an English teacake.

NARCISSUS (Trumpet)

"*Daffodils,
That come before the swallow dares
And takes the winds of March with beauty.*"
(Shakespeare: Winter's Tale.)

"*A host of golden daffodils
Dancing in the breeze.*" (Wordsworth: "The Daffodils")

"*O fateful flower beside the rill—
The daffodil, the daffodil!*" (Jean Ingelow—Persephone. St. 16)

THE GOLDEN-TRUMPET NARCISSUS, in our garden, stimulates memories of a happy early-spring in France's Auvergne. There one, from a vantage point, could see at one time millions of wild blooms. The Auvergne was the land of Caesar's Arverni. At its northern end is Gergovia. The American in France could do worse than desert Paris for the thrill of Gergovia, . . . of reading—on the plateau where that battle was fought—his Caesar's Commentaries.

Golden-trumpet Narcissi are not as numerous around Gergovia as they were when brave Arverni were decimated by Julius Caesar. . . . Later, liquidation of the brave was extended by the avaricious clergy who made Louis the Fat their puppet. At nearby Claremont, Peter the Hermit began his First crusade sermons. From Claremont Cathedral's tower these golden lilies can be seen carpeting the rolling North Auvergne hills. Thru all these twenty centuries, Vercingetorix never has been forgotten. The wild narcissi also never have disappeared in all that time. The golden trumpet, also Vercingetorix, both continue to be the very personification of Gallic freedom.

The springtime visitor may not find the steeply escarped basalt of Gergovia plateau as golden with narcissi today as when in 53 B. C. Caesar met his first reverse in Gaul. If so, then let him wander deeper over the real Auvergne massif.

Jean Duval, village sabotmaker, was a heretic. Among his tools afront him was a well-thumbed Voltaire! He did not stop shaping the wooden block that was soon to be footgear. Drawknife and tongue moved in unison. He gossiped about the village cure. The latter had posted a notice forbidding certain reading. Therein French translations of "Buffalo Bill" were denounced as "corrupting youthful morals."

Jean lived in, loved the Auvergne. This is the land made

AUVERGNE VILLAGE, IN NARCISSUS LAND

ARCADED STREET, MONTAUBAYI

immemorial by Robert Louis, the well-beloved, in his "Travels With a Donkey." Our Geogardener left Jean and his stack of sabots to motor across the high limestone semi-deserts of the Auvergne.

Here our Geogardener was again to learn about bulb-value as a survival factor. With ample bulb storage of food elements thru summer months, the narcissus manages to persist. This is despite high temperatures, despite a leakage-drainage limestone formation. Narcissus has a high birthrate due to bulblet reproduction. There had come, therefore, a narcissus-population that probably had long ago reached the saturation point. The Auvergne Massif, therefore, is enamelled with daffodils.

It will be remembered that Narcissus was a beautiful young Greek. The nymph Echo loved him but he repulsed her. As punishment, he fell in love with his own image, reflected in a fountain. This unattainable, he pined, died. When the Naiads came to bury him they found only the golden flower.

"*Daffy-down-dilly came up in the cold*
Through the brown mold.
Altho the March breezes blew keen on her face."
(Miss Warner: Daffy-down-dilly.)

"*Better, no doubt, is a dinner of HERBS,*
When seasoned by love, which no rancor disturbs,
And sweetened by all that is sweetest in life
Than turbot, bisque, ortolans, eaten in strife."

(Meredith: Lucile)

ALBI'S CATHEDRAL, IN NARCISSUS LAND

BEZIERS, WHERE MILLIONS OF TRUMPET NARCISSUS BLOOM

BIBLE STORIES PICTURED IN STONE, NARCISSUS LAND

At quaint Besse-en-Chaundesse in Narcissus Land, a festival was being held next the church. Bagpipers played the old Auvergne songs. There was folk-dancing in the ancient peasant costumes. If one tired of the piper's music, the capitals in its church of the 1200s were ever fascinating. When one goes a geogardening, the by-products are worth while.

CHAPTER 63

NASTURTIUM

"She had composed . . . an incomparable elixir by
mixing five or six kinds of SIMPLES, which we used to—
gather on the Alpilles—With the help of Saint Augustine,
I might recover the composition—Then—put it in bottles.
This would allow the community to grow rich quietly."
(Daudet's "The Elixir")

TROPAEOLUMS were found growing "sauvage" by our Geogardener in Peru. Leaves and pods thereof had been called by yesteryear's housewives: "Indian cress." They were used as "herbs" by the Incas, probably even by the Pre-Incas. Different species of this genus grow along the Cordilleran chain from Mexico to Chile. A near relative of nasturtium is oxalis. This family includes (a) the carpet-plants of the California redwoods, (b) the edible sorrels of the Californian High Sierras, (c) the European sorrels, basis of France's *"potage sante."*

The name "nasturtium" is said to come from Latin *nasus,* (nose) and *torquere, tortum,* (twisted). Thus it is supposed to picture the wry face caused by its pungent taste. The name, however, originally was given to certain European crucifers. These included horseradish, also watercress. Later this cress-name was transferred to "Indian cress," the Western Hemisphere plant which our gardens now know as "nasturtium" . . .

Our Geogardener and his friend, the Professor, were at luncheon one Monday. They had an *omelette des fines herbes,* fluffy as only the French can make them. "Can one find one of the old peasant women skilled in herb doctoring?" The Professor, after a moment's pause, countered with: "Can you paint signs?"

"Yes,"—"Ah, then we will go to the *magazin* at the corner, buy brushes and a couple of small cans of paint. You shall earn your knowledge" . . . The village to which they motored that weekend was 20 minutes off the trunk highway. With a good glass one could see from the ridge above the village the very tips of Notre Dame's towers. The village never had known a doctor. Madam Touslemonde, as midwife, had brought its children into the world. The tiny proprietors of the neighborhood each had his plot of tax-free tobacco plants. Government required a sign with owner's name and the hectorage.

"These signs each cost 10 francs (then about 70 cents). Mon-day night I wrote," said the Professor, "I would arrive next Satur-day morning with a friend, a sign-painter, and who was a little de-ranged about studying weeds." He continued: "There is nothing these peasants will not do to save a franc. You can prolong paint-ing tobacco signs at your will. Meantime you can probe for herb-lore. They all are well informed about herbs, from Jacques Archi-bault, the cressonaire, to old Madam Touslemonde herself."

It proved the cressonaire had contracts with several swanky restaurants and hotels in Paris for his watercress. His wells were noted for the purity of their water. He had a small fortune in-vested in the Funds, based on his cress-crops. It was Madam Touslemonde, however, who proved an encyclopoedia of informa-tion: a worthy successor to Daude's Aunt Begon.

> *"Aunt Begon knew more about the HERBS of our mountains than . . . yes, more than an old Corsican black-bird."*

(Daudet's "The Elixir")

> *"He held a basket full*
> *Of all sweet HERBS that searching eye could call,*
> *Wild Thyme . . . and cresses from the rill.*

(Keats' "Endymion")

"IT PAYS TO ADVERTISE"

Comparative sizes of Rayflower and Disk Flower of the Desert Sunflower, sketched from San Bernardino County, California, specimen.

Mother Nature concentrates on publicity to attract pollenizing bees. Thus, the Rayflower, mathematically, is colossal compared with the tiny diskflower or seed-making flower. "It pays to advertise" i. e., invest in public education.

CHAPTER 64
NEW ZEALAND FLAX

"The glint of the sun
On our flax
Is the same
As the sheen of that sun
On Auckland Water."
(Old Maori folk-saying.)

SOME 19TH CENTURY WRITERS, certainly nearer the redskin than we of today, assert our Amerinds* took no enjoyment in sunset color. The Maori saying above, nevertheless, discloses enjoyment of sunlight-sheen on both water and foliage. . . . This New Zealand flax is one of the plants as peculiar to Maori Land as is the celery-leaved pine, the giant forgetmenot, the vegetable sheep.

Our Geogardener found wild New Zealand flax growing vigorously on the road between Napier and Rotarua. The flax then was in full bloom with tall spikes of mahogany-colored flowers. It seemed to thrive luxuriously up to the edge of the pumice semi-desert. Mottled conifer forest is common in the California Sierras. Chaparral spots the pines where moisture supply is irregular. So, too, in New Zealand, areas of flax alternate with forest. New Zealand belongs to the Wild-pigeon Province, just as our West is dubbed by some botanists, the Lupine Province. The pigeons arrive in huge flocks to feed on the berries of a tree somewhat resembling our California junipers. As the wild pigeons arrive they commence gorging on the fruits. After a fortnight, they have put on fat as do corn-fed hogs. The diet makes them uncommon' thirsty. Of this, the Maoris took advantage. They would place pigeon troughs below the trees. For several days, these freely would supply water. To these the pigeons become accustomed. Snares then would be cunningly placed around the water so as to trap the thirsty pigeons. The catch often would be so great, the Maoris would "lard down" pigeon-meat in pigeon-fat for winter use. This technique parallels that of our Covered Wagon folk. Our Geogardener has eaten pork chops cooked a year after they similarly had been "larded down" in their own fat.

A curious New Zealand plant, never introduced into Northern Hemisphere gardens, is "vegetable sheep." The plants, on a dis-

---

* American-Indian.

tant hillside, look like a flock of sheep. When one has a vegetable
sheep at his feet, one has the impression of a colossal puff ball. A
section thereof, in one's hand, proves to be a colony of tiny, daisy-
like composites. These are crammed together like the cells of a
honeycomb. Each is an individual plant about an inch long. If
the "sheep" is two feet high, it may represent 24 generations of
"daisies." These are superimposed on each other. For years the
underneath plants have formed a spongy mass. This moisture-
reservoir is as efficient as our cacti* in an environment of dessicating winds, porous soil, irregular rainfall. This spongy accumulation of past years harbors a parasite. It is a fatty white grub,
about the size of a child's thumb. It is not unlike similar grubs
California trout fishermen used to extract from fallen timber.

KEA, OR SHEEP-KILLING PARROT, NEW ZEALAND

Of these larvae, the kea, or sheep-killing parrot is inordinately fond. Most parrots have bills adjusted to fruit-food, such as
bananas. The kea bill, however, is hawk-like. It is evolved to tear
the woody "vegetable sheep" for this fat grub. . . . Keas undoubtedly had feasted on vegetable-sheep worms for centuries. Then arrived sheep-breeding Scots. If a lamb died, its pelt would be hung,
fleece underneath, on a back-block barbed-wire fence. In skinning,
the fat near the kidneys often adhered. This fact the parrots discovered. Soon they were alighting on the backs of live lambs.
With their powerfully hooked beaks, they would tear open the
lambkins for kidney fat. Followed, naturally, a sheepman's war,
with consequent near-extermination.

To find *keas*, our Geogardener had to go into South Island's
mountain fastnesses. There a Maori called them *"Kea-a, Kea-a!"*
They came to a saucer of melted butter beside a lighted candle. . . .

---
* See chapter of cactus re. water storage.

The roof of the Alpine hut where our Geogardener slept was of corrugated iron. Next dawn, several *keas* amused themselves sliding, again and again, down the roof. Apparently they enjoyed the scraping of their claws against the iron.

The thrifty Scots who brought sheep-raising from their Highlands to New Zealand are the backbone of that Dominion. Their adjustment, over centuries, to the Caledonian environment, has fitted them for successful living in, particularly, South Island. Illustration of this is in a tale told our Geogardener by a MacDonald of Invercargill. The two were climbing Mt. Cook together. This hairy-chested, red-polled MacDougall boasted he was "born with his red flannel shirt already on." He unbuttoned his shirt collar as evidence. Of a neighbor, one MacDougall, he yarned thusly: "In the wee sma' hours of the night, MacDougall rang the Invercargill chemist's bell. Down the tube came a sleepy: "What's wanted?" "A pennyworth of bicarbonate of soda for Mrs. MacDougall's indigestion." "2 a.m., for a penny sale? Why, man, a cup of hot water would have sufficed." "Oh, thanks," answered MacDougall, "Now don't bother dressing and coming down!"

However much we joke about such caution in spending, an American travelling man said his New Zealand corporation's sales were the highest per capita of their worldwide business. Our Geogardener found these Southern-Hemisphere Scots,—tho carefully

TATTOOED MAORI WOMEN
Some exhibit high intelligence in utilization of fauna, flora of their environment. The leadership type multiplied, the weaklings were bred out.

thrifty—generous, hospitable. . . . They are, too, most canny gardeners. A certain community botanical garden, wisely located on a South Island moraine, specializes in veronicas. It ranks, in planning of vision with the Alpine Botanical Garden on Lake Geneva.

New Zealand flax is, along with agave, a favorite on the many larger gardens in California. Like agave, it needs space. Like it, pleasing results are obtained when garden-owners strive for exotic effects.

ELABORATE MAORI WOODCARVING

Even wild pigeon drinking troughs were thus carved. These were used in snaring wild pigeons after gorging on ripe berry-like "cones" of New Zealand conifers. New Zealand has even a "celery-leaf" pine, in lieu of our pine needles.

CHAPTER 65

OLEANDER

A N OCCASIONAL OLEANDER in bloom peeps over a wall as one strolls along a street in Fez, in Damascus, or in Peshawar. One knows, too, that at a hundred latticed windows in second stories above, black eyes are watching. The atmosphere of Arabian Nights is ever present. There seemed to be a passing gust of breeze. Was it, however, really a flitting ghost? Was it Ali Baba's? Was it Harun al Rashid's? What one took for a great fleecy, drifting, sunset-tinted cloud, was it really the Magic Carpet? On it, was there riding the shade of Fatima? Or of Suleyman the Mignificent. The little clouds near it . . . were they wraiths of Janisaries, Christian-born, captured in boyhood, trained in Mohammedanism for the Sultan's bodyguard? That spinning dust-devil, was it a tenuous Whirling Dervish? You must remember you ARE under the Crescent Flag. The lure of the Desert IS around you. Sunlight is blindingly brilliant in Oleander Land. One winks, and blinks. In the warm breeze, 'tis easy to drop into Dreamland. . . .

Oleander's blooms in your garden, therefore, should recall Islam. They should stimulate further a-wanderlusting to the Oh-so-different Belt. This ranges from Morocco to Malaysia, from Tunisia to Hyderabad, from the three Somalilands to Persia, then East to the Mohammedan Philippines.

Moisture-loving oleander takes the place, in the North African flora, of the water-cherishing willows of more northern climes. Many a "gorge," to use the French word, debouches out of the hill-desert. From same, there trickles streamlets, soon to be lost in the tawny sands below. These gorges are lined, on either side, with, not willows, but oleanders. It was as his camel came toward the sand-desert, descending such a canyon, that our Geogardener found his first "sauvage" oleanders.

Said camel, leaving the oleander-ornamented gorge, proceeded over sand-dunes to an oasis. Here was his caravan-serai. Its court reeked with camel-stench. It was crowded with gesticulating camel owners. In one corner was the inevitable coffee shop. Checker-players gambled there. Outside, little girls played "jacks" with date stones, that fell "ridged" or smooth. Mercenary *Ouled Naails* eyed the incoming caravan. They estimated their "pluckings," whose goatskins of dates were being exchanged for silver. Much of that metal was to be added, eventually, to the ornaments of these allegedly-beautiful sirens.

Our Geogardener never can forget these, his first *sauvage* oleanders. He was coming out of the rock-desert range. It was an outrider of the range to which, 'tis said, had come the Roman General, Strabo. He had looked down on the oases-mottled sand desert. He then had exclaimed, of the dark green blotches in contrast with the tawny-golden desert's sand-expanse: "Spotted like a leopard's hide." On the margin between the rock-desert and the sand desert, our Geogardener tarried. There he first met, at a French Army post, that brilliant Gallic administrator, the beloved Marshal le Autay.

From this outlook vantage of Strabo, the camel-trail streaked down thru a gorge. It contained a typical tiny stream. It is such streams, deep below the sands, that, yonder, furnish the water for wells. These are the basis of oasis life. They irrigate the gardens of dates. An Arab proverb describes date palms as "Feet in the water. Head in the sun!" The entire course of this streamlet was a sinuous line of oleanders, their roots, too, in the damp, their massed blooms in the desert sunlight above.

Because of its heavy and long-continued bloom, oleander has been suggested for roadside forestry effects in semi-tropic areas like California. The single pink variety has an especially pleasing color. Avenues planted solidly to oleanders, especially beside ditches of running water, would thrive in what resembles their native environment. Effects could be obtained thusly with oleanders that would rival the world-renowned flowering cherries at Tokio. . . . Here is something worth the attention of city planners, of profit-eager Chambers of Commerce.

Double oleanders often are seedless. Single garden varieties, like the wild bushes, have a noteworthy mechanism for wanderlusting. These fuzzy, tawny seeds are evolved to utilize the hard piercingly-cold winds of the Saharan winter. The water-canalling gorges act as natural draws for air currents. Thus the food-need that underlies all migration, human or oleander, is solved by wind-transportation to terrain distant from the parent plants.

There are 2 colors of the true oleander. Both are of the same species, *Nerium oleander*. It is cousin to the blue periwinkle, a ground-cover plant native to Europe. Other genera of the Apocynaceae or Dogbane family are (a) Allamanda, found from Guatemala south. Its flowers when first found make one wonder:

"Whence a yellow oleander?" (b) Frangipanni* of the tropics, with its heavy fragrance. . . . In California's Sierras are found plants of the type-genus Apocynum. Common names thereof are "Indian hemp," also "dogbane." These, too, like oleander, have a milky sap. Dr. Hall reminds us the Pah-utes used its fiber for fishline twine, also small baskets.

> * *"Then comes the wish to*
> *Es-cape from pris-on*
> *A wish grown deep-er*
> *When full moon shines,*
> *And o-dors heav-y*
> *Of FRAN-GI-PAN-NI*
> *Blend with the scent from*
> *Moonflower vines."*
> (Mexican Pulque Song. See Chapter on Agave.)

CAMEL CARAVAN

The oleander is willow-like as to thirst. To the right, a little above the camel colt, can be seen the shadow of an attempt at the nearer of two retaining walls. The **"wadi"**, or arroyo is, at times, pipe for those rare but copious desert cloudbursts. Beyond the left, this wadi was lined, both sides, with blooming oleanders. Despite drought, also heat, the desert's biota, from Bedouin and camels to oleanders and date palms, succeed in reproducing. Only among our Occidental highpowers is the natural birthrate excessively reversed.

CHAPTER 66

PAEONY

"At the roots of paeony,
Bushels lay, in rose-red heaps,
Or snowy, fallen bloom."

(Jean Ingelow.)

THE PATIENCE of Chinese workers-in-jade, as to delicate details, equals that of their countrymen who train young hawks for falcony. Our Geogardener's wanderlustings in China gave opportunity to see the jade carvers at work. There were, too, occasional glimpses of the output of the devoted old masters. Of all these, the memory he most prized was of a natural-sized paeony. It was in white jade. So exquisitely, so cautiously had it been cut, one might, at some distance, have mistaken it for a recently-plucked bloom.

Fashions in flowers proceed in waves as regularly as in gowns, in hair-dos, in perfumes, in millinery. Our grandmothers delighted in their "piney" gardens. To these we today are reverting.

One never-to-be-forgotten plantation of colorful paeonies was in a rural Vermont cemetery. One headstone therein told of death in battle during the French-and-Indian war. This was the conflict that fixed English dominance in North America.* The next generation, according to a paeony-decorated grave, yielded a sacrifice when Burgoyne was decisively defeated near Saratoga. Here was forever settled the schism between Britain and the 13 colonies. By 1812, a grandson of the 1755 soldier fell about the time the Star Spangled Banner was written. Then a great-grandson's blood crimsoned the sands beside a Mexican maguey on the Buena Vista plain, when General Zachary Taylor bested Santa Anna. Next came the needless Civil War. At its close a great-great-grandson watched his lifeblood color a blue uniform. He had struggled with the men under the Stars and Bars of General Robert E. Lee. Each generation seemed doomed to lose a man in

---

* A sage once said: "When a nation commences to forget its history, decadence has begun." Perhaps these Vermont paeonies can do their bit in calling attention to the elimination, in our schools, of American history. The need thereof startlingly was made apparent by a recent event. On the Fourth-of-July, an editor gave a reporter 3 questions. All tested one's knowledge of the origin of the Fourth-of-July. He detailed said reporter to stop, one by one, 30 pedestrians on his city's principal street. Some questioned were soldiers, sailors. Only 1 of the 30 answered all 3 questions correctly. One said "I think 4th-of-July is a holiday because of something that happened in World War I, but I don't know what!"

COMBINED WATER-MAIN AND SEWER

An Occidental, landing at a port with above lack of sanitation, may shudder. He may wonder how the Far East could have taken scrawny, **sauvage** flowers and built them into show-winners when transplanted here. . . . Human excreta was dumped into an open drain uphill. Drinking water then was taken from same lower down. Here was complete disregard of biologic law. Yet, amidst a tragic infant mortality, a horticultural wizard lived there. His tree paeonies made an Occidental turn green with envy. A British friend interpreted his answers to questions about methods: "Simple. I SCOUR THE PROVINCES FOR GOOD ANCESTORS . . . I KEEP SEVERAL TRAINED BOYS WATCHING MY GARDENS. (For mutations). WE ORIENTALS KNOW, TOO, HOW TO MANURE. IF, ONCE IN TEN YEARS, I ISOLATE A PRIZE, SOME MANDARIN, SOME RICH MERCHANT-FANCIER BUYS!" THEN, TOO, UPCOAST TRADERS KNOW, IF THEY BRING ROOTS THAT PROVE ACCEPTABLE, THEY WILL HAVE WHAT, TO AN ASIATIC, IS A HANDSOME REWARD. ONE DOES NOT HAVE TO PAY MUCH TO HAVE HUNDREDS OF PEASANTS, DAD, MOTHER, NUMEROUS KIDS WATCHING. A STUDENT OF EUGENICS WAS INTERESTED IN HIS: "YOU SEE WE CHINESE EMPHASIZE ANCESTORS!"

———————

war, for Cuba's deadly fever laid low a great-great-great-grandson. Then came the Kaiser to dream of a "Place in the Sun." A great-great-great-great-grandson was at the storming of a Hohenzollern machine-gun-nest in the Argonne . . . a wooden cross represents him in France . . . Wooden crosses do not beget warriors. This family of devoted fighting men now is extinct.

While we of the Occident had been eliminating, in ceaseless wars, our bravest, the peace-loving Chinese long emphasized—not warfare—but education amidst peace. This Peace-concept continued to dominate Chinese thought despite Japanese aggression, despite crushing poverty resulting from overpupulation. . .

Buying oranges in China, our Geogardener found, does not carry title to the peel. In China tens of millions live on rice, rice, only rice. Any flavoring therefor has a market value. In West China, a sunrise-to-sunset workday earned, about 1910, less than a 3c postage stamp. Yet such folk clung to a philosophy of, not War, but Peace.

A Chinese piledriver's power was the muscles of women. A score circled it. At a signal, all pulled together to raise the weight. Wages 5c a day, dawn to dusk. Asked why an American machine was not used, the boss said: "Here we make each job support as many as possible." Still these piledriving women of Paeony-land dream of Peace, of education of their brainiest amidst Peace.

On a wheelbarrow trip in China, our Geogardener found rice-growers who dared not eat their rice. Its sale price, invested in the cheaper millet, yielded a margin. This covered the cost of a few primitive needs: a loin-cloth, a pellet of opium.

It is because of this bred-in-the-bone desire for Peace, that deep was the impact of Protestant missionaries in Paeony-land. The minds of many Chinese accepted the Good-will-toward-men teachings. One factor therein came under our Geogardener's observation. He, before first starting a-geogardening in China, had been advised by an American diplomat. The latter, long resident in the Flowery Kingdom, said "If you wish to peer into the Chinese soul, avoid tourist-ridden treaty-port hotels." Get into the interior. Then stay with missionaries. They will welcome you."

These indeed did, for his family was a missionary one. One grandfather had died a martyr overseas. Another of the family was born on a southern plantation. Louisiana, during Slavery, was like a Eugenics' layercake as to differences between "house negroes" and "farm-work negroes." Out of early plantation years, this kinswoman sensed how to most wisely enter China. She aimed to break the shackles of Chinese womanhood. Analyzing her success therein, our Geogardener was profoundly convinced her educational work there succeeded because she concentrated on EUGENICALLY-HIGHPOWERED CHINESE GIRLS. With several decades of such work, she made a real contribution to the present fortunate understanding between China and U.S.A. Hundreds of Chinese girls came from homes where paeonies were lovingly grown. With Christian ideals they married men governing China. Today they intelligently are helping their husbands in their gigantic task.

This could not have happened had work been among the lowest coolie class. She concentrated on leadership types. This has brought great spiritual dividends. . .

Wild species of paeony show remarkable adjustment to varied environment. The wild paeony of California is at home with yucca and cacti in the semi-arid mountains of the San Diego hinterland.

When our Geogardener was sleuthing the classic paeony of China to its sauvage beginnings, he neared the Siberian border of Manchuria. His trip, delayed until autumn, prevented his finding it flowering wild. He met, however, an American who had been exploring the Coast of Siberia. At some 450 miles north of Vladivostock, wild paeonies—white, pink, magenta—were found in impressive color masses. This explorer remarked they reminded him of the color-sheets of California poppies. These "sauvage" paeonies were mostly single. Some, however, even among these wild ones, showed tendencies toward "doubling."

Occidental gardeners owe a deep debt of gratitude to that master Geogardener, Baron Phillip Franz von Siebold (1796-1866). Chamberlain credits him with the introduction of PAEONIES, aralias, chrysanthemums, and scores of other interesting and beautiful plants with which they are now adorned.

He wrote many books, in Latin, in German, on the zoology, botany, language, and bibliography of Japan. Like Kaempfer a century and a half before him, he judged, and rightly, that the Dutch East India service was the royal road to a knowledge of the then mysterious empire of Japan. Appointed leader of a scientific mission he landed at Nagasaki, August, 1923. By force of character, by urbanity of manner, by skill as a physician, he obtained an extraordinary hold over the usually-suspicious Japanese. The court astronomer, Takahashi, presented him with a map of Japan. It was high treason to give this to a foreigner. The affair leaked out. Takahashi was cast into a dungeon where he died. Siebold's servants were arrested, tortured. Siebold had to appear on his knees before the Governor of Nagasaki. He adroitly saved, however, his chief treasures including the map. He was, nevertheless, banished in 1830.

"The lion and the paeony, because the former is the King of beasts, the latter, the King of flowers."

(Chamberlain.)

*In Bacon's Essays, where he recommends gardens
"for all months of the year" we have a glimpse as to the
April favorites of England of his time, when he recommends: "Flower-de-Lices, THE DOUBLE PIONY, and
the Lelacke Tree.*

"Day after day
   I labor in my garden,
   And the interest in my work
   Grows with the day."
(Tao Guan Ming, Circa AD 420
   Dr. H. H. Hart's Translation.)

**AIR TRAVEL, BUT NOT BY
PLANE, IN CHINA**

To parody the slogan of the
Campbells of Loch-awe " 'Tis a far
cry from" the wind-aided wheelbarrow of China to the recently an-
nounced seven-hundred-miles-per-
hour airplane. However, we Occidentals could well pause to consider
that extremely conservative China,
due to various causes (including
ancestor-worship and planned early
marriages of talented youth), has
a population trend which is decidedly eugenic. America's present
highpower birthrate since 1900, has
become more and more dysgenic.

**HOME OF CALIFORNIA'S WILD
PAEONY**

CHAPTER 67

PALM (Washingtonia)

JUAN AGUASCALIENTIES—we anglicized his name to Johnny Hot-water—was a Pass-Cahuilla redskin. This was when the sand wastes between Whitewater and Figtree John's never yet had dreamt of asphalt highways, of desert dogshows graced by flaxen-haired Hollywood movie stars, of realty sub-divisions, of dude ranches. Johnny Hotwater knew where the desert bighorn browsed. He could trap packrats for the squaw who brewed that marvelous broth, "sure-cure for pneumonia." He could lead to where chimney swifts nested up Taquitz Canyon. He showed our Geogardener how to gain a sherbet from the bisnaga. He brought in the best seed-palm nuts. This was when nurserymen bid against each other, for Washingtonia was in demand. It was Johnny Hot-water who guided our Geogardener to Palm Canyon when redskin Pass-Cahuillas plus the Desert-Cahuillas outnumbered 10 to 1 the whites, or "desert rats" in the Colorado Desert.

Washingtonia, the native California palm, is a fan-palm. One American humorist, with a philosophy decidedly Benjaminfrank-linesque, invented the term "as useless as a palm-leaf fan in Spitz-bergen." He probably did not know that fan-leaf palms, during one of the earth's mightly oscillations, actually grew north of the Arctic Circle. It has been found fossil in Greenland. There are several Puget-Sound fossil palm leaves in University of Washing-ton Museum at Seattle.

Washingtonia created the Mutt-and-Jeff combination long be-fore they appeared in yesteryear's comic strips. Tall crafty Mutt, to use Shakespeare's "Yon Cassius has a lean and hungry look," was anticipated by the Washingtonia type that grows very tall and slender for a palm. Runtish, but big-hearted, little Jeff also was in Palmland. Long ago he, too, was seen in a dumpy, potbellied Washingtonia. One may see impressive and pleasant avenues of the tall, or Mutt, type, also of the Jeff, or dumpy kind. The tall willowy kind planted together with the squat, corpulent variety, without nice discrimination, jars one's sense of uniformity. When selected for regularity of type, as those surrounding Capitol Park in Sacramento, they form pleasing collonades. With the years, they remind one of the naves of great Gothic cathedrals. The to-bacco-brown trunks with glorious fans glinting in the sun, offer a pleasing color contrast.

To know Washingtonia intimately our Geogardener went repeatedly to Palm Springs. Here were old friends: Phainopeplas fed on mistletoe berries in the catclaws. Canyon-wrens, from nearby talus heaps, sang at dawn in a never-to-be-forgotten symphony. Their sisters, the cactus-wrens, were busy nest-building in the cholla. That honest cuckoo, the roadrunner, who scorns parasitism, also was absorbed with making his own nest. He earns his living cleansing the desert of sidewinders and horned lizards.

Here, in the desert, was creosote-bush, smoke-tree, paloverde. After that heavy rainfall, that comes once in a blue moon, there was to be enjoyed the quick rush of gorgeous desert wildflowers. First must come a cloudburst. It would roll ten-ton boulders down the canyons on to the desert fans. These would tumble in such numbers one could hear the roar some miles away. A few weeks later could be expected the rush of sand-verbenas, of desert-primroses. The ocotillo then burst into bloom. The latter's flower cluster is so brilliant one cannot tell them from a cardinal at rest.

All this is Washingtonia country. . .

Verily the geogardening-lust is worth cultivating. As a hobby, what can be more satisfying than tracking down to their native haunts, such garden items as Washingtonia. Especially is one gratified when there is engendered thereby a love of the desert.

MODESTLY PETTICOATED PALMS

It was Johnny Hotwater who guided our Geogardener to Palm Canyon when the redskins . . . outnumbered 10 to 1 the white . . . "desert rats."

WASHINGTON'S BIRTHDAY

In Johnny Hotwater's day, Figtree John had never dreamed of asphalt highways across his desert—of desert dogshows graced by flaxen-haired Hollywood movie stars. Both Johns—Figtree and Aguascalientes—enjoyed the annual redskin Washington's Birthday fiesta. It was connected somehow with the Great White Father in a distant village also called "Washington." Neither John knew spectacled scientists also had christened their native palms "Washington-ia". Both Johns, however, celebrated by over-eating, over-drinking and watching the redskin Beau Brummells. One Indian's idea of full dress was eagle feathers and a wildcat pelt. The other, who had seen baseball played in the Pass at Banning, sported a cast-off baseball uniform.

CHAPTER 68

PAMPAS GRASS

*"Everybody works but Father.
He just sits around all day."
etc., etc.*

As THIS is written, the radio describes a husband's attempt to obtain an injunction against his wife. He is a candidate for Congress. Against him runs his wife. His prayer for such restraint asserts that, at marriage, she promised to "love, honor and *OBEY*." He had ordered her to withdraw. She refused to thus *OBEY*. The judge declined to grant his requested injunction. . . .

The relation between the sexes as to birds is quite different in Pampas-Grass-Land. At least, a gaucho there so told our Geogardener. The latter had traveled to Patagonia to track pampas grass to its "sauvage" environment. The gaucho had returned, with his *bolas,* from an ostrich hunt. He had no bird but did have several eggs. . . .

If down in Patagonia you have the rare good fortune to find a flock of these rheas, or South American "ostriches," you may even flush a male from the nest. It is this daddy-bird that can be made the basis of arguments overlooked when in 1913, London suffragettes then were pouring acids into the royal-red cylinders that are the British General Post Offices mailboxes.

Mamma-bird, of course, lays the eggs. In fact, several of the ladies, who must have joined a rhea labor-union and are careful not to overwork—make one nest. Here is what the French call an *ap-part-te-ment.* It's as good as a community kitchen as a labor saver. The eggs are deposited. Thereafter, however, Dad does all the housework. Incubation is his lonely task. The head of the harem raises, educates the chicks. He alone, down there in Pampas-Land, bears all the household worries!

CHAPTER 69

PANSY

"I send thee pansies while the year is young,
Yellow as sunshine, purple as the night;"
(Sarah Dowdney—"Pansies.")

"Pansies for ladies all—(I wish
That none who wear such brooches miss
A jewel.)"
(E. B. Browning—A Flower in a Letter.)

WHETHER producing attractive hybrids by crossings of various California mountain-lilacs or creating new roses with fresh stocks from Persia's desert-like mountains, the Gallic imagination excels, as it for centuries has, as to charming gowns, pleasing perfumes, or tasty cookery.

The French are most resourceful in combing the globe for new materials. The above mentioned rose-breeder sent his collectors to the Persian hinterland for a yellow rose. Upon this he built a whole series of desirable novel varieties. Two he named for his only sons. Both fell in World War I. These young men had been schooled in their father's methods. Eugenically they both had inherited his intellect, his manual deftness. The world may be poorer by a several score fine roses because these, in making the supreme sacrifice, also made extinct that rose-breeding line.

French success in rose breeding was paralleled with pansy-culture. Herein their progress was so marked, French gardeners used to declare that perfection had been reached. Further improvment was impossible.

Such satisfaction is a Gallic characteristic. Our Geogardener was searching in Tours for the Balzac house. He inquired of one, who proved to be an ardent Legitamist. "Which way to the Rue de la REPUBLIQUE?" he was asked. The old man's black eyes flashed, "Tours contains no such street. But, if, perhaps, Monsieur seeks the Rue *ROYALE* (the old name of the street in Bourbon Days) it is the third turning ahead to the left. . . ." Perhaps, the day will come, too, when even the giant colorful French pansies may be improved beyond "PERFECTION."

Our Geogardener was passionately fond of pansies. One of

THE DEVIL'S NEEDLES, LE MONT-DORE, FRANCE

It is in such meadows as the one in the middle distance of above photo-graph that our Geogardener found millions of pansy blooms. Under the space of a single blanket could be found all color-variants from milk-white, through yellows and light blues to deep magentas and almost black purple. Botanizing here one came to understand what a wealth of material French breeders had from which to isolate mutations for their crossings. Le Mont-Dore and its pansy-enamelled meads is up stream from Dordonge and from Cro Magnor grottos.

The Cave Man's association with the Cave Lion, the Cave Bear, the Cave Leopard, the Cave Hyena continually has intrigued the circus-love that per-sists from boyhood into manhood. . . . The caves Cave Man favored muchly during 1,500 centuries were in the Dordogne Valley, whose river rises in the snow of Mt. Dore's central peak, and flows thru our pansy terrain.

his late-winter delights was, a mass of yellow ones. These were bedded to contrast with the black-green of deodars behind. Strong was his desire to study the *"sauvage"* material of the French pansy breeders. Twice therefore, while at work in Europe, he invested vacation time in studying France's wild pansies. One of these outings centered at Le Mont Dore. Above its beechwoods stretched vast mountain moorlands. There bloomed millions of wild pansies. The other *"vacance"* was at Besse-en-Chundesse, with similar terrain. Here, too, the grasslands, at the flowering season, were enameled, for miles, with "thought-flower" blooms. On these two expeditions our Geogardener found the whole range of pansy-colors. They ran from pure whites, also pale yellows, thru the red-browns, to the blues and the purple-blacks. In their own highlands the French enthusiasts could, and did find, though sometimes only after prolonged search, every element needed to produce the pansy* marvels now known worldwide.

One is reminded, year after year, in gardening, in geogardening, what breeders accomplish by Artificial Selection. What could not be done with Homo sapiens?

---

* The pansy long has gripped folks as can be imagined from its names, the French being connected with "pense." The German is "Stiefmutterchen." The designation "The little stepmother" is based upon proportion of sepals to petals. This stepmother (the upper petal) selfishly grabbed 2 sepals. Each of her own blood daughters, (the next 2 petals) was assigned 1 sepal each. Hence the poor little stepdaughters (last two petals) had to sit together on 1 stool (the last sepal). In its hold upon human affections, it ranks even above the passion-flower.

"Pansies in soft April rains
Fill their stalks with honeyed sap
Drawn from Earth's prolific lap."

(Bayard Taylor—Ariel in the Cloven Pine.)

FARMSTEAD IN NORWAY

This mountaineer's dwelling was shingled with birch bark. Same was held in place with sod. The roof was purple and golden with massed wild pansies rooted in the sod. One wondered if the blue-and-gold tiles of far away Persian palaces were similarly rooted in folk memories of the tall blonde conquerors who had wandered into Iran from the Baltic Broodland.

SAETER GIRL

Combined dwelling, goat shed, and cheese factory, this Saeter Girl's cabin had a roof heavily weighted with sod against early winter gales. Rivaling the tiles of Akbar, of Shah Johan in color, this sod had sprouted an amazing mass of those tiny pansies the kiddies call "Johnny-Jump-Ups" . . . Saeter girls' weird songs for lovers in the Polar codfish fleet formed the motif for much of Greig's music. Such sturdy women, for centuries until recent excessive birth-control, were the mothers of the large families that peopled Scotland, Ireland, Iceland, even our Pacific Northwest.

CHAPTER 70

PASSION FLOWER

"Passion-flower! . . . thy pure corolla's depth within,
We trace a holier symbol; yea, a sign
'Twixt God and man; a record of that hour
When the expiatory act divine
Cancelled that curse which was our mortal dower.
It is the Cross!"

TO TRACE THE PASSION FLOWER of our gardens back to its native haunts, one must go to tropical jungles. The red-flowered species is found in Bolsa-Land, i.e. the rain-forests of Colombia, and Ecuador. These also produce that feather-light timber. The scarlet passion-flower climbs from the dank mud to bolsa's sunlit heights. In this jungle, you may have to rely, in places, for transport upon Indian dugout canoes:

"If you are slipping down the
Coast toward Quito,
Black monkeys in the jungle screaming,
Macaws blue, or red-and-green and yellow
BOLSA growing in the jungle muck so dank." (Sailor Chanty.)

The blue-and-white passion-flower, much more common in yesteryear's gardens than the scarlet species, also has a West Coast habitat. It is found particularly at forest clearings in Costa Rica, thru Panama to Colombia. There the natives call it *"quate-guate."*

In yesteryear's Mexican *fondas,* one's breakfast was served without fruit. Then, into the dining room, would come a peon fruit vendor. His basketwork tray would be piled with mammaes, chicos, zapotes, (both white and black-fleshed), avocados, cherimoyas, and—of course, graniditas. The latter are the yellow fruit of one species of Mexican passion-flower. Its eggshaped, woody encasement is about one-third filled with seeds. These are in a mucilaginous mass. Our Geogardener never saw monkeys in the jungle feeding upon this tasty pulp. He could imagine, however, stickiness had a survival value. It resembled the similar secretions on both the oak and the desert-mesquite mistletoes. The seeds of these adhere to the bills of birds. Thus seed transportation to distant food-producing terrain.

It is in Australia, however, that passion-fruit gains its summit in cookery. It apears there in salads, fruit punches, ice creams, candies, cake decorations. Always these are most acceptable. The passion-flower family is rather close in botanical classifica-

WILD ROYAL PALMS, BAMBOO RIVER, CUBA

Passion Flower Land is almost identical with Royal Palm Land. The terrain is spotted, stretches of savannah with the palms, bits of jungle or of chaparral with passion-flower vines. In the jungle are many cousins to the pineapple. Often these are epiphytic. The cacti, too, frequently are epiphytes. They are not terrestrial, as in Arizona. One also finds many heliconias, including the beefsteak heliconia. . . Vanilla vines compete for sunlight with passiflora climbers. There are custard-apples, the Madre de Cacoa, the Cabbagebark, the Sandbox trees, dye plants like the Bixa. One also finds here, as winter visitants, the homeland's summer birds: tanagers, linnets.

tion to that of the toothsome papaya. Papaya fruit fortunately lacks the woody covering of passion-flower fruit. Papaya is a much esteemed pulpy melon-like fruit. Papaya seed is sometimes eaten by Brazilian natives. The whites there call it "Brazilian caviar." The name "papaya", used almost everywhere else in the tropics, is tabu in Cuba. There it has an obscene meaning. A Cuban therefore calls it not "papaya" but *fruta de bomba."*

Are you garden-enthusiast? Botanist? Nature lover? Perhaps, just a plain sufferer from Northern blizzards? Would you escape from weeks of steam heat. Then hop aboard a plane for Passion-flower Land. . . . You'll be thrilled by flying over craters like Orizaba, Popocatapetl, Ixtacchuital . . . You will flit over clearing that once were mahogany forest. You'll peer down on checker-board-like coffee *fincas,* their peons moving like ants . . . You'll revel in the Oriental-rug patterns of jungle trees. Their flowers, massed at branch-ends, glow vermillion, scarlet, lavender, cerise, carmine, indigo, orange, canary, violet. All these are backed by the whole range of greens. Then, when you land, there will be introduced to you Passion-flowers and their neighbors, the Royal Palms. From a cousin of the latter, the "Panama hat-palms (Carludovica), come your headgear. They have some so skillfully made they can be passed thru your ring. You will pay a price, however, for these finer sorts.

Should your Geogardening be limited to your home garden—like Thoreau's "traveling much . . . in Concord" . . . you, nevertheless, ever can learn from the 6-footed who are your co-tenants. At the morning enjoyment of the rising sun's rays seen thru bougainvillea bloom, one notices a mayfly on the window pane. The adult humbly makes his unique double moult. It seems to feel the need for sartorial perfection for his wedding dance. It seems to know its adult life has brought imperfect mouthparts, that it cannot hope to eat. It must quickly dance its wedding-dance before mating. Then follows egglaying, finally, death by starvation. Its name has given us the concept of the opposite of permanent castled strength. From it has come our adjective "ephemeral." The mayflies are the "Ephemeridae." They often last but one day. . . . We have been taught humility is foremost among Christian virtues. One's garden's mayflies may be an impressive lesson in humility.

PEPPERTREE LAND'S ROADSIDE MARKET

In Peppertree Land's markets, Indian women squat on the ground. One may have a turkey for sale. Another firewood, cut from sun-baked chaparral. Always there is one with a square of homespun afront her on the ground. On it are spread tied bunches of red peppertree berries. The Hidalgo family will buy these for its tame parrots.

Below is a gathering of **alcaldes** in Pepper-Tree Land. These village headmen have assembled for what we Norte-Americanos would call "a convention." Each has a "secretary" who blows ostentatiously on a conch. Note the staff-of-office. Time was when Spanish-California villages, even Monterey, also were **alcalde**-ruled. These elders, who evidently were not afraid of a 13-party, returned home on foot trails. These were thru a chaparral of peppers. Because of the altitude these were high-mountain-stunted, were not trees, but mere bushes. Some of these **alcaldes** lived down-mountain on the fringe of the Upper Amazon jungle.

CHAPTER 71

PEPPER-TREE

GUADALUPE SANCHEZ supported herself and aged father selling pepper-tree seeds. For these, there is a market. They are used for parrot food. 'Lupe's squatting-place was in the Zocolo bird market. This is almost under the shadow of Mexico City's great Cathedral. Afront her, and spread on the ground, was a tattered *serape*. On this were rows and crossrows of pepper-tree seeds. These were tied in bunches. 'Lupe was pure Aztec. Her bent father was intensely anti-Spanish. He complained that to build the cathedral, the old *teocalli*, on the same site, had been leveled to provide stones for the present structure.

Our Geogardener was invited by Guadalupe's father to visit the Sanchez home. There he learned much of Aztec lore. This passed orally, in Homeric style, from father to son, thru the generations. There were tales of Cortes' treachery toward the Montezuma. Yarns were told, too, of the pink-cheeked, blue-eyed Alvarado. "His hair—so different from that of the Aztec, senor. It was of the color of the silk of the full ripe maize. You know, senor, of which, after harvest, my daughter grinds the flour on the *metate* and makes the *tortilla*." Old Juan had tales of the Aztec Goddess of fertility . . . of Quetzalcoatl, the Fair-haired God "just like Alvarado," who gave them the maize . . . Tales, too, Juan told of the gorgeous feather cloaks* of Montezuma. "That is why 'Lupe sells at the bird market. She is a good girl. She carries on in the Aztec tradition."

There seems to be some doubt whether the pepper-tree is native as far north as Mexico. Our Geogardener found a clump—either *sauvage* or escaped—in the hills near Zacatecas. In Peru, however, on the headwaters of the Amazon, the chaparral, for miles upon miles, is almost entirely STUNTED pepper-trees. At these high altitudes the pepper is hardly llama-high. At about 8,000 feet, the slopes are steep, with rapid drainage. They there do not attain the luxuriant growth seen nearer the Amazon jungle. In this chaparral one would hardly recognize their cousins of the well-watered avenues of Southern California. Even at this higher altitude, however, the peppery seeds are eagerly eaten by

---

* Two were still in existence in 1935. Before the Spanish Civil War, one was preserved at Seville. The other was in Stuttgart Museum.

birds. Perhaps the wide distribution of this stunted pepper-tree chaparral along the Brazilian slope of the East range of the Andes is due to this almost ravenous hunger of birds for the seed. They evidently pass thru the digestive tract unimpaired as to vitality. The birds seem to obtain thereby a narcotic-like stimulant. They apparently are as lustful as an addict for his cocaine or heroin.

When the kitchen can-opener circles the tomato can, did you ever stop to think of the origin of its protecting veneer of tin? It probably rode as a tin-brick from a 2-miles high mine to the railroad on a living freight car. This was a rubber-necking llama. Its driver, when he reaches destination, probably spends most of his pay drinking *"leche de tigre"* or "jaguar milk." As one descends to Cuzco, one passes a little lake. It is in a pass. There they tell you a North gale will blow a cork on its way to Lake Titicaca. A South wind, however, will whiff it over the lip into a brook. Thus, finally, with the help of other brooks, it reaches the mighty Amazon. In this Tibet of America, our Geogardener saw probably 100,000 llamas. In some of the out-of-the-way places, occasionally can be seen vicunas. His blankets, in very high altitude, were robes of alpaca and of vicuna. A good vicuna blanket makes a fur coat prized by the ladies.

This pepper-tree-chaparral area is true Inca-Land. Our Geogardener was there, trying to trace out the clandestine routes of Japanese infiltering. The little brown men, barred from Atlantic ports, were sneaking in from Peru. They were headed, not only to their Amazonian colony, but toward Sao Paulo. Their strategy herein was most clever. The fertile state of Sao Paulo is the very heart of the great Brazilian empire. In East Peru are the many-skirted Indio women. It is said they add petticoat atop petticoat, never removing those beneath till they rot away. Our Geogardener was dismayed to find Japanese spies almost to the edge of the Amazonian jungle. Some of these posed as dye-vendors. These members of the Nipponese secret-service needed no funds from To-kio. They could easily support themselves from the profits of aniline dyes, "made in Japan." Our Geogardener noted with sadness how the new colors attracted the squaws. They were evidently displacing the old Inca dyes. These had, for centuries, been distilled from roots, barks, berries. Thus in Pepper-tree Land, one witnessed the decay of another priceless Amerind art. The redskin folk themselves were decimated by paleface diseases, against which they had no immunity. In like manner, their skill in dye-making was disappearing.

CHAPTER 72

PINE (STONE)

"A FAT-TAILED SHEEP, who did not want to die,
bleated lamentably at my tent door. He was scuffing with
the prime minister and the director general of public edu-
cation. He was a royal gift to me and my camp servants.
. . . The prime minister adjusted his turban, which had
fallen off in the struggle. . . . I dispatched two bottles as a
foretaste, and when the sheep had entered upon another
incarnation," etc. etc.   (Kipling: "Namgay Doola.")

THE STONE-PINE of the Mediterranean Basin stimulates memories of fat-tailed sheep. Our Geogardener rumaged the Near
East for "sauvage" narcissi, cyclamens, anemones, ranunculi and
other bulbous plants. He then frequently had to dine off the greasy
fat-tailed mutton. Often, too, the meat meal came as a pilau
of fat-tail rice, of raisins and pinenuts. These, too, rather un-
hygenically were soaked in the fat-tail grease.

Stone-pine trees are not common in American gardens. They
do find, however, California's climate congenial. There is a fine
group in Sacramento's Capitol Park. In cultured communities such
as Berkeley, California, whose residents have traveled widely, one
also finds good stone-pine specimens.

The Italian people accelerate the pine's branch-shedding habit
to meet their fuel needs. Your peasant meal may be an omelette
created via stone-pine twig fuel. Pinenuts make a welcome addition to any meal, especially if the cook, in preparing the pilau, is
careful not to overemphasize the fat-tail lubricant.

Whether the Geogardener enjoys, at Baalbec, a pilau of fat-
tail sheep mutton, rice and pinenuts . . . or cracks the hardshell
Sabine pine's nutlets for dessert of a hiker's campfire's chili con
carne . . . or bargains with a Pah-ute squaw for pinyons . . . or,
down among the laddered Pueblos, takes refuge from a desiccating snowstorm, thus enjoys the original succotash of beans and
corn topped off with a handful of pinyon softshells . . . the agree-
ably-flavored fruit of the needled pine is always most acceptable.

Our American pines yield products utilized as food, also
medicinally. The northern tribes are especially familiar with
the value of the cathartic properties of the sugar which is
often found as an exudation on the partially burned base of
the sugarpine tree.

STONE PINE, APPIAN WAY NEAR ROME

BURNING GHATS, BENARES

Some Hindu pundits assert the conical domes of certain temples in British India were modeled upon the pines of the faraway Northern Broodland, south of the Baltic. Many Hindu seem proud of their "Aryan" ancestry—diluted as it is. Kipling, indeed, introduces one of his heroes as "Pagett M-P was a liar."

> "April began with the punkah, coolies and prickly heat.
> Pagett was dear to mosquitoes, sand flies found him a treat.
> He grew speckled and lumpy—hammered, I grieve to say,
> ARYAN BROTHERS who fanned him in an illiberal way."

CHAPTER 73

POINSETTIA

L ION—OR ZEBRA—MOVIES naturally show African backgrounds. One may notice therein, branched, candelabra-type plants. These resemble the organpipe cactus of Mexico. Such African plants, however, are not cacti. They belong to the Euphorbiaceae.

One member of the Euphorbia family is widely planted in Southern California gardens. Its actual flowers, like those of bougainvillea, are inconspicuous. To attract insects, their "publicity" is gained by remarkably-conspicuous, highly-colored bracts. This plant with strikingly-colored inflorescence is the Poinsettia . . .

On Florida's Gulf Coast two similar Euphorbias* grow wild. They have the same milk-like juice, the same bits of bright color. If the latter were sufficiently expanded in areas one would have a poinsettia of which even Angeleans could boast. The kiddie name for both these wildlings is "hypocrite." Children show rare imagination in such christenings.

One wonders, therefore, whether the gorgeous poinsettia of our gardens was gained from *sauvage* beginnings like "hypocrite." Similar progress has been made with potatoes, tomatoes, maize, pecans, plums** from other unpromising beginnings deepens the wonder.

---

* Our Geogardener found his "hypocrites" as this book was ready for press. He had therefore no time to investigate further whether they may be the "sauvage" beginnings of our garden poinsettias.
** For data on all five, see appendices of the author's "War Profits . . . and Better Babies." in most local libraries throughout U.S.A.

ICELAND'S THINGVILLIER

Here was held the world's first Parliament. At the celebration of its 1,000th anniversary, the statesmen representing Britain graciously stated: "Ours on the Thames is called the 'Mother of Parliaments.' If that be true, Thingvillier is the grandmother of Parliaments." That first gathering at Thingvillier was, indeed, grandmother to the Parliaments of Canada, Australia, New Zealand, South Africa. It also was ancestress to our American Congress and to all our 48 State Legislatures. . . . The lava flows from Rejavik to Thingvillier were brilliant with masses of "Iceland" poppies.

CHAPTER 74

POPPY

"In Flander's Fields the POPPIES grow
Between the crosses, row on row,
Which are our place,
And, in the sky
The larks still bravely singing, fly
Regardless of the guns below.

Short days ago, we lived
Saw sunset glow,
Loved and were loved.
And now we lie in Flander's Fields.

*   *   *   *

If ye break faith with us who die
We shall not sleep,
Tho' POPPIES grow in Flander's Fields."

"A mischievous morn, that smites the POPPIES cheeks
Among the corn, till they are crimsoning
With bashful flutterings."

(Margaret Preston.)

THE RED "CORN-POPPY" of Flander's Fields—and nearly all the rest of Europe—takes its name from the wheat, or "corn", amongst which it grows. The old wives use narcotically dried-petals for colic, whooping cough and other coughs, also for certain fevers. These herb-prescribing dames insist that a poppy petal infusion will cause sweating. They probably often have relieved illness in much the way of the California redskins in their sweat-houses. The red corn-poppy in Northern or Central Europe usual-ly grows in cultivated grain. In Spain, however, the soil is less fertile. In grazing areas, one may see the streamsides in valleys streaked with blood-red flowers. The peasants will shudder as they repeat tales of the Inquisition. They declare poppy grows in memory of the Inquisition martyrs on Spain's blood-drenched soil. . . . One wonders whether the Shirley poppies of our gardens are not based upon the Europe's red or corn-poppies. If so, they are a further testimonial to the intelligence of plant breeders. The poppy of Europe's wheatfields often is a scraggly bloom. At times it has hardly more glamour than the imitations sold on Veterans' Poppy Day. Compare this scrawny corn-poppy with the attractive Shirleys. Here one has convincing evidence as to what can be gained by careful breeding. By systematic persistent watching of this highly variable flower for desirable mutations, plant breeders successfully have built up various strains. The beauty of a May poppy garden just after dawn, with the rising sun's rays aslant the pinks, the scarlets, and with accenting whites, is a never-to-be-forgotten sight. . . . Have we not in such a garden a glimpse of humanity of the future? If we spend as much care in improving our human stocks as we have on poppies, what may not the future hold in store?

Gardeners call one attractive European species the "Iceland" poppy. Perhaps this is just as well. It thus may link, in our minds, this attractive garden flower to the land of the "Grand-mother of Parlia-ments." However "Iceland" poppy is about as accurate as the now discarded bird names: "Louisiana" tanager, "Arkansaw" goldfinch. Our Geogardener once was en route to Jan Mayen Land. This is where, for one dollar, one could buy, from Norwegian hunters, polar-bear pelts suitable for rugs. He tarried awhile in Iceland. It was an opportunity to botanize. It permitted study, too, of the curlews, the wild swans and other birds that nest in the Far North. It was above all a pilgrimage by one passionately devoted to the republican form of government. This, because in Iceland had been held the first Parlia-ment. It seems to emphasize the "type of government" where policies are "parley-ed" or talked over, are discussed. It is the very antithesis of autocratic orders from above, enforced by a parasitic, plotting Gestapo. Nevertheless, christening this golden bloom "Iceland" poppy is hardly accurate description. Its blossoms brighten the heights of,—not only Midnight Sun Land at North Cape, and all down the backbone of Norway,—but even under the alpenglow-blushing Dolomites. Our Geogardener found them also in Spitzbergen. His fellow collectors gathered them likewise in Greenland, as well as in Franz Josef Land.

"Sleepy poppies nod upon their stems;"
(Anne E. Bleecker—"On her return to Tomhanick.")

A VENDOR OF WEED-STALKS FUEL
The innkeeper's English permitted only "No opium". Our Geogardener finally guessed he was trying to impart that the fuel, on one cold November morning was, not opium-poppy, but wild, Oriental-poppy stalks. They were his only fuel.

The livingroom floor had a papier-mache covering. Under this were hollow tiles. These snaked from a below-floors' oven over to the base of a walled-in chimney. A guest was permitted to squat on the floor just above the oven. Thus he had a bit of heat. The host, his children shivered in a circle around their visitor. Here was galling poverty, tragic ignorance, but—at least—freedom—until the Japanese conquerors came. One regrets above photo is not a Koda-chrome. The background up to the skyline was ablaze with giant burnt-orange poppies. It was worth the discomforts of a Japanese freighter to have them burn such a color-memory into one's geogarden-brain. If you are not already a passionate Conservationist, study our photo of "A VENDOR OF WEED-STALKS FUEL." Korean deforestation, (see also above photo) was carried so far that the current fuel again was weed-stalks.

The opium poppy has been grown from almost prehistoric days in Anatolia and Egypt for the narcotic obtained from its milky juice. Its culture for opium extended Eastward to Hindustan, finally to China. Curiously, the same opium poppy long has been grown in France and in Germany for the oil of its seeds. These have no narcotic properties. The seeds contain approximately 40% oil. This is used for the same purposes as the olive oil of the region immediately to the South. The poppy-seed poppy is another species that is cultivated in Germany and in Austria. Its dried seeds atop little cookies make Teutonic kiddies beg for *"mohnkuchen"* . . .

An opium tale was told our Geogardener when traveling from the Malay States to Burma, the captain of his vessel was a kindly, unassuming Britisher. Later in Calcutta was obtained the story of this heroic man. He had saved one burning vessel near Aden,— had finally reached the head of his company's fleet. Then came orders to load a cargo at Calcutta, partly of opium. He insisted his Christian religion did not permit him to engage in a trade so evidently debauching to his fellowmen. Came a curt reply "Take that opium to China, or take the run from Kurachee to the stinking reaches of the Persian Gulf." . . . Captain Carre accepted demotion, had grilling years on the world's most detested sea-run. Only when that company was absorbed in a great maritime trust, did the Board of the new corporation reverse the injustice by restoring his rank.

In "City of the Dreadful Night" Kipling gives an illuminating description of Gaziphur Factory. "An opium mint" he dubs it. . . . Reread therein about the Keeper of the opium den. A pet mongoose is coiled about his neck. He kicks a smoker on the floor. In pidgin-English he snarls: "Hi-ya, you. Show how, Opium smoking!" . . . The adjoining chapters give a rare description— of commercialized vice at its very worst—in a Hindu slum.

Let us climb from the Bengal plain, with its cultivated opium poppies. Let us go over the Himalayas toward Tibet. Our Geogardener's track ran thru these passes when he tried to locate the blue Tibetan poppies. That Himalayan trail illustrates how thrilling may become geogardening. In crossing the Himalayas he was advised to hire a string of Nepalese coolies. The only means of transportation was *dandywallah*. This was a cheerful, coffin-kind of a Pullman. You sat upright where the corpse's face is exposed for the last time. There was a crossbar beyond head, beyond foot. Each of these rested upon the shoulders of two tough little Gurkha coolies, one right, one left. Four coolies were always "in action." Relief coolies trotted behind, ready to take the load from blistered shoulders. There was no labor union, no 40 hour week. Hours 4 a.m. to 8 p.m. There was, however, a kind of guild, like the beggars' guilds of China. One had to hire 12 coolies per passenger with baggage. This seemed an appalling expense to Mr. and Mrs. Geogardener. English friends counseled, "Do not be alarmed. We will find you a good Number One Boy." His bid for all 24 bearers was $1 daily. We were told each was to have 4c daily. Actually each had 3½c. Number One Boy had his 4c, but he also gained the good old Oriental "squeeze" of ½c daily on each of

the remaining 24. This 12c plus his 4c or 16c per day meant
wealth. He was known as the village moneylender. He shy-
locked his savings at 10% per month, waxed corpulent accordingly.

AMBER-BEADED KOREAN TEACHER AND PUPILS

Oriental-poppy terrain commences with Korea, stretches across Manchuria
and thru Siberia to the Urals. Hundreds of miles at times, will look as if
Mother Nature, was annoyed at the fickle, short-lived sunsets. Had she, perhaps, angrily snatched one evening's clouds and dragged them over the steppes?
. . . Czarist Russia produced a few good botanists. However, one recalls but
few Siberians that have become garden favorites: Siberian iris, Oriental or
Siberian poppies . . . and from Siberia's Pacific Coast, some paeonies via Chinese breeders. There are some few specific names—"siberiea." Could not flower-
breeders send there a flower-searching expedition or two, as English garden
lovers sent Douglass, also Jeffrey to our Pacific Coast? After our gains from
the Himalayas' area, can we not expect much from up Siberia way? In any
event, the inhabitants are fascinating, as the Korean kiddies in our photograph.
      Above school children of Imperial days are learning Korean A.B.C's.
Korean since ruthlessly has been destroyed as a Living-tongue. Note how carefully they parked their rice-straw sandals. One must not disrespectfully soil
the Center of Intellectual Light with dirty shoes.

From Tibet let us go still farther north, across Mongolia, into
Siberia. "Oriental" poppies of the Siberian steppes also are poppy
cousins. One missionary, long resident in Japan, made his last
trip over the Trans-Siberian railroad. He said that journey yielded two never-to-be-forgotten pictures. One was the sunset over
Lake Baikal. The other was the steppes, ablaze, day after day,
with Oriental poppies.

In our *sauvage* poppyquest, we have traveled from Iceland
and from Norway with their Arctic poppies, from Flanders and
from Germany with their corn-poppies to Turkey, to Egypt and

Our Geogardener used to wonder what poppy-mass thrilled most. In California's hot Sacramento Valley, the miles of eschscholtzia-gold . . . or the Santa Barbara Coast's matilijas, ... in the Dolomites, the "Icelands", edging the talus . . . or the Tibetan blues. Perhaps the latter . . . for the girls there seem to have captured the poppies' blue in their turquoise ornaments, nose discs, bracelets, anklets.

to Hindustan of the opium-poppies. We crossed the passes into Tibet, with its blue-poppies, thence northward into Eastern Siberia with its vast steppes of Oriental poppies. Now let us take ship at Vladivostock to glimpse California's native poppies.

One of its members is the Matilija poppy of the Southern California Coast. With its silky white blooms, it is like a queenly bride. Its plebeian first-cousin is the prickly Desert-poppy. It ranges from California's trans-Sierran deserts and from Nevada southward far into Mexico.

California's state flower is the golden eschscholtzia, or *copa de oro*. An illuminating poppy experience came in our Geogardener's own native state. The dominant figure therein was the late Luther Burbank. The two were discussing the theaters of ancient Magna Grecia. They talked of the seascape which was the drop curtain of that at Segesta. They chatted about the Mt. Aetna background of the theater at Taromina. They debated the "violet-crown" coloring of ancient Athen's "Theater of Bacchus." The twain compared possible California backgrounds. Then Mr. Burbank exclaimed: "Those brainy Greeks of Pericles' time knew how to evaluate color: Seagreens at Segesta, seen thru pinkish almond blossoms—the white plume of Aetna's smoke contrasted with that cobalt sky—the rare "violet crown" of Attica. . . . I wish," he said wistfully, "I could try a color experiment with moderns. I would like to be able to seat in an outdoor Greek Theater, say, 10,000 American leaders. To them I would like to display—on back-curtain hills—3 color-ribbons of my poppy blooms. The first would be a broad band of my variants' original sowing of seeds of *golden* eschscholtzia. These I planted to isolate color. To its right, to the left would be plantings of seeds from color-mutants. The right hand belt would be half white, half pink. The left hand planting would be my scarlet eschscholtzias. Then I would shout "Gentlemen, you see the possibilities of a few years of Artificial Selection." It is based upon a flower at which Mother Nature has been working, for probably over one million years. Then I would remind them I once had written "The Training of the Human Plant." I would beg these 10,000 leaders to consolidate their brainpower into a movement to improve that Human Plant. What I had done with my Burbank potato, my Earliest-of-all tomato, my Shasta Daisy, THEY COULD DO BY EUGENICS; WITH HUMANS!

The poppies of your garden then—minuet-ing Iceland's, flirting Shirley's, arrogant eschscholtzias, gorgeous Orientals, or aristocratic matilijas . . . may speak symbolically to you. They are floral signs of the age-old concept: Good and Evil,—Jehovah (or Jawe) and Satan,—Heaven and Hell,—Saint George and the Dragon.

Was not Kipling anticipating the Life-Zones* of later biologists when, in "The Overland Mail" he penned:

> "From aloe to rose-oak,
> From rose-oak to fir,
> From level to upland,
> From upland to crest,
> From rice-field to rock-ridge,
> From rock-ridge to spur,
> Fly the soft, sandalled feet,
> Strains the brawny brown chest."

* For description of Sierran Life Zones see "Sierran Cabin . . . From Skyscraper," Chapters 3 to 8 both inclusive

REINDEER HIDES ARE LAPP'S LUMBER

Your garden's "Iceland" poppies will bring you increased pleasure if, in
addition to their mottled orange, canary, milkwhite hues, they speak to you
continually of the Arctic, of Iceberg chromatics, of savage polarbears, of
tricky arctic foxes, of staring snowy owls, of the efficient seasonal camou-
flage, of ptarmigan and snowshoe rabbit. Greenland, Iceland, the Lapplands,
all, in their summer, are covered with varihued poppy rugs. These would make
a burnoosed sheik fairly itch to swap his carpets—(camels and sandstorm
"thrown in") for reindeer and a Midnight Sun that could paint such colors!

One wonders, however, whether these stolid Lapps are sensitive to all this
color. Their one obsession seemed to be: Coffee! Said Lapps, like Eskimos,
are short. Dr. Mjoen emphasized one danger of human hybridization: Norwegian sailors, along Lappland's coast, crossed with Lapp girls. Resulting
children, according to Dr. Mjoen, often inherit the lung-size of the Norwegian
six-footers. The small heart of a runtish Lapp mother makes, for such a
breathing apparatus, an inadequate pump. Tuberculosis' rate among such hybrids, he said, was excessively high.

Both photographs courtesy Chief Ranger Calvert, Anza Desert State Park
RIOT OF SAND VERBENA COLOR

What Geogardening thrill could be deeper than one's first sight of massed color in Nature's Desert gardens after one of those rare, heavy rains? It may come once in 10, even 20 years. Then the dry, dormant seeds rush thru sprouting, leaf-making into the bloom that must precede the next seed-making. Our Geogardener has just returned from another Desert trip. For several decades, he, almost annually, went to study plant adjustment to desert drought, plus heat, with consequent rapid evaporation. The Nature Guide called his attention to a desert plant called the "Humble Gilia." Each plant was about the size of his thumbnail. Its cousins in the forest are tall. A perfect seedmaker, it is evolved, like a hummingbird, toward reduced size. Yet, in masses, its bloom is unforgettable.

"DESERT GOLD" RECALLS '49ER GOLD RUSH

THE DOLOMITES AT SUNRISE AT SUNSET BLUSH WITH
ALPINE GLOW

Having enjoyed each January for many years, his garden's borders of
dainty little lavender primroses, our Geogardener started tracking them to
their wild beginnings. From the North Sea to the Mediterranean he found,
at each spring's opening, the characteristic primrose-hued primroses, but no
lavenders.

Spring comes in midsummer in the high altitudes. One July day Mr. and
Mrs. Geogardener were caught in a heavy Dolomites' thunderstorm. They took
shelter in a limestone abri. The talus below was bordered with a line of nodding lavender primroses. Later they found whole meadows carpeted with them.

DOLOMITE'S TALUS IS COLORFUL WITH GOLDEN "ICELAND"
POPPIES BLOTCHED WITH PRIMROSE LAVENDER.

CHAPTER 75

PRIMROSE (LAVENDER)

Three bunches a penny, PRIMROSES!
Oh, dear is the greeting of Spring,
When she offers her dew-spangled posies,
The fairest creation can bring. (Eliza Cook—Old Cries.)

WILD LAVENDER primroses cover acres in a Tyrolese meadow at the head of which stood the inn hereinafter described. To the Dolomites of the Tyrol our Geogardener went a-sleuthing, since lavender primroses were listed as to be found growing *sauvage* there.

It was here he found most convincing "Before-and-after" pictures. You know "Before-and-after" portraits. Baldheaded barbers dare use them . . . an alleged remedy for baldness. They are so convincing some folks do not hesitate to buy the advertised hair tonic. They were a tribute to American inventive genius. Similar contrast pictures belonged to this Tyrolese innkeeper. They showed the "Before-and-after" aspect of the mountain behind his hostelry. The mountain seemed like a bit of elevated ancient peneplain. Steep cliffs at both ends but a mesa-like skyline between. It was level enuf to support an Austrian division in World War I. This was said to be 15,000 soldiers. There was a side ridge below the summit. The whole was like a gigantic letter "T." The top was Austrian-held. The stem ran down to the Italian lines. *Bersagleri* has won and held the stem ridge. Then they commenced tunnelling into the side of the mountain. The rock was soft. The work proceeded rapidly. It was superintended by an Italian engineer. He had been trained in the use of high explosives in California Mother Lode gold mines. As he tunnelled and cross-tunnelled for the coming TNT charge, his soldiers' drilling finally could be heard by the Austrians above. Our Tyrolese innkeeper belonged to that division. News had filtered through, the explosion was to come on a certain Friday night. 15,000 Austrians would be blown to atoms. The innkeeper went to his colonel. "I am father of 8 . . . In the village below. Do let me escape." "Such a remark means the firing squad" snapped back his commander. That evening, nevertheless, he was ordered to carry a message to an officer stationed in his native village behind the lines. At midnight came the explosion. 15,000 Austrians, with their colonel, went to their doom. This one soldier alone escaped death.

The old photograph showed the original mountain. The second one gave proof that the innkeeper spoke truth. The 2c tip that stimulated the tale was a good investment in producing photopraphic support on the yarn.

Our Geogardener's interest had been awakened, years earlier, as to the Alpine origins of certain garden plants when visiting the Alpine Botanical Garden near Geneva. Here wise Swiss botanists had grown specimens of high mountain plants from worldwide sources. Here one also learned of the marvellous adjustment of high-mountain plants to their remarkable environment. They had to combat, say 10 months of snow, with only 2 snowless ones. Into these two were telescoped brilliant but dessicating sunshine. There were high and drying winds. There were gravel slopes with rapid drainage. Plants that were annuals near sea level here had to utilize two or more years to build root systems. Then came, finally, a summer of quick flowering, cross-fertilization, seed-making. Our Geogardener therefore was stimulated to study the Alpine flora of the Dolomites. This included typical high-mountain wild-flowers. These numbered not only our lavender primrose—but also forgetmenots, saxifrages, "Iceland" poppies. There were, too, whole series of high-mountain orchids, also of cinquefoil and, one relished, too, delicious forest-strawberries. These thrive, sauvage, from the Dolomites across North America, to California's Yosemite, then down-coast to the mountains of Chile.

This Tyrolese adventure included a fascinating "climb." It was the type where, on the ice-slopes, one is roped to one's guides. Our Geogardener's head guide was Alois Hofer. He cautiously led the cutting of steps in the ice-slope. The night before our Geogardener had a rare glimpse into the soul of this flaxen-haired, blue-eyed Tyrolese! He was describing Fascist attempts to make the South-Tyrolese Italians. Hofer complained!

"Rattlebrained Mussolini thinks he can snap his fingers, bark a "Presto" and lo! we Tyrolese, of a thousand years' breeding, become instantly macaroni-munchers. To make sure we don't backslide, he has everywhere his *carbineri* twins. They think they carry out his orders. True our schools no longer teach German—only Italian. However, tho it is forbidden under death penalty, we teach our kiddies German at night. Along with this we give liberal nightly doses of hatred for the Tyrant of Tiber-bank!"

"Her modest looks the cottage might adorn,
Sweet as the primrose peeps beneath the thorn."
(*Goldsmith—Deserted Village*).

PRIMROSE (YELLOW)

"A primrose on the river's brim
A yellow primrose was to him
AND IT WAS NOTHING MORE!"

(*Wordsworth*)

Going a-geogardening to the World's only tax-free nation! It is along a road lined, both sides, for miles, with blooming yellow primroses. The road ascends the French slope from Foix to the snowline. Remember the headaches that came with tax-evolution in World War I. Then let us peep at this tax-free nation and see if we like THEIR system.

The "Primrose Path" from France's Foix, thru Andorra, is a main highway to Spain's Urgel. The poet may have been thinking of the leagues of primroses when he wrote:—

"And every road's a good road
That leads toward Spain."

This tax-free nation, tiny Andorra, is bastioned on all sides by Pyrenees' peaks. Napoleon once exclaimed *"Les Pyrenees, elles non exist pas!"* You stand in front of the National Capitol of this tax-free republic. You remember a saying of the Corporal. Had he partaken too much of a certain brand of alcoholic stimulant that still claims to have been his favorite. The Pyrenees still do exist! They tower all around the little capital of this tiny "republic."

One forgets the primroses as one stands on the steps of Andorra's capitol building. One holds one's nostrils. Across the cow-path, that also is the boulevard facing this structure, is a cowbarn. It is about as big as the Capitol. Its accumulations of manure occupy its half of the street . . . The standing army of the state compels it to "shinny on your own side." In tax-free Andorra City filth is everywhere. One's menu contains a national dish: Rice with minced chicken-combs. Other delicacies are peculiarly Andorran. They make one wonder as to the origin of such a cookery. It is sandwiched between a France's, with *"Caneton a la mode de la Valance,"* and Spain's *"Arroz con pollo."*

Yes, one may be tax-free. But one lives in a nation where everyone seems a smuggler . . . One almost forgets the

"Primroses. The Spring may love them
Summer knows but little of them."

(*Wordsworth—Foresight.*)

"Primroses by shelter'd rills."
(*Keats—The Eve of St. Mark*).

RUE de ST. JULIA, ANDORRA

An American judge, if he used the old test—"No visible means of support"—might sentence most of the population of the tiny republic of Andorra for vagrancy. There are only tiny bits of cultivated land. It is gossiped, however, that most of its citizens are exceedingly busy with smuggling. The laws of Spain encourage this as much as they did in California of the days of the serape-ed and sombrero-ed Dons . . . And France? . . . well the Gauls have a tobacco tax that keeps Andorrans from dying of ennui.

CHAPTER 76

SAXIFRAGE

SAXIFRAGE LAND lies north-of-the-Artic-Circle. In our Hemisphere, one could enjoy, during the Klondike rush thereto, the raw songs of the Sourdough. In the other Hemisphere, the folk-music is older. Composers like Greig have found in, the wild measures of the Arctic fisherfolk, motifs rare. To feel the real message of Grieg, one must hear it when the Venturesome

> *"Tell how icebergs great are made,*
> *With crashings wild like thunder,*
> *From glacier-nose in ocean thrust*
> *Where sea-waves have cut under."*

Our Geogardener was studying saxifrages in Spitzbergen. He wanted to understand the conditions under which the Arctic floras pushed down into his native California during a succession of Ice Ages. Spitzbergen was where pioneer aviators used to take off for their early North-Pole flights. Our Geogardener's companions were fond of Grieg. Hence there "Anitra's Dance," also "In the Hall of the Mountain King" was played. One's garden saxifrages recall the glacier's music. They remind one of the high trebles of the tinkling of melting ice in the crevasses. They make one remember the deep bass booming of icebergs falling from "glacier nose in ocean thrust."

The saxifrages are remarkable in that they seem to include pre-Rosales radiated into what might be called the "glacial niche." Their evolution has been along the line of a remarkable adjustment to coolth.

Our Geogardener's garden contained a collection of saxifrages. These started from dainty coral-bells, or "St. Patrick's cabbage" as the Scotch Highlanders call them—to the broad-leaved Tibetan variety. Both these are examples of color-lust as described in our Foreword. Coral bells, massed in contrast with wild verbena's deep purple, make a delightful color show. This contrast would thrill the heart of a Burmese market-woman, puffing her "whackin' white cheroot."

The Gaelic Scots plant St. Patrick's cabbage as borders around garden plots of strawberries. A Scottish host, picking berries for our Geogardener, exclaimed, " 'Tis an unwarranted injustice. St. Patrick was Scottish-born. Though they say we never give anything away—we gave this human-snake-medicine to the Hibern-

REINDEER PAW SNOW FOR REINDEER-MOSS

Saxifrage Land truly is Snow Land. The snow blanket melted, saxifrages lift their dainty flowers. Reindeer wander long distances for reindeer moss like camels in Africa, Asia. Both move far annually to gain even a meager living. Even Southern Norway lacks fertility. Population therefore is sparse . . . This has given Norway an unusual homogeneity . . . Because of same, quick, nation-wide appreciation of betterment proposals like Dr. Mjoen's Windern Laboratorium* CAN result. In such an environment, social service ideals are more quickly translated into actualities.

*See account thereof in the author's "War Profits . . . and Better Babies."

SPITZENBERG IS TYPICAL SAXIFRAGE LAND

Photograph from steamer anchorage in Magdelena Bay. Fine example of a cirque.

ians!" He continued, "Folks tell cruel stories about us Caledonians. The other day a Glasgow man spoke to one of our Aberdeen youths. 'You selected as wife a bonnie apple-cheeked lassie.' 'Aye, so that she'd no be a-wasting my pence at the chemist's for cosmetics.' "

The Tibetan saxifrages recall Himalayan passes. Their broad leaves are as almost Scottish in their thrifty use of sun-energy. Parallels thereto of similar big-leaved plants are the cineraria,* also the wild thimbleberry of California. Being thus accustomed to poverty-of-sunlight, as well as to cold, Tibetan saxifrages make a colorful show when blooming in Californian gardens at Christmas. Our Geogardener's shady spots on Christ's Birthday are great blotches of rose-pink bloom, bright against the broad spatulate leaves . . .

Saxifrages blooms are, however, mostly milk-white. One finds white ones in Norway, in Iceland, in Alaska. Pale, too, are saxifrage flowers near moraines in Rainier, or Glacier National Parks, or the Canadian Rockies. White, too, are most of those down the Cordilleran backbone, as in the California Sierras.** At this latter place, they represent polar plants pushed southward with each down-range advance of the Great Polar Ice Cap in successive Glacier Ages. These include what Eastern Geologists call the Nebraskan, the Wisconsin, the Illinoisian and the Kansan Ice Ages. Saxifrages persist in California's mountains. More than a half dozen species of true Saxifraga grow there, also Boykinia, Bolandra, several Hucheras, Mitella, and the dainty Tellima. There they bloom in late winter. Even then one finds them in shady coolth. They seem to say "We, too, have had the genius of adjusting ourselves to a changed environment, just as Mexican tarweeds blossom in August's sunblasted valleys below. Did not some philosopher write of humans somewhere:—

"The truly educated man is one who successfully can adjust himself to environmental changes."

---

* See chapter on Cineraria.
**For Andean saxifrages, however, see chapter on Escallonia.

CHURCH-BOUND NORWEGIAN "TIN-LIZZIE"

When next you see your saxifrages venturing
into bloom in late winter, remember they are
used to frost. After church, our Geogardener
proceeded up-fjord to the glacier. A white triangle in our photograph above and to the left of
the man standing shows that glacier. In the
glacial till between the terminal moraine and the
glacier's nose were blooming dainty white saxifrages.

"TOTEM POLE"

A Sourdough Song
(*From Western Hemisphere's Saxifrage-Land*)

Totem Pole! Totem Pole!!
Silently Alaska's pebbled beaches guarding,
Where the black-green forests stand,
The sea's advance retarding.

Totem Pole! Totem Pole! !
Speak, and tell of when Northern Lights are flashing.
Tell of when the storm-whipped waves 'gainst
Rock-ribbed coasts are dashing.

Totem Pole! Totem Pole!!
Tell of when the walrus bulls are wallowing in slaughter,
Ripping with their reddened tusks
Till bloody is the water.

Totem Pole! Totem Pole! !
Tell how icebergs great are made, with crashings wild like thunder,
From glacier nose in ocean thrust
Where sea-waves have cut under.

Totem Pole! Totem Pole ! !
Tell the Tale of Father Wolf whose sons were Bear and Dolphin
Eagle bold, and Alca fat, and
Shark with cruel back fin.

Totem Pole! Totem Pole ! !
Sing of Raven black begetting frog and owl and salmon,
Honking goose, sea-lion sleek
All laughing loud at famine.

Totem Pole! Totem Pole! !
Tell of hunting spouting whales, each spear attached to bladder
Made of hide of seal well sewn
With sinews of seal leather.

Totem Pole! Totem Pole ! !
Tell of winning food by sinews woven into bird nets,
Walrus-Ivory balls attached
Help gather game for banquets.

Totem Pole! Totem Pole! !
Tell of salmon-smoking moon, of moon of salmon-drying
Kelp-bulb bottles neatly made
For salmon oil's out-frying.

Totem Pole! Totem Pole ! !
Tell of those who gorge themselves on blueblack tundra berries
For cream is smeared the oil of whales
Smacked up like pie of cherries.

Totem Pole! Totem Pole ! !
Tell of making picks for ice from sharpened deer-horn antlers . . .
Of beds made, not of sweet fir boughs,
But from the creekside willows.

Totem Pole! Totem Pole ! !
Tell how bark of cedar trees is woven into matting,
Of Haida braves in wild war dance,
While squatting squaws are clapping.

Totem Pole! Totem Pole ! !
Tell of Haida baskets made from roots of twisted cedar
Holding soups and ven'son stew
With never drop from either.

Totem Pole! Totem Pole ! !
Speak of parrots of the sea, their bills made into rattles
Tell how Thlingit braves went forth
Red war paint smeared for battles.

JOACHIMSTHAL, SCABIOSA; HOME OF THE DOLLAR

One of the scabiosas, the beautifully-tinted lavender kind, is found in the Caucasus, from which it is named. It also ranges thru the hill countries of Czechoslovakia and other parts of the old Austria-Hungary empire to France. Our Geogardener found this scabiosa growing wild in St. Joachimsthal, shown in our photograph. A mine-dump will be noticed in left of center in the foreground. The mines of this delightful little Czechish valley were famous in medieval times for their silver. Later they were to play quite a port in the discovery of radium . . .

The old Count of St. Joachimsthal was the very opposite of the typical robber baron. Like many other petty medieval rulers, he coined bracatate money. All kind of tricks were used to give, to a small amount to bullion, the appearance of an honest coin. These ranged from under-thinness to over-baseness. Much of the silver of these dishonest counts hardly deserve the name. In fact, the standard of morality among some of these mints was as low as that of the Hanseatic League merchants at Bergen, Norway, who opened each new ledger with the caption: "IN THE NAME OF GOD, AMEN." These then proceeded to record their profits by buying long weight and selling short weight, thus gaining 3 profits: the legitimate one as well as the long weight and the short weight.

Most widespread was this adulteration of coinage in Europe. Silver was only too scarce. The great silver mines of Mexico, Peru, had not yet been discovered. Metal coins were regarded finally with almost as much suspicion as the later paper *assignats* of the French Revolution. In this world of chicanery, the honesty of the Count of St. Joachimsthal became conspicuous. His coins were 100 percent pure silver. His Joachimsthaler, later was called "Thaler," finally "Dollar." It became almost as much a standard of real value as France's Louis' d'or, or the pound sterling of England's East sterlings.

Before World War II broke a world-renowned metallurgist tried to awaken Americans. If a War came, he declared, it would finally be decided by those who control the underground wealth, the oils, the metals. The "dump" in the foreground of our photograph shows an old silver mine. It yielded also sphalerite, or zinc blende. This in the United States also often is found in the same veins as argentiferous galenite. With the cubical crystals of this silver-bearing lead-sulphide is found the zinc sulphide. Dr. and Mrs. Curie became convinced that there was contained in St. Joachimsthal's greasy, brown-black zincblende, some rare substance. They said it possessed little understood possibilities of power.

Our Geogardener, while in St. Joachimsthal, was told that its city fathers had rare foresight. They granted the Curie's request for a shipment of sphalerite. From this, was extracted our first radium. Almost miscroscopic were the first beads. Some time after the discovery a hospital lost its treasured supply. The search extended even to the hospital's sewer. It was found therein. It had been washed down a washstand drain.

TRULY, WHEN ONE GOES A-GEOGARDENING, EVEN FOR SCABIOSAS, UNEXPECTED THRILLS ARE BY-PRODUCTS.

**CHIMES AT ST. SERGIUS AND HERMANN, VALAMO MONASTARY,
LAKE LADOGA**

In the middle of the Lake (almost in sight of Czar-of-all-the-Russia's St. Petersburg) persisted this Greek-Orthodox worship. And in Leningrad was the museum of Irreligion, planned to teach Communist youth that all that Valamo stood for was Nonsense. All this in Scabiosa land. All garden varieties grow in "sauvage" in Russia from the Caucasus to Lappland—then across all the Lapplands (Russian, Finnish, Norwegian) and indeed all Scandinavia to the coast of Fjord-slashed Norway.

**GRANDMA CARRIES WILD GRASS HAY FULL OF
LAVENDER SCABIOSA**

CHAPTER 77

SCABIOSA

A N UNUSUAL SCABIOSA, skyblue in color, which he first saw there, recalls memories of our Geogardener's studies in Copenhagen. He was advised that, as to nature-guiding, Denmark exceeded the world in its intelligent use, for the blind, of wild-bird music.

At Klampenborg, up-Sound from Copenhagen, were concentrated a number of fascinating recreational activities. At its outdoor theatre, one may hear Danish translations of Hamlet. Their acting is almost within sight of that hero's castle . . . Most fascinating were the excursions of inmates of Danish Schools for the Blind.

TEACHING BIRD SONGS TO THE BLIND

This is one of the author's photographs of Danish nature study field excursions for the Blind. This and the following one were used in attempting to awaken an interest in wild bird music in Blind Schools throughout the English speaking world.

One of these excursions was to the Deer Park beyond Klampenborg. The young folks would squat in a circle in the meadow near the giant beech trees. Then commenced competition as to who would first distinguish the songs of the birds which they had already been taught. Each one of the blind kept the score on his fingers. One would exclaim, "bullfinch." Another would say, "I hear a chitchat." A third would declare, "There's a greenfinch singing." Yet another would call, "I'm sure I hear a redwing thrush off in the distance." The teacher would listen and approve. Then another would say, "There's a nesting blackbird."* Then another would say, "missel thrush," yet one more would call "black-

---

* The story of Theodore Roosevelt and the blackbird is given in the author's *Sierran Cabin from Skyscraper.*

cap warbler," and another "tree pipit," again, "a redbreast."

Points in this game of the blind were allowed one for each common songster. Three points were allowed for the first skylark, it being such a highly prized songster. Five points were allowed for the nightingale. This bird is not heard as often in Denmark, or even in Britain, as it is in the Mediterranean basin.

This game was played regularly. It was said that a treat was given the 3 highest winners at the end of the season. These excursions were apparently made in clear weather all through the nesting season, when the males were singing. The sightless looked forward to the picnic lunch, eaten *al fresco*. There was, also, the invigorating ride on the little steamer from Copenhagen to Kempborg. Followed the land hike from steamer landing to the Royal Deer Park.

The joy of the blind was so evident that the author published an account thereof. This was sent to every blind school in the English-speaking world. It was suggested that here was rare opportunity to bring joy to the afflicted. Thrilling correspondence that resulted from the radiation of this pamphlet. Came one request from a Western U.S.A. Blind School for the music of the Meadowlark. A musical friend was asked to reduce to written musical notes said song. Same was sent to this inquiring school. Later they wrote: "Played your music on the piano for our younger blind children. They clapped their hands and exclaimed, "Meadowlark Song!" Our Geogardener attempted surveys as to the persistence of such wild bird music courses. The last study shows 28 Schools for the Blind still carrying on.

This story is reprinted here because it shows what can result from geogardening, or traveling to satisfy one's curiosity about the wildflower origins of cultivated plants. Like all travel by those who wanderlust with seeing eyes, there may be developed, as by-products, those things which add to the joy of living of one's fellowmen.

It is not only the stricken who can thus be educated. In the author's native city, Sacramento, scores of blocks of streets are lined with tall elms. The first of these were planted in the years of the Gold Rush. This was done by arrivals from New England and the states into which New England migration had spilled. These elms contain, in spring time, hundreds of nests of the red-headed linnet. This bird winters around such places as Cuernevaca, Mexico. It annually migrates in summer to the North. Immediately on arrival it commences nestmaking. The songs of these red-polled males constitute much more than 50% of the spring

NATURE STUDY CLASS
FOR BLIND
ROYAL DEER PARK,
HAMPENBURG,
DENMARK

dawn-chorus in parts of California. Yet one of California's most brilliant clubwomen had never noticed linnet songs. She had spent, however, nearly 4 decades of her life where linnet music in spring is constant from dawn to dusk . . . This incident shows that not only the afflicted, but many who live without observing eyes and ears, can add much inexpensive joy to their living.

The innocent children call Scabiosa: "pincushion." (The flower DOES have many "pins" in its "cushion.") Old wives, however, who have accumulated the barnacles of suspicion and hatred, dub it: "Devil's Bite." If Satan's bite did not cause scabby skin diseases, he seems to have had a bit in its making. The *sauvage* scabiosa is bitter, is astringent. SCABiosa *IS* used in SCAB-diseases by the witch-like herb women in France's Midi use as a "cure" for herpes, also eczema. The word is rooted in the Latin *Scabo* (to scratch). (All know what a Labor Union man thinks of a "scab").

European flower-shops supply a demand for the attractive fringed Caucasian varieties, none-too-well-known in U.S.A. Our plant breeders, about the time sedum was popular, isolated a fine range of colors and giant Scabiosa blooms from milk white, thru attractive pinks to reds, garnets, and purples. This fad did not last long—one seldom sees them today in florists' shops. Did the Devil's bite superstition dog them into disfavor?

FENCES TIED WITH WILLOW TWIGS

Wild scabiosas, wild violas, wild pansies often blossom from the heavy moss on Norway's farm houses. Out of such homes came manpower for Norwegian codfishing, whaling fleets. Leadership was developed, since weaklings could not survive. From farmsteads like above often came Norwegian researchers. These gave Mankind the first fertilizers made from air, also Dr. Mjoen's Eugenics Laboratorium.

CHAPTER 78

SEQUOIA

T HE SEQUOIA, at least, is to be seen in almost any large California
garden. Californians are most boastful of the height of their
redwoods. This, despite St. Peter's turning back Californians at
the pearly gates. In his saintly judgment, 'tis said, they had enjoyed so much on earth they would continually grumble at what
Heaven offered. This would only cause discontent among St.
Peter's other tenants.

Californian's competitors therein are the Australians. They
yarn about certain towering eucalpyts. Australians have been
pioneering, simultaneously with our Americans. Their tales parallel ours. It is only recently that exact measurements have settled the tree-height score in favor of California. The Australians,
however, still can tell the tallest stories.

Geogardening Californians need not travel far for sequoias.
The *sempervirens* groves are strung along the coast, like pearls
on a dazzling necklace. *Gigantea*, forming great apartment houses
of bark-dwelling, white-headed woodpeckers is scattered in the
Sierras from Placer to Mariposa.

Sequoia can be proud of its family record—aristocratic as is
any Briton's whose forbears came over with William the Conqueror. Sequoia's noble birth has been set forth elsewhere.*
Sequoia has, however, an additional value to the Geogardener.
When he started tracking the Redwood into its genealogical records
written in the rocks—'way back in Cretaceous—he passed thru
groves of another great fossil forest which might be dubbed the
"Mississippi Basin Hardwood Forest."** It was to our Geogardener's dear friend, the late Madison Grant, to whom came first the
concept of "Save-The-Redwoods."***

---

* See Sierran Cabin from Skyscraper, page 33.
** As this is written our Geogardener and his friends are trying to reproduce the conservation
work with the near-extinct Bison, Pronghorn Antelope, Roseate Spoonbill, the American and
Snowy Egrets and other near-extinct species. Already the Northern conservationists have saved
the Michigan remnant of what the Grand Rapids furniture men did not cut. Porcupine Mountain is now a Michigan State Park . . . At the Southern end of said Mississippi Valley Hardwoods is Louisiana's Tensas River Forest. This is already reduced to a tragic minimum. Some
wise governors, however, are cooperating to save these virgin trees as well as their dependent,
the magnificent Ivory-billed woodpecker.
*** Grant was author of two remarkable books that should be read by every American "The
Passing of the Great Race" and "The Conquest of a Continent" . . . The amazing censorship
of the latter was the subject of a Presidential Address to the Eugenics Research Association
in 1936. The suppression of this book parallels any similar work by Hitler, Mussolini or Tojo.
It strikes at the very Freedom-of-Speech guaranteed by the Atlantic Charter.

CHAPTER 79

SNAP-DRAGON

"And Christ went up into a mountain
And from thence the Devil
Showed Him the Kingdoms." (St. Matthew XV 41.)

THE DEVIL in the form of a Dragon colors folklore from England to China. Snapdragon's curiously-staring flower earned its children's name. Easily can it be imagined to resemble a dragon. Also, with a bit of thumb-and-finger pressure, it can be made to "snap," to the constant delight of kiddies.

China's Manchu* dynasty's flag, the blue dragon on a yellow field, was, of all the world's banners, probably unique. The triangular ensign not only was different from the usual rectangular one, it had, also, a deeply religious symbol. After all, its dragon was another picturization of the Devil-Myth. It portrayed the story of the eternal struggle between The Good and The Bad. Here was something which continues daily in the soul of Everyman. . . .

Into the name "snap-dragon" our kiddies have embalmed folk-tale memories of the Atlantic Coast version of St. George-and-the-Dragon. The crystal-clear imagination of these wee poets does this very often in naming wildflowers.†

Our Geogardener knew snapdragon (both white-yellow and purple-red types) was credited to the Mediterranean-basin flora. He unsuccessfully searched during two decades to find it growing *"sauvage"*, as the French say. Finally, on two different trips he made his discoveries. The white variety he found in the Spanish slope of the Pyrenees where the peaks are called "Puig". The yellow one he located soon afterward, on the Smugglers' Road. This runs from Urgel in Aragon, northward thru Andorra to Fort Romeu. The next trans-Atlantic trip held another geogardening thrill. It came in Normandy, close to Caen, where our allies' troops are fighting as this is written. He located *sauvage*, the reddish-purple variety.

Pyrenees peasants insist that snapdragon is poisonous to grazing cattle. The latter certainly seem to avoid it. That the plant

---

* Our Geogardener was exploring, the last year of the Manchu dynasty, in Manchuria itself. It was so close to the Siberian border that Russian influence was evident even with an occasional droksky. He was trying there to sleuth certain garden plants to their natural haunts. That year he saw the Dragon triangle displaced by Sun Yat Sin's red-white-and blue, cornered with a Sun.

† For children's names for California wildflowers, see the author's "Sierran Cabin From Skyscraper."

contains some medicinal properties* is apparent. The French
country-folk declare it is a sedative. It also is declared it has
astringent qualities. It further is classed as a "vulnerary," or
wound-healer.

---

* In another chapter, French peasant use of artichoke as a liver medicine is recorded. There
is no European nation wherein old-women's herb remedies are valued as widely as in France.
Americans who used to do Europe with a day each for London, Paris, Berlin probably do not
know that, within sight of Notre Dame's towers are backwaters where a doctor never enters.
The midwife who attends to births is all-wise as to roots, berries, barks, and, herbs.

    Kiddie names of flowers evidence remarkable childish imagination, such
as fox-glove flowers on little Bridget's fingers at Ireland's Park-nasilla. One
learned from this dainty colleen how gloved-Reynard stalks his prey. The
youngsters also find Cinderellas in these pansies, goldenhaired Gretchen calls
"*Stiefmuettechen*." Blue-eyed Mary in Manchester tells about St. George and
the Dragon. If you doubt Mary, watch the landing of a small bumblebee on
a snap-dragon in your garden. The bee lights on the air-strip, enters the
tunnel, enjoys his honey, backs out. As it flies away, watch, and you'll learn
how canny is the wee bairn who calls it "SNAPDRAGON."

THE "ALIGNMENTS" OF CARNAC, 'CROSS CHANNEL FROM STONEHENGE

    Snapdragon is generally credited as "native to the Mediterranean Region."
It was in Spain our Geogardener found growing wild both white and orange
snapdragons. He searched in vain on both the African and the European
rims of the Meditteranean Basin, also in Anatolia for any "sauvage" individuals that gave promise of being the basis of the darker colored flower
of our gardens. Then the search abandoned, he found the redding-purple ones
on the coastal plain of Brittany not far from the "Alignments of Carnac."
Whether these blossoms were truly native there or whether they were
"escapes" is not certain. The habitants when questioned said "not cultivated,
but wild." That, however, is flimsy evidence. It may be, however, that the
little ones of the Sun-worshippers of Carnac played "foxglove" "stiefmutterchen" and "snapdragon" games.

CHAPTER 80

STRAWBERRY

"It is the oldest fight of all, the seeds against the weeds."
—Wife Hannah, to husband, Captain Sam Wyatt, in
Harris' Pulitzer Prize Novel, "Trumpets at Dawn."

WILD-STRAWBERRY ICECREAM-SODA was, in the early days of Yosemite's Camp Curry, a *specialtie-de-la-maison*. It ranked with other "specialties"—the famous tripe of Caen—the *pate de fois gras* of Foix, eaten judiciously with proper alternations of lettuce-leaf—*Cancton a la mode de la Valence*. Tiny wild strawberries thus were enjoyed by palefaced visitors to yesteryear's Yosemite, as probably for centuries before, similarly they had been relished, sans ice-cream, by redskin kiddies. . . .

"Fill your lap and fill your bosom,
Only spare the strawberry blossom."
(Wadsworth: Foresight.)

Our big garden berries can be geogardened back to native sub-Alpine haunts. These include the Cordillera backbone of both Americas. Wild strawberries occur from Alaska, thru the Californian Sierra, to Chile's* Magellan's Territory. Our cultivated species, however, is based upon those of Europe's mountain "dals." These extend from Norway's perpetual snowfields, to the Dauphiny Alps, to the old Italo-Austrian World War I battleline in the Dolomites, to the Boemerwald of Czechoslovakia. In such continental locations, they add substantially to peasant income.

Our Geogardener's adventures in Scotland brought glimpses of some most attractive cultivated strawberry beds. Their rectangles were loaded with gigantic berries. These most evidently were the pride of those devoted and lovable men, the highly-trained Scotch gardeners. The border of each strawberry bed seen tastefully was planted to some colorful flower. Often this was St. Patrick's cabbage.**

American breeders have, of recent years, come forward with improved races. These are so advanced that we are competing successfully with all the world. No longer can Europe sneer: " 'Tis only the American DENTIST that excels." We have developed big strawberries. We have isolated varieties that stand

---

* One California species is Fragaria chilensis.
** See Chapter 76 (Saxifrage)

THREE ROSALES, STRAWBERRY'S COUSINS

"YES, AND THE STRAWBERRIES"—Chapter 7 (the Apricot), records other fruit-bearing rosales: blackberries, raspberries, salmonberries, Loganberries, Youngberries, phenomenalberries, likewise apples, pears, peaches, plums, prunes. This array of luscious fruits should deepen our interest in the type genus, Rosa,—both as to garden and wild varieties. To the left of the cultivated roses above is Adenostoma. It is a native California rosale. The Covered Wagon folk dubbed it "greasewood." To withstand Upper Sonoran zone temperatures (up to 115°) it has evolved (a) reduction of leaf, (Compare its short needles to the center's garden rose) and (b) it secretes a moisture-conserving resin (like the tarweed's) which gave it high fuel value for a hasty meal of antelope steak or venison. . .To the right, another rosale of our Arid West. It is Mountain Mahogany. Small leafage tells of its ability to persist in hill-desert's August heat. Note, too, the fish-hook like seed mechanism.

shipment half way across continent. Now strawberry breeders offer runnerless varieties, with all that means to the grower.

> *"When the fields are sweet with clover,*
> *And the woods are glad with song,*
> *And the brooks were running over,*
> *And the days are bright and long,*
> *Then, from every nook and bower*
> *Peeps the dainty strawberry flower."*
>
> (Dora Goodall: Strawberries.)

For strawberries ripening in Forest Snow, read the Czechish fairytale which comes to us through the French "Les Quatre Saisons." French children delight in this variant of the Cinderella myth.

The *frais de bois*, the tiny wild strawberry of France's forests long was used medicinally by the herb women. A heavy-set, mustached one asserted, "We know more than the doctors with all their books. How many of them can end stoppage of urine by powdered strawberry roots?" She used an infusion of the root of the common blackberry for checking diarrhea . . . Dr. Erwin H. Ackerknecht, Proceedings, N. Y. Academy of Sciences, 1145, page 26, reports:

"Even today, our own pharmacopoeia is heavily indebted to the primitives. Picrotoxine, the powerful stimulant of the respiratory emetine, the alkaloid of ipecacuanha and specific in amebic dysentery—all are of Indian origin. Salicylic preparations for rheumatism were first used by the Hottentots. Yet our culture, which, somewhat prematurely, but all the more firmly, believes that the test tube is superior to the plant cells in synthesizing drugs, refuses in general, to analyze the primitive material which anthropologists and missionaries have brought back from the field. A large scale analysis of primitive drugs would be of great practical importance to modern medicine."

*The yellow SUNFLOWER by the brook in autumn beauty
   stood.*

> (Bryant—The Death of the Flowers.)

*And here the SUNFLOWER of the spring
Burns bright in morning's beam.*

> (Elliott—The Wonder of the Lane.)

*As for marigolds, poppies, hollyhocks, and valorous SUN-
FLOWERS, we shall never have a garden without them,
both for their own sake, and for the sake of old-fashioned
folks, who used to love them.*

> (Henry Ward Beecher—Star Papers.
> A Discourse of Flowers.)

*On the hill the golden-rod, and the aster in the wood,
And the yellow SUNFLOWER by the brook in autumn
   beauty stood
Till fell the frost from the clear cold heaven, as falls the
   plague on men,
And the brightness of their smile was gone from upland,
   glade and glen.*

> (Bryant—The Death of the Flowers.)

*Eagle of flowers! I see thee stand,
And on the sun's noon-glory gaze
With eye like his, thy lids expand,
AND FRINGE THEIR DISK WITH GOLDEN RAYS;
Though fix'd on earth in darkness rooted there,
Light is thy element, thy dwelling air,
Thy prospect heaven.*

> (Montgomery—The Sun Flower.)

*Ah, SUNFLOWER, weary of time,
Who countest the steps of the sun,
Seeking after that sweet golden clime,
Where the traveller's journey is done;*

> (William Blake—The Sunflower.)

*Light-enchanted flower, thou
Who gazest ever true and tender
On the sun's revolving splendour!*

(Shelley—Translation Calderon's "Magico Prodigioso.")

CHAPTER 81

SUNFLOWER

Unloved, the sunflower, shining fair,
RAYS ROUND WITH FLAMES HER DISK OF SEED.

(Tennyson—In Memoriam. Pt. C.)

IF, AS TO ADVERTISING, you are a Doubting Thomas, go you, not to the lilies of the field, but to its sunflowers. Study their ways, and gain wisdom. Note, too, that most botanists place the successful sunflower-group atop all plants, flowering or nonflowering. Truly they have, thru COOPERATION, not thru Nazi-like terrorism, found their "PLACE IN THE SUN."

"It pays to advertise." One can substantiate this by studying the compositae. Dissect a sunflower by laying, side by side, one of its disk-flowerettes and a ray-flower. Then take a pencil. Outline, mathematically, the area-proportions of the two. It should convince any doubting Thomas that "it pays to advertise." This because, while the reproduction machinery is in the disk-flower, the ray-flower's only task is the publicity job. It flaunts these bright yellow banners, each many times the size of the modest ray flower. Such publicity calls all pollenizing bees to its honey stores.

The sunflower has a remarkable quality.* It might be imagined that the sunflower, describing its own *Zeilstrebigkeit*, says "I AM INTERESTED, ABOVE ALL, THAT MY REPRODUCTION EFFORTS SHALL BE CANALIZED TOWARD THE HIGHEST POSSIBLE EFFICIENCY. ALL THIS, THAT I MAY—IN THE FACE OF FIERCEST COMPETITION FOR FOOD—CONTINUE TO EVER PROGRESS TOWARD A BETTER RACE. Therefore I have reduced my disk flowers as severely as does one packing luggage for an airplane. I, on the contrary, devote much flower-area to the attraction to my honey-stores of progress-building pollenizers. I, utilizing the sunshine, have extracted these sweets, by a marvelous chemistry, out of soil-salts. With these, I recompense those who transport to my disk what I NEED FOR EVOLUTION UPWARD."

The sunflower tells us several important stories.** One is the

---

* For which we have no word for it in English. . . . The Germans call it "Zeilstrebigkeit." It parallels, indeed at times almost shames, what in humans we call "Intelligence."

** In Sierran Cabin . . . From Skyscraper the author has called attention to the cost of BIOLOGICAL ILLITERACY. Billions of dollars could have been saved. We need not have wasted lives of HUMANITY'S VERY-BEST EUGENICALLY. (THESE INCLUDED THE "A-1" TYPE IN-ALL DRAFTS FROM RUSSIA TO CANADA, FROM GERMANY TO AUSTRALIA.) All this waste came because a score of men were ignorant of one biological fact. This is: The ISOLATIONISTS in the Vegetable Kingdom, centuries ago, began to yield terrain to the COOPERATORS of the sunflower family, the compositae.

above one as to the value of publicity, a second is that Cooperation is better than Isolationism. A third is the survival value of concentration on reproduction.

Members of the compositae or sunflower family go yet further under the urge of *Zeitstrebigkeit*. Compare them with their less successful competitors. A borrage, say, fiddlenecks—a gladiolus—a petunia—even a passionflower along its climbing stem matures but one flower, say daily—so as to require SOME fertilization thru several weeks. Our composite, however, is not content with a daily single flower. Through a whole month it matches each fiddleneck's single bloom with a succession of blooms, each of which has A WHOLE RING OF DISK FLOWERS. To do this, bulk is economized as carefully as with the Pony Express rider or with the hummingbird. Evolved to dine during wing-beats, it finds survival in diminution of weight.

> *But one, the lofty follower of the sun,*
> *Sad when he sets, shuts up her golden leaves,*
> *Drooping all night; and, when he warm returns,*
> *Points her enamoured bosom to his ray.*
>
> (Thomson—The Seasons. Summer.)

Other composites are the daisy, and the thistle:

> *A foe had better brave the diel*
> *Within his reeky cell,*
> *Than our thistle's purple bonnet,*
> *Or bonny heather-bell.*
>
> (Hogg, "The Flowers of Scotland.")

> *"Of all the flowers in the mede,*
> *Than love I most these floures white and rede,*
> *Soch that men callen daisies in our toun."*
>
> (Chaucer—The Legend of Good Women.
> Canterbury Tales, Line 41.)

CHAPTER 82

SWEET PEA

"Here are sweet peas, on tiptoe for a flight;
With wings of gentle flush o'er delicate white,
And taper fingers catching at all things,
To bind them all about with tiny rings."

(*Keats—I Stood Tiptoe Upon a Little Hill*).

PEASANT CART, SWEET PEA LAND

IT WAS in Sicily that our Geogardener discovered his first wild sweet-peas. They were insignificant little plants. Each had but two flowers. These were on short, weak stems. They were blooming in the cracks of a Greek temple. These plants contained, however, all that upon which sweet-pea breeders based the magnificent foot-long stemmed 5-blossomed giants that are the pride of California's gardens from January to August.

Our Geogardener's spiritual experience here in discovering this weakling was next deepest to that of reading the "Sermon on the Mount" where Christ preached it. In Palestine he located wild anemones, cyclamens, narcissi, tulips. Here, telescoped into a most primitive plant was the whole story of ARTIFICIAL SELECTION. Mother Nature had evolved, from a pre-Legume, a wild sweet-pea. It was cousin to clover, alfalfa, acacia,* even the leaf-less paloverde of the desert. Mother Nature's best was a sturdy, little weed with tiny, but bright-colored flowers. It had wings of purple, keel of scarlet. The whole plant was only a few inches in height. It was tough, wiry, EFFICIENT. It had taken probably millions of years to evolve the Sicilian sweet-pea from its ancient pre-Legume ancestor. Then comes along Man. He telescopes into mere decades important improvements. He is restless, impatient. So, by watching for mutations, Man develops improvement quickly. Imagine the wild Sicilian sweet-pea growing beside our garden sweet-peas. Almost any gardener contemptuously would uproot the Sicilian as a weed. Our Geogardener, sitting where Pythagoras had taught, wondered when there would arise another eloquent, convincing teacher who could awaken his fellowmen to the possibilities of eugenic SELECTION among humans thru Positive Eugenics. He dared hope the good strains could be multiplied that Man thus could parallel the development of, say, FRILLED Spencer sweet peas from the humble Sicilian "weed."

---

* See Chapter on Acacia.

MOROCCAN "ADOBE"

Our Geogardener found tamarisk growing, apparently wild, along natural watercourses, also irrigation ditches from Morocco, across North Africa, into Asia Minor. Both these photographs were taken in a French-African oasis. The picture above shows how adobe, or sun-dried bricks, reached California-of-the-Missions by way of Mexico, and before that Spain. They are an invention of the Moors.

CARAVAN-ASARY, FRENCH AFRICAN OASIS

This picture shows the century-old transportation of desert camels, desert donkey. These first were domesticated in the Neolithic, perhaps during the time referred to in the chapter on Crab-Apple. Apparently invention occurred in the desert and semi-desert regions, then spread northward into the forest of Europe.

CHAPTER 83

TAMARISK

"Gray Dusk behind the Tamarisks—
the parrots fly together—As the sun is sinking
slowly over home."

(*Kipling "Christmas in India"*).

"SAUVAGE" TAMARISK areas stretch from Gibraltar and Tangiers, on both African and European sides of Mussolini's *Mare Nostrum,* past Palestine, to Hindustan. The tamarisk is a semi-desert shrub. It is closely related to the ocotillo of our own arid Southwest. In Palestine, in Transjordania, tamarisks grow wild along desert water-courses. Herein it resembles the oleander,* of North Africa. The tamarisks of our gardens are, therefore, shrubs that have radiated, under population-pressure, into their peculiar niche. Such radiation into a new or an unoccupied environment may become finally the organism's niche.** Such expansion means use of new sources of nourishment. Let us always remember that food supply must precede reproduction.

One observes such radiation-into-niches everywhere. When all Americans are biologically-literate, our nation will commence to grasp the profound meaning of the Philosophy-of-the-Niche. Then they will read new meaning into the tamarisk, whose branches of rose-pink, also ash-pink, bloom charmingly. Our tamarisks then will be more than colorful flowering shrubs. They will be organisms that, too, have travelled under the stimulus of *zeilstrebigkeit.* Thus they have found new food supplies, even in that forbidding terrain, Jordan's banks at the Dead Sea.***

The tamarisks are cousins to the willows. In fact, one eminent bontanist suggests that the tamarisk may be great-great-granddad to our willows. He wrote: "An interesting relationship exists between the tamarisk family and the willow family. Willow flowers are SIMPLIFIED from the tamarisk type." Thus arises an inter-

---

* See Chapter on Oleander.
** For a listing of various birds finding their different NICHES in a single California Blue Oak see "Sierran Cabin . . . From Skyscraper," page 94.
*** It was the spot where once the walls rebelled, collapsed at too much saxophone-jazz. While lunching in tamarisk shade at Jerico our Geogardener met a Presbyterian dominie, from the Land-o'-Kilts. The churchman described the contrast between the Sea of Galilee and the Dead Sea: "Munch sweet Jerico oranges. Sip a bit of Dead Sea water when we arrive there. Then, as you go out toward the country of the Druses and the Circassians, tarry beside the Sea of Galilee. Wash down your meal of Peter's fish with a bit of lake water." (The dominie was as careless of bacteria as is a funeral procession to Mother Gunga at Benares.) Continued this fervent Scot: "Dead Sea water is bitter . . . Galilee's is sweet. Why? because streams flow into the Sea of Galilee. However, a stream also flows out. Galilee not only accepts, but gives. The Dead Sea accepts the sweet waters. Selfishly, however, it gives forth nothing." The dour Scot could not help adding his moral: "Its self-centeredness gains its ill fame as a DEAD Sea. And so it is, my friend, with YOUR LIFE."

esting question: Was the generalized ancestor a puritanically-"dry," a desert-loving tamarisk, whose daughters, the willows, became bibulously "wet"? Or did the bone-dry tamarisks radiate out into aridity from the willows? Willow-feet are so much in the water that, were they humans, their pneumonia rate would be appalling!

TAMARISK BESIDE A 'DOBE RUIN

"A large low moon turned the tops of the plume grass to silver, and the stunted camelthorn and sour TAMARISKS into the likenesses of trooping devils . . . aimless little winds blowing across the rose gardens of the southward brought the scent of dried roses."

(The Incarnation of Krishna Mulvaney . . . Kipling).

TAMARISK-LINED HIGHWAY COACHELLA DESERT

CHAPTER 84

TULIP

"To Kermishaw for us they travelled, . . .
To where summer finds the high steppes
ABLAZE WITH RED TULIPS,
Where pink flamingoes, etc." (*Old Song of the Harem*).

TULIPS GROW wild in the great, camel-trodden Near-East. This includes an area from Dan, also from Beersheba to the Zarafshan's steppes near rug-weaving Samarkand. It also stretches up to Dagestand of the Caucasus, with its rugs intriguingly marked with circles and polygons. It runs on down to Sheraz, whose rugs are of undying blues and reds. It continues out to Bokara, likewise possessing many looms. One must, therefore, to know the wild tulips, wander to Oriental-Rug-Land. It is no accident that its bulb-bearing relatives produce blooms dear to the poets who plan these carpets. One must therefore go travel at least to Palestine. Better yet, wander far beyond. Go to where the rug-makers dissolve pigments of vegetable blue, of vegetable brick-red in camel's milk, to color their textiles. Venture to Samarkand, to Karmishah, to Sarak. Have, in the land whose tent hangings became our Occidents' carpets, the thrill of gathering wild tulip blooms. These reach skyward from bulbs deep in lava cracks. Here is the terrain that evolved the water-storing stomach of the camel, also its sand-enduring foot-pads. It also was favorable to the persistence of bulb-plants like the tulip. Those colorful lilales can store, in the underground dark, food and drink, fully refrigerated, despite August's 135 degrees.

The Persians, 'way out there in Farther Tulip-Land, are said to have been the world's first gardeners. These Moslems invented, (along with the Arabic numbers that give one a headache as one figures income tax), the indoor bouquet. It was first used, not in a house, but in a tent. It appeared, not on a table with Thanksgiving turkey-and-cranberry, but by hookah-sucking, henna-bearded Moslems. These, squatted around a ground-carpet, had the first bouquet of tulips. In a bowl, they were midway between a dish of fat-tailed mutton and a basket of dates. There the turbaned mixed pleasure with intrigue.

The youthful Occident can learn, if it be not too conceited, much from the strategy of these scheming but age-wise folk of Tulip-Land. It is only when they venture into Western speech that they become tangled. Our Geogardener had this adventure with one of these:—

An unclean, illiterate vendor of Oriental rugs, brought out from a filthy bosom, a tattered testimonial. He whined: "From the Duke of Blank . . . All about me." It read "This depraved rascal would cheat his own mother. Most of his rugs came from Manchester looms. Occasionally, however, he has a real antique. If you be a judge thereof, offer this swindler 1/10 of his first price. You'll get it at 1/5. Even then you will be worsted." Followed a ducal signature well known at Buckingham Palace.

To one who has sleuthed tulips to their native lands, they stimulate recollection of gossiping cameldrivers . . . of importunate

TULIPVELDEN IN HOLLAND

coaxing from the numerous beggars of the Near-East, for "blacksheesh," . . . of the persistent, annoying arguments of vendors of "made-in-Japan" souvenirs.

It is a far cry from turbaned Tulip-Land to the tulip-gambling of yesteryear's Holland. One recalls the record of a certain scurvy-weakened sailor. At the height of the craze, he walked into his shipping firm's office. In the absence of the Factor, he slyly stole—commenced munching—an "onion." It proved to be a 10,-000-florin tulip bulb.

Tulips still bulk heavily in "Dutch bulbs" shipments. They awaken memories of creaking Dutch windmills, of the clatter of kiddies' wooden shoes on brick-faced dikes. The Geogardener, therefore, must hie himself to the Land of Windmills and Wallons, of Leyden-jars and Limburger, if he would become intoxicated with tulip color. Let him climb the belfry of a Groote Kerk in some Dutch town. Let him then peer North, South, East, West over the tulip breeders' polders. Then he sees the world's brightest masses of flower color.

Since tulip-built gambling long has been ended, and since the Five-and-Ten's now stock tulip bulbs, everyone can afford the delight of mid-winter potted tulips as well as garden ones. When potting them, have a few extras for the later-on sick. If, to the hospitalized, you also can carry Geogardening concepts of camel caravans trekking loads of bulbs from the Persian hinterland-also dreams of Windmill Land-you may help lighten hours of pain.

"The tulips, out of envy, burned
Moles in their scarlet breast." (Hafiz.)

CANAL BRIDGE, MARKEN, HOLLAND

Extravagant yarning is characteristic of all Asia. This is true of the Tulip-Lands of Anatolia and Persia. It is likewise so of the Camellia areas of Japan. One Japanese garden tale is told by Chamberlain:—

The painter Kanaoka, whose horses were so life-like that at night, they quitted the screen which they adorned. They trotted off into a neighboring garden and munched the shrubs. Then some ingenious person hit upon a plan. He added a rope to the picture in order to tether these lively steeds.

CHAPTER 85

VERBENA

"With 'er arm upon my shoulder
And 'er cheek agin' my cheek,
We watched the steamers passing
And the elephants pilin' TEAK.
Watched the hathis pilin' TEAK,
On the muddy, sludgy creek," etc.
(Kipling's "Road to Mandalay.")

IT WAS off the Italian colony of Eritrea, later to be quite a conquest in World War II. A continental Botany-Professor was at the ship's rail. He asked: "Do you, in what you call 'geogardening,' want an interesting field? If so, try, on this trip to the Tropics, to call at the homes of the clansfolk of some of your common garden flowers. Take verbena for example. You have been discussing its charm of color contrast, its masses of the red, the pink, the white kinds. I advise you somewhere in Asia to make the acquaintance of a collateral branch of this not inconsiderable family. The verbena clan in the tropics has some tall timber-trees, the Teaks."

Instantly there flashed into memory Kipling's lines above. Came later experiences in Burma, Java, Ceylon. In Burma there was a steady stream of logs. Certain parts of the transport seemed possible only by elephants. They were most intelligent in their handling of the great heavy logs of this woody "verbena."

In Ceylon, our Geogardener witnessed an example of religious devotion in temple-building paralleling the worship that went into constructing the great Gothic cathedrals of our Occident: York Minister, Canterbury, Exeter, Notre Dame, Chartres, Brouges, Cologne. In Kandy is perhaps the most renowned of all Buddhist shrines—the Temple of the Tooth. It is, of course, constructed of the prized wood of our aborescent verbena, the teak. The temple is built against a cliff. The beams on the outside had been artistically carved. In Kandy the saffron-toga'd priest gave its building date. Its construction evidently had occurred about the time Charlemagne had completed welding his great empire.

Teak long has been used, 'tis said, for the packing between

A CHINESE PROVERB SAYS: "It is most unwise to expect a duck's egg to hatch a Phoenix."

the inner and the outer turrets of battleships. It is the only timber that does not dangerously splinter under shell fire.

When next you enjoy the verbenas of your garden, think of the timber yards along the Irrawady, with the stink of over-ripe fish . . . think also of the rattan-hung jungles of Farther Java, which are crossed going to the Comic-opera Court of the Susushan of SoerAkarta, "Nail of all the World."

VILLAGE IN THE TEAK JUNGLE

Verbenas are very satisfactory for summer color-contrasts. Their habit of matting means survival when, during that fortnight at the California seashore, your home garden's irrigation may be neglected by a careless substitute . . . Our garden plant should not be confused with the California sand-verbena. The latter is an Abronia. It belongs to the Nyctaginaceae or four-o'clock family. It mats sand. It is, therefore, a valuable binder in controling sand dunes. The species of the California beaches are (a) yellow, A. latifolia, (b) lilac, A. villosa, (c) pink, A. umbellata, (d) magenta, A. maritima, (e) white or A. fragrans. Curiously there are desert species. They also are sand-binders. One colorful kind is common at Palm Springs.

CHAPTER 86

VERONICA

"Ihr lieblichen Kinder, wie strahlt euer Blick
Den heiligen Frieden der Unschuld zuruck
Ihr, rein noch, wie Engel, seid Englen verwandt,
Sie reichen im Traume euch liebend die Hand
Drum strahet es im Aug'euch, wie himmlischer Scheen—
Ach, selig ist's, selig, ein kind noch zu sein!

* * * * *

"Es Kommen die Jahre in flichtigen Schritt,
Und jedes bringt Sorgen and Schmertzen dirmit,
Und wie du auch kaemphest fuer Wahrheit und Pficht,
Der Kummer, du Armer, entgehest du nicht.
O, bleibet ihr Kinder, unschuldig und rein—
Ach, selig ist's, selig ein kind noch zu sein!"

BUSY MOTHER Nature, seems to steal time once-in-a-while, for a few loving maternal thoughts. She remembers *"Ihr Lieblichen Kinder."* She recalls that *"Der Kummer, du Armer, entgehest du nicht."* She therefore brings, out of her apron-pocket, toy plants. One of these is veronica. She probably gave it originally to brown Maori kiddies. They call *"koromiko."* Kiddies have much in common the world over. Studying palms in Saharan oasis, our Geo-gardener found wee maids playing "jacks." This was on a bit of clay-hardened sand beside the well. Instead of the metal-pronged ones of U. S. A. girls, they used date seeds. They called, "rough," or "smooth" as the seeds fell on ridged or unridged side . . . So, too, American youngsters learn as quickly as Maori kids to snap veronica buds. This is done to see the ever-smaller leaf-twins. These are encased like Chinese nests of boxes.

Only two veronicas are commonly grown in American gardens. They represent a family of many species.* Ours are both bush, or chaparral, types. One has magenta, the other violet-colored racemes. Some, perhaps, never grown outside New Zealand, are adjusted to desert-like conditions. One which grows on the Tasman Glacier's lateral moraines, is as small as dwarf ageratum. It thrives under conditions of extreme drought, such as obtain in the Arizona-cactus country. Even this dwarfling, however, has the peculiar protection-twin-leaf-envelope that makes our kiddies dance when they first discover its hidden mystery.

---

* There are more than 100 species of koromiko, or veronica, native to New Zealand. In fact, a New Zealand botany in the author's library calls the Scrophulariaceae, the "keromiko" family.

Our Geogardener once was studying the evolutionary adaptation of mighty Tasman Glacier's moraine flora. This flora is as remarkably unique as the alkali-adjusted one of the "hog-wallows" of California's Sacramento Valley floor. It was then that he heard this story of a party of his predecessors.

At Tasman's veronica-covered terminal-moraine were waiting two silver-haired Britishers. A quarter-century earlier they, and 3 others, had tracked up mighty Tasman. One was a friend. The other two were guides. These mistook, for firm footing, the snow-choke atop a crevasse. Three were precipitated several hundred feet into the "cold-storage" below. The two survivors, after the first shock, ascertained the rate of glacial advance. They then estimated the year that unfeeling Tasman Glacier would disgorge its corpses. They were there to give them, among the veronicas, that brightened the Tasman's Moraine, a Christian burial . . .

Our Geogardener's trail led from the camp of these expectant but aged mountaineers up to Tasman's alpine-hut. Here our Geogardener expected to, did find, the sheep-killing parrots. This trail was over more than 20 miles up glacier. It apparently substantiated New Zealand's boast that Tasman is the longest glacier —except in the Himalayas—outside the Polar Regions.

Both on South Island, where both Scots and English colonized, and on North Island, with a preponderantly English population, one finds evidence of typical British success in colonization. It parallels their remarkable foresight in planning seen in their colonies of the 1600's in Massachusetts and in Virginia. It was with a Maori Chieftain of North Island that Wingfield consummated a realty deal. Wingfield was a born colonizer. He wanted 100,000 acres of reasonably good land on the best obtainable harbor. He bought it finally for a bale of night caps, plus a barrel of Jew's harps. The scene of the tatooed, yet night-capped, Maoris out in the manuka and New Zealand-flax scrub—making noises more fiendish than any jazz composer ever imagined—would be worthy of a new Gilbert-and-Sullivan opera.

When, therefore, you watch excited children in the garden snapping open veronica's unique leaf-defenses, travel, in memory to New Zealand. Think of mining there for fossil *kauri* gum for varnishes. Picture tattooed Maori chieftains. Recall Hochstetter of the ice-fall. He swapped moa bones all over the museum-world to build up the Christchurch Museum. Close your eyes and see again the unique plants: the biddy-biddy, the "Irish emigrant." Watch the honey-eaters on the *pakutahawa*. Observe the Maori maidens at Rotara, their cabins inlaid with abalone pearl. Remember, too, her Anzacs, that died cheerfully at bloody Gallopili to make the world safe for democracy. Are we discharging our responsibilities to them?

When geogardening, as is faraway Veronica Land, recall the old German Gypsy song:

> *"Wir sind arm. Der Wald das Feld*
> *Ist uns Haus und Speicher*
> *DOCH SO GLUECHLICK IN DER WELT*
> *LEBT' WIE WIR KEIN REICHER!"*
> (*Ziegeunerlied.*)

**MAORI GREETING IS
NOSE RUBBING**

The high intelligence of the Maori group made it possible to adjust racial differences, so that they live peaceably side by side of the whites. These loyal Maoris furnished some of the finest fighting men in the Middle East campaign in World War II.

Veronica chaparral forms the background. In some parts of New Zealand, the Bush is Veronica, in others, Antipodean heaths. Again it may be masses of manuka or New Zealand flax or tree lilies. Where glacial till or moraines make for rapid drainage, there are dwarf veronicas spaced apart, like the prostrate opuntias of Montana.

**MAORI CHIEFTAIN IN
CEREMONIAL ROBES**

Maori chieftain in ceremonial
robes. Such a type is described in
our Maori Story.

A geogardening byproduct is knowledge of faunas which
often interact with floras. Topping any "fauna" are the humans.
Hence, tracking veronica, manuka, fuchsia, New Zealand flax, tree
lilies—to mention only common garden material—to their sauvage
haunts, the geogardener comes to know and to respect the Maoris.
To hear a Maori orator in the Dominion Parliament gives one a
glimpse of redskin debate in a Fenimore Cooper tale. A student
of eugenics further learns that chieftainship is won and held only
by those of superior mental attainments as well as physical
strength. Under a polygamous economy, the chief gets the most
attractive girls. Also, however, if he be a good, shall we say "poli-
tician," or "statesman," he selects the most intelligent. The feminine underground, in any tribe, is a source of power. Hence the
chief's offspring tends to be fittest to rule. In time Evolution works
upward. It has taken the Occidental intelligensia (?) to reverse
Mother Nature and breed from our worst.

CHAPTER 87

VIOLET

"Morgen bring ich der die VEILCHEN
Die ich frueh in Wald gefunden."

(*Old German Love Song*).

ST. JORY'S Pierre La Fontaine, aged maker of candied violets,* was sad-eyed. None had had to face Depression-difficulties more crushing than his. The cream of his trade was with Paris-residing youths from Buenos Aires, from Lima. These cared nothing for ever-mounting mortgages on homeland *haciendas*. One Juan yearned for the smiles of a thoughtless, black-eyed senorita. He was competing therefor with Pedro. He learned his rival had sent, the evening before, a 5-pound box of La Fontaine's candied violets. He promptly dispatched a 10-pound one. In a few days this was eclipsed by Mateo's 25-pound one . . . Now the Depression had devastated South America from the coffee *fincas* of Guatemala, of Venezuela, to the great cattle *estancias* of Argentine's *pampas*. Hence Pierre Fontaine, at St. Jory, down near Toulouse, maker of candied violets, was immersed in gloom . . .

Can we not take the violet as a symbol of the triumph of Science over Superstition? It is curious that even violet seed was the basis of a superstition. Not many centuries ago, it still was believed that fleas** were born of violet seeds. The breakdown of the violet-seed and of other superstitions has come largely through the efforts of research workers . . .

Americans cut the Panama Isthmus where others failed. Our success came because we had a new control of insect-born tropical disease. Researchers, who had been called "crazy about bugs," had found the way. Americans, too, were first to harness millions of

---

* In the Tewa language "violet" is "pin-ka" ("Pin" means heart or heartshaped, "Ka" means leaf). Our Geogardener once botanized on the Ramon Vigil Rancho, near Tshirege, and later, around the Rito de los Frijoles. This is Tewa Land. The ethnobotany of this region has been covered by Robbins and Harrington . . . Some of the Tewa names of our common garden plants show imagination . . . Galium or bedstraw in Tewa is "hot-tooth," because chewing makes the gums burn . . . The wild geranium, resembling our filaree, is the "5-stick flower." Our kiddies call these twisting 5-seed stalks "clocks" . . .The locust is the "cat-stick" or sticker, while the Spanish there call it "una de gato" or catsclaw, a name given on California deserts to a kind of mesquite . . . Sage brush, artemisia, is in Tewa the "mist-plant" or "fog plant." It at times does look like mist arising in the early dawn . . . Gooseberry is the "throws-out-water" plant. Is Tewa here not more descriptive than our English? . . . Cocklebur, which the Tewa's use for a diarrhea cure, is the "very thorny plant." Our "Indian paint brush," (Castilleja) curiously is also called in Tewa "painted root-plant." The Tewas reproduce this on their pottery . . . Penstemon in Tewa is "hummingbird flower" . . . Clematis is the "downy vine," not a bad description of its seeds. The shield fern (Dryopteris) is the "mountain-lion-foot plant."
** All this occurred at the time learned medicos were grinding yellow lichens into a yellow-jaundice cure. Even to the great Linnaeus it had not occurred that swallows could migrate. He believed they hibernated every winter in mud! Indeed, this was also in line with the myth that the Earth was the center of the universe, that Sun revolved about us, a fallacy that existed until Copernicus advanced his heliocentric theory.

VIOLET FARM, GRASSE, FRANCE

Violet plantations in Olive Trees' Half Shade. Some violets are grown commercially for candied violets. The picture, however, is one of the violet farms feeding the perfume factories of Grasse.

horsepower where, for untold ages, had been only waterfalls. Americans were first to really solve the airplane problem. The beginning of each such an advance was in ONE highpowered human brain . . . Since the days of the first stettlement in Virginia and New England, until recently, brainy parents were noted for their large families. Now we have tragically reversed this favorable birthrate, to having families of 2, 1, 0 offspring. Meanwhile morons multiply like rabbits. With our still high percentage of pioneer blood, which never quailed at any menace, we can still stem this unfavorable tide. It needs only a clear understanding by every American of the eugenic significance of the Differential Birth Rates Law. Then we can hope to conquer more superstitions of which an example is the above-mentioned one of fleas from violet seed.

In Bacon's Essays, we are reminded of March blooming, that "then come Violets, especially the Single Blew."

The VIOLET'S *charms I prize indeed,*
So modest 'tis and fair,
And smells so sweet.
(*J. W. von Goethe—The Beauteous Flower*).

The timid, bashful VIOLET,
(*Phoebe Cary—Spring* Flowers.)

The VIOLET *in her greenwood bower,*
Where birchen boughs with hazels mingle,
May boast itself the fairest flower
In glen or copse, or forest dingle.
(*Scott—The Violet*).

Where the VIOLET, *brimmed with sweetness o'er,*
Lifts its small chalice up.
(*Julia C. Dorr.*)

Again the VIOLET *of our early days*
Drink beauteous azure from the golden sun,
And kindles into fragrance at his blaze.
(*Ebenezer Elliott.*)

Where at the foot of the rocky steep,
The sweet blue VIOLETS *below.*
(*Julia C. R. Dorr—Over the Wall*)

VIOLET! sweet VIOLET!
Thine eyes are full of tears;
Are they wet
Even yet
With the thought of other years?

                                        (Lowell.)

The VIOLET is a nun.
            (Hood—Flowers.)

After the slumber of the year
The woodland VIOLETS reappear.

                                        (Shelley.)

The snowdrop and primrose our woodlands adorn,
And VIOLETS bathe in the weet o'the morn
                    (Burns—My Nannie's Awa.)

And from his ashes may be made
The VIOLET of his native land.
                    (Tennyson—In Memoriam.)

The VIOLETS whisper from the shade
Which their own leaves have made;
Men scent our fragrance on the air,
Yet take no heed
Of humble lessons we would read
(Christina G. Rossetti—"Consider the Lilies of the Field")

Stars will blossom in the darkness,
VIOLETS bloom beneath the snow.
                (Julia C. R. Dorr—For a Silver Wedding.)

CHAPTER 88

VIRGINIA CREEPER

"I know a spot where the wild vines creep."

(Julia Dorr).

"VIRGINIA" CREEPER is named from the Old Dominion. This Commonwealth gave us the Revolutionist, Patrick Henry, the Biologist-President Jefferson, Madison, defender of the Virginia non-conformists; Monroe of the Monroe Doctrine, and Washington, Father of His Country. This state also has steadily supplied U. S. A.—largely out of its F. F. V's.—with a steady stream of statesmen. In the last two decades, Virginia senators, again and again, have demonstrated, by their courageous patriotism, the wisdom of a 2-house Congress.

Virginia Creeper is one of the most striking wild plants of the Southern Appalachians. It belongs to that grand forest of Hickories, Black-Walnuts, Oaks, Tulip-Trees, Sweet-Gums and Dogwoods of North Carolina, Kentucky and Virginia. Miss Lounsberry describes the rather humorous fate of its use for decoration at Blowing Rock, North Carolina.

When one goes a-geogardening, he may overshoot as above his mark. To locate ampleopsis wild, a Californian should have tarried near home in woods that rightly give it its name of "Virginia" Creeper. Long, however, before our Geogardener had collected *"sauvage"* Virginia Creeper, he had enjoyed its brilliant coloring overseas. It was in the thatched cottages of the "tight little isle." The autumn hues of ampleopsis had thrilled him, wherein had evolved, since the days of The Magna Charter, the folkways that had become the foundation of our American republic. "Virginia" Creeper is particularly esteemed in Wiltshire.

There were compensations, however: a most colorful array of ampleopsis was passed when motoring to Stonehenge. It was October. The thatched Wiltshire cottages were ablaze with scarlet Virginia Creeper. The "promenade," as the French call it, terminated in Stonehenge.

As to the survivorships of both Stonehenge, and of Carnac, its twin across in Brittany, we know far less than we do of the Zoroastrians or of the Inca devotees of the Sun God. All we know is that both groups are extinct.*

---

* For additional data on EXTINCTION, see "War Profits & Better Babies."

FRIAR'S HEEL FROM CIRCLE, STONEHENGE

"When motoring to Stonehenge . . . in October . . . the thatched cottages were ablaze with scarlet Virginia Creeper."

STONEHENGE RUINS

CHAPTER 89

WALL-FLOWER

"THE WALL-FLOWER—THE WALL-FLOWER
How beautiful it blooms!
It gleams ABOVE THE RUINED TOWER,
Like sunlight over tombs;
It sheds a halo of repose
Around the wrecks of time.
To beauty give the flaunting rose,
The Wall-flower is sublime."

(Muir—The Wallflower.)

CHEIRANTHUS' ORANGE banners grow high on castle walls. Its folk-name of "wall-flower" indicates its peculiar habitat. It somehow gains food and moisture almost miraculously. Mother Nature, with her artistry, frames the golden wallflowers with a wall-growing fern, a polypody. Fern-lovers think of the lush fern-growths of California's Coast north of the Golden Gate. They recall the rank tree-fern forests of Java, of Australia's Tasman-Sea frontages. They remember humid Jamaica's varied fern-flora. They hardly expect to find ferns growing abundantly from the gray lime-stone-interstices of France's chateau towers. They are amazed to see them abundant on even the walls limiting their closes.

Other wall-stone-growing flowers* are: both species of toad-flax, snapdragon, stonecrop. One is not surprised to find stone-crop, or sedum, prominent in these castle-wall floras. Being a true succulent, it is adjusted to moisture-storage in its obese, cravan-etted leaves. Whether one collects sedum from a castellated tower in Dauphiny, or from a quartzite outcrop atop a California hill, with an August shade temperatures up to 110 degrees, one can imagine it shouting to the August sunbeams: "Fiends, do your worst!" In the Great Beyond, the wicked should not be surprised to find stonecrop thriving over the Gate of Dante's Hades.

---

* The wallflower-polypody-toadflax flora of continental castle walls and enclosures illustrate the value of a hobby. Our Geogardener found relief from the mental strain of long hours of labor on certain sociological problems in France by making, as a hobby, a tiny herbarium of this stone-wall flora. It compared in uniqueness with certain other restricted plant associations such as those of the semi-desert New Zealand moraines or the alkaline "hogwallow" ones of California's Sacramento-San Joaquin Valley. Here is a hobby suggestion: Select, then master a peculiar flora, like that of the wall-growing wallflowers . . . Others include the peculiar Mediterranean beach floras, such as that with the acanthus-stachys complex . . . (Common or yellow toadflax is Sinaria vulgaris . . . The ivy-leaved is L. cymbularia . . . Polypody is the Common polypody.)

**WALLFLOWER TERRITORY. NOTE THE SHRUB ABOVE AND
TO THE LEFT OF THE GATE OF THIS FRENCH CHATEAU.**

THE CORDILIER'S GATE (XIII CENTURY) FALAISE, NORMANDY

The walls of old Chateaux have a flora all of their own. Of these, wallflowers are the brightest-hued. There are also (see text) stonecrops "as much
at home in a castellated tower in Dauphiny as in a quartzite outcrop atop a
California hill, with August shade temperatures up to 110 degrees." It might
be noted in passing that since World War I ended, stonecrop culture became
quite a fad. Some of the plant breeder's improved stocks are fascinating.

Wallflower, however, is not a succulent. Neither is the yellow, nor the dainty lavender toadflax. (Can you image the mother frogs gathering it? They, later, so the folktales have it, will spin it for fairies' tablecloths linen. This will be used as the fairies picnic, squatted on their toadstools.) Wallflowers, and the 2 toadflaxes, tho not succulents, economize moisture, however, like their companion the polypody. All three manage, somehow, to gain that nourishment that must precede reproduction. Was it not Victor Hugo who said:

> *"There is none so poverty-stricken but that he*
> *can find solace in helping some one even poorer."*

TRAIL SONGS WHICH GEOGARDENERS MAY ENJOY

> *"I've bartered my sheets for a starlit bed,*
> *I've traded my meat for a crust of bread,*
> *I've changed my book to a sapling cone*
> *And—I'm off to the END OF THE WORLD again."*

> (*Author unknown. Used as Trail Song in California*)

> *"Gypsying to ANYWHERE*
> *Where each day has its glory,*
> *Where life was still untrammelled*
> *And its jest was still unstale,*
> *Where each new turn held joys most rare,*
> *In all their amber glory*
> *Along that road to ANYWHERE,*
> *We watched the sunsets pale."*

> (*Again, Author unknown . . . Used as Trail Song in California*)

CHAPTER 90

WALNUT

THE WALNUT has been cultivated for so many uncounted centuries it is not easy for a Geogardener to sleuth it to native haunts. In North America we call it—to distinguish it from our native black walnut—the "English walnut." In Britain one sees quoted "French walnut." Cross Europe to the Balkans. There it is "Caucasian walnut." Take a camel at Haifa, cross Palestine, Iraq, Iran, Mongolia, North China. There it is "Manchurian walnut."

In England of the "English" walnut, they tell one of the real Scots, the painfully-thrifty, are to be found,—not North of the Tweed, but in France. The Britons relate their yarn about an American uncle: This wealthy bachelor had numerous spendthrift nephews. Latter could not conceal from the shrewd old fellow that his speedy decease was "a consummation devoutly to be wished for." His estate was in giltedge bonds. These he one day, in anger, converted into bills-of-exchange. He then took steamer for La Havre. Uncle Knickerbocker thus had the Atlantic safely between him and his heartless kin. He then promptly advised the latter he disinherited all of them . .. In France, he bought a walnut-shaded chateau from a sporty last-survivor. With said French estate he acquired a staff of trained servants. They were faithful—within certain limits.* Knickerbocker soon discovered his blunder. He had hoped to find a substitute for family affection in his servants. Despite disappointment herein, he remained, however, obstinate to the last . . . His will read "I leave my estate to my servant staff provided each thereof shall wear, for one year, the uniform described. ½ of estate to concierge (Esquimaux suit). 1/10 to his wife: (Hula-hula grass skirt). 1/10 to cook: (Zulu shield and assaigi). 1/10 to housekeeper: (Elizabethan costume, including neck ruff). 1/10 to chauffeur: (Monte Carlo carnival dress with mask). 1/10 to gardener: (Uniform of Admiral German Navy)" . . . The testament concluded with "Object of this will is to demonstrate there is nothing the French servant will not do for a few thousand francs!"

One may smile at such sardonic humor. The typical American spendthrift, however, might be wiser to appreciate the thrift of rural France. It was this rare quality that carried through the later 1870's. It made possible paying Germany an indemnity that "blood-

---

*See Daudet's novel "The Nabob." However, Uncle Knickerbocker soon grasped the meaning of Daudet's scene between the dying Duke de Mornay and his avaricious chamberlain . . .

and-iron" Bismarck had supposed would "bleed France pale." As a part of such thrift: Our Geogardener, who had spent much time in rural France, often noticed the precaution the average small proprietor took always to have a walnut tree* with its abundant food possibilities.

---

* Read about Pierre Beauregard's Walnut Tree in "War Profits . . . And Better Babies." This suggested that many households, over much of U. S. A., could, with gain, plant in gardens one walnut or other nut tree, also one fruit tree.

A properly-planned garden, with its contrasting flower hues, gives us a radiant joy, a spiritual satisfaction. This is akin to the coloration of Constantinople's Sancta Sophia. Of this Van Mulligan wrote:

"Only one thing more was needed to make the fabric artistically complete —to spread over it what Ruskin terms, that most subtle, variable, inexpressible colour in the world—the colour of glass, of transparent alabaster, of polished marble, and lustrous gold. Accordingly, all that porphyry, verde antique, white marble, marbles of variegated hues, in the form of pillar, slab, capital, inlaid patterns, could contribute, all that delicate carving, with its lights and shadows, all that mosaics bright and soft as sunset tints could lend, was brought into requisition, until every part of the interior surface was suffused in a splendid coloration, and the solid fabric stood transfigured into a pavilion of some iridescent tissue, over-wrought with gorgeous embroidery, and held up on shafts of porphyry and emerald . . . Justinian exclaimed, when he first crossed its threshold, 'O Solomon, I have surpassed thee'."

"And what is so rare as a day in June?
Then, if ever, come perfect days;
Then Heaven tries earth if it be in tune,
And over it softly her warm ear lays;
Whether we look, or whether we listen,
We hear life murmur, or see it glisten;
Every cloud feels a stir of might,
An instinct within it that reaches and towers,
And, groping blindly above it for light,
Climbs to a soul in grass and flowers;
The flush of life may well be seen
Thrilling back over hills and valleys;
The cowslip startles in meadows green,
The buttercup catches the sun in its chalice,
And there's never a leaf nor a blade too mean
To be some happy creature's palace;
The little bird sits at his door in the sun,
Atilt like a blossom among the leaves,
And lets his illumined being o'errun
With the deluge of summer it receives;
His mate feels the eggs beneath her wings,
And the heart in her dumb breast flutters and sings;
He sings to the wide world, and she to her nest,—
In the nice ear of Nature which song is the best?"

(Lowell: "The Vision of Sir Launfal.")

"FLOATING" GARDENS, XOCHIMILCO, MEXICO

CHAPTER 91

WISTERIA

"What would life be without coffee?
But then,
What is it
Even with coffee!"

(*Louis XIV*)

Wisteria sinensis, as its name indicates, is a native of China. Being thus Asiatic, it has spread as a drinking-house ornamental vine. Eastward it has gone to the Nipponese islands off China. Westward we find it penetrating thru to the *kaffeeneons* of Anatolia, of Turkey-in-Europe, even of Greece.

An ancient wisteria grows in a certain *kaffeeneon* in Constantinople. Its trunk is thick as a telegraph pole. So twisted is it that one imagines it never recovered from writhing in agony when, at the Sancta Sophia, the Christian cross was lowered. This wisteria has grown for a hundred feet right, also left, from its root. In spring, it is hung with thousands of lavender blooms. Turks stroll out from their downtown timber-houses to this *kaffeeneon* to sip the molasses-thick coffee. They there enjoy the wisteria color . . . and the gossip. To this coffee-house, our Geogardener was fond of repairing. At it he would enjoy coffee plus a typical Turkish meal. This was a black-bread loaf, plus an onion. Since lack of sanitation required caution, it was possible to obtain a bacteria-free interior by peeling the onion. The breadcrust was similarly under suspicion. To it was attached revenue stamps. These adhered because of moistening with unclean saliva. The crust therefore went the way of the onion's outskin. At heart, however, both were sound.

Another wisteria-decorated *kaffeeneon* is at Yebub. Venerable cypresses form the garden of its thrice-sacred Mosque. Yebub's tomb and shrine overlook Constantinople's Golden Horn. To its coffee-house, too, came befezzed, baggy-trousered Turks. There again was served the violently-strong coffee. Its patrons declare a tiny Turkish coffee-spoon, inserted upright at cup-center, remains pointing to the Zenith. The thick, ropy liquid is all-supporting. The Wisteria clusters at Yebub resemble the long, lighted lanterns Japanese rickshaw runners once held, at pole-end, to light the way.

At the other end of the great Asiatic land-mass, one sees wisterias at not coffee- but tea-houses. A certain teahouse in Japan

JAPAN'S GARDENS HAVE PERENNIAL CHARM

was annually the object of strolling Nipponese intellectuals. This ended with the Marco Polo Bridge incident in 1937. This teahouse also possessed an ancient wisteria. Its trunk truly tree-sized. Its branches extended so far one hesitates quoting figures—'Tis too much like that "trout that got away." The same is true as to the length of the pendant racemes of lavender flowers. To give the real statistics would sound like Californian boasting as to the size of Golden State watermelons—one fills a flat car.

The Japanese, too, are fond of yarning at such tea-houses. Watching them sipping tea under the wisterias, one is reminded of the old whaler captains at Nantucket wharf.

Colossal Asia, both in its Near-East and its Far-East, has learned the wisdom of inexpensive recreation. High among recreation that is re-creation ranks the sauntering toward a Refreshment House. It is said "sauntering" was originally a Sanct'-Terring—or Holy-Landing, i.e. Pilgrim-age making. We no longer, in our Scientific Age, go with hearts full of adoration to some hilltop shrine. However, the best way to travel still is afoot. Perhaps we may come to have less of "Keeping up with the Joneses." We may gain a lesson as to the folly of "conspicuous spending" if we can come to SAUNTER. We hectic Americans may learn to appreciate the suburban garden. It may consist of but a single well-tended wisteria. There we may understand how to enjoy wisteria beauty while sipping a cup of Turkish coffee—or of Japanese tea.

If not a palmer's palm-leaf, then wisteria, in a circle, might

well be the device of an "Encourage-Pilgrimage-Making-League."
Wisteria-garden drinking places are the foci of pilgrims out of
some one billion humans. Is not philosophy of the Pilgrimage afoot
worth careful Occidental reflection? Can we not learn herein even
from the Japanese?

The pilgrimage habit is formed in childhood. Adult Nipponese after much childhood training are seen hiking regularly to
Pilgrimage points. One may be a Buddhist shrine. Arrived, the
pilgrim reverently may add his pebble to the heap raised to shaven
Jizo, God of children . . . More likely, however, the pilgrimage's
object may just be a 5-miles-away teahouse. Reaching it, he sips
tea. Gossip will be about the flowers. This time it is WISTERIA.
En route, he has enjoyed the par-excellence method of intimate
acquaintance with his environment and its creatures. According
to season, his teahouse may show iris, chrysanthemums, lotus.
Among the summer wee beasties, our pilgrim meets, are the cica-
das. Their "song" so grips him he catches one. He fashions a
2-inch-cube of bamboo splits. He takes it home to remind him of
his pilgrimage.

As he has walked, he also has had time to observe the roadside beauty of—do not be surprised: A marestail! One untrained in
botany would hardly notice, among the roadside plants, the less
colorful marestail. It parallels the fence-lizard as an example of
descent from glory. The lizard is a survival of the giant reptiles of
the Jurassic, such as the Brontosaurus, or Thunder-Lizard. So, too,
the marestail, or scouring brush, is a plant survival of former
giants. In the writer's collection is a bit of fossil marestail from a
plant of the Pennsylvanian. It must have been treesized . . . Our
Japanese en route to his WISTERIA teahouse, has noticed a 30-
inch marestail. Here is material for DWARF GARDENING . . .
At one dinner in Tokio's Imperial Hotel of yesteryear, the sole
"table bouquet" was a dwarfed marestail. It was fully mature, yet
but 3 inches high. Some gardener had succeeded in reducing its
normal growth 90%, thus equalling the dwarfing of ginkos and
pines by these patient gardeners . . .

As this is written, news comes of the final last stand of the
1,500 Nipponese on Saipan. Of these, 1,350 fought the suicide-fight.
Our Geogardener's observations in Japan, commencing shortly after the Russo-Japanese War, led him to believe there are several
powerful factors behind such fanatical fighting, as on Saipan.
Among these was: The deliberate utilization of certain characteristics by the War Lords. These militarists had the task of substi-

tuting, for a decadent Buddhism, their newly-invented Shintoism. The proud old Samuri had sent their sons to every nation in the Occident they were studying. These-content to even accept positions as butlers, valets, houseboys—were sending home systematic notes about us. Some were gathered from the cloistered interiors of our homes. (Imagine the oldest son of the Duke of Devonshire waiting on the table of a Chinese Mandarin!)

In accepting such tasks, the Japanese learned much from the Swiss. These mountaineer-democrats had shrewdly, as will be hereinafter set forth, discovered the value of building love-of-country by an intimate knowledge of the wee-beasties, birds, the bees, beetles. So the Japanese developed highly the Nature-Study-Pilgrimage. This was interwoven, as a Navajo at her loom weaves her woof and warp, with the decades-old Pilgrimage. The boys were under teachers trained in War-lord strategy. These lads were to be the rank and file in the wars to establish dominance of the Yamotos.* Such were indelibly tattooed during the Pilgrimage, now become a combined Nature-Study plus History Field Excursion, with a fanatic patriotism. It was exactly this that would make possible cheerful acceptance of suicide-warfare.

Occidentals, because of apparent courtesy, often, at the century's turn, called the Nipponese "The French of Asia." The term was based upon a superficial knowledge of the Japanese mind. The unthinking westerner did not grasp how the supposed politeness was based upon cruel discipline exacted by the Samuri code. It might have been more accurate, therefore, to dub the little brown folk "The Swiss of Asia." This, because Nipponese thinking as to education had been moulded upon that of Swiss leaders. The story of how what developed into National-Parks Nature Guiding was discovered by the author and his wife on the *Vierwaltstaetersee* has been recorded elsewhere. Let it be written here that the Swiss studies thereof disclosed this one dominant note:

"Switzerland is forever doomed geographically to encirclement by great nations that are powerful militarily. Each rising generation must, therefore, be led to grow strong, to remember Morgarten, also Sempach. Systematic trailside nature study, along with historical suggestions, must be persistently taught. In other words, the child that, each summer, is led to climb for edelweiss, for alpenrosen, comes UNDER PLANNED LEADERSHIP, to have stamped, indelibly, upon its character, love of country. It was thus that Scott acquired his love of Scotia's flora as recorded in

---

* For further notes on the Yamoto Race see the Author's "War Profits . . . and Better Babies."

"The Lady of The Lake."
>   "*E'en the slight harebell*
>   *Raised its head*
>   *Elastic to her airy tread.*"

It was thus that he came to have affection for Scotland's aspens.
Their feet were washed by Loch Kathrine's ripples, whose music
we almost hear in his:
>   "*Breathes there a man with soul so dead*
>   *That never to himself has said*
>   *This is mine, my native land.*
>
>   * * * * *
>
>   *O Caledonia! Strewn and wild,*
>   *Meet nurse of a poetic child,*
>   *Land of the brown heath and shaggy wood,*
>   *Land of the mountain and the flood.*"

The Swiss school child's heart comes to beat with that of Sir
Walter. Young Helvetians know their biology, their history. It was
no accident that the author found a nature-guiding excursion of
school kiddies collecting fascinating varieties of fungi on the battle field of Morgarten. It was clearly planned that, as he climbed
Rigi with another directed group, rucksacks were bulky with the
vasculum, the cyanide-bottle, the geologist's hammer. As they
ascended their trail song was:
>   "*Ich bin von Berg der Hirtenknab.*
>   *See all' die Schloesser hier herab*
>   *Die Sonne stralt am ersten hier,*
>   *Am laengsten blieb'et er bei mir.*" etc., etc.

Such HABITUAL HIKING has the advantage of being INEX-
PENSIVE recreation. It contrasts favorably with automobile riding as to muscle-building. Love of scenery, of wild flowers, of trees,
of butterflies, of bees and beetles was stamped indelibly upon the
Swiss Kiddies. Need one wonder that German Nazis, plotting with
Italian Fascists, did not dare, even after the Norway, Denmark,
Holland, Belgium and France conquests to press shut their gigantic
pincers over Switzerland. To the North, to the South of the Alps,
the Totalitarians knew the danger of mountain passes. In each of
these few determined men could hold at bay a whole division!

**CHINA'S POPULATION
IS DENSE**

Geogardening in China, the native land of Wisteria, one is constantly impressed that population pressure is painful. One has little hope of finding any sauvage plant where the terrain has been cropped for several milleniums. No wild Wisteria was found. It is possible, however, it still grows in the Hinterlands as in Yunnan.

We have a glimpse as to the influence of flowers on the cultural, the religious life of Holland in the following from Motley's "Rise of the Dutch Republic."

"The Guilds of Rhetoric . . . existed, in greater or less number, in all the principal cities. These were associations of mechanics, for the purpose of amusing their leisure with poetical effusions, dramatic and musical exhibitions, theatrical processions, and other harmless and not inelegant recreations . . . In the outset of their career they gave theatrical exhibitions. "King Herod and his Deeds" was enacted in the cathedral at Utrecht in 1418 . . . As they were all connected with each other, and in habits of periodical intercourse, these humble links of literature were of great value in drawing the people of the provinces into closer union. They became, likewise, important political engines . . . Philip the Fair enrolled himself as a member in one of these societies. It may easily be inferred, therefore, that they had already become bodies of recognized importance. The Rhetorical Chambers existed in the most obscure villages . . . Their presiding officers were called kings, princes, captains, archdeacons, or rejoiced in similar high-sounding names. Each Chamber had its treasurer, its buffoon, and its standardbearer of public processions. EACH HAD ITS PECULIAR TITLE OR BLAZON, AS THE LILY, THE MARIGOLD, OR THE VIOLET with an appropriate motto. By the year 1493, the associations had become so important, that Phillip the Fair summoned them all to a general assembly at Mechlin. Here they were organized, and formally incorporated under the general supervision of an Upper or Mother-society of Rhetoric, consisting of fifteen members, and called by the title of "JESUS WITH THE BALSAM FLOWER."

WHEN IS A MAN EDUCATED?

Joseph Fort Newton, famed clergyman of Philadelphia, gives answer: "When he can look out upon the universe, now lucid and lovely, now dark and terrible, with a sense of his own littleness in the great scheme of things, and yet have faith and courage. When he knows how to make friends and keep them, and above all, when he can keep friends with himself. WHEN HE LOVES FLOWERS, CAN HUNT THE BIRDS WITHOUT A GUN, AND FEELS THE STIR OF A FORGOTTEN JOY IN THE LAUGH OF A CHILD. WHEN STAR-CROWNED TREES, AND THE GLINT OF SUNLIGHT ON FLOWING WATERS SUBDUE HIM LIKE THE MEMORY OF ONE MUCH LOVED AND LONG DEAD."